SMALL
TALK

BRINGING LISTENING AND SPOKEN LANGUAGE
TO YOUR YOUNG CHILD WITH HEARING LOSS

ELLIE WHITE AND JENNA VOSS

© 2015 Central Institute for the Deaf
825 South Taylor Avenue, St. Louis, Missouri 63110

www.cid.edu

Library of Congress Control Number: 2015944292

ISBN Number: 978-1-931480-00-0

For more information, please contact us at cid@cid.edu.

314.977.0132

Acknowledgments

■ ■

This book is dedicated to our children,
Joseph, Michael, Mary, Francis and Ramona.

For years of infinite love and support, special thanks go to our
spouses, Ben Voss and Patrick White, and to our parents,
Mike and Jean Bollinger and Jerry and Maryann Rice.

With grateful appreciation, we honor the hundreds of children
and families who have taught us, inspired us and motivated us.

Credit, adoration and praise go to the many colleagues and
professionals who made this book come together:

Julie Aldridge, Lynda Berkowitz, Greta Bohnenkamp, Betsy Brooks,
Chris Clark, Meghan Cohen, Lisa Davidson, Robin Feder,
Meredith Gronski, Dianne Gushleff, Patricia Hoffman, Ann Holmes,
Kathy Holtman, Erin Hopfinger, Lisa Inch, Victoria Kozak-Robinson,
Shashikant Kulkarni, Susan Lenihan, Melany Nitzsche, Dorie Noll,
Terri O'Donoghue, Andrea Osman, Kim Readmond, Mary Rice,
Marie Richter, Megan Samson, Cathy Schroy, Sara Stever and Claire Soete

Cover photo by Tom Rollins

Additional images by Chris Malacarne, Mike Martin Media,
Danielle Pipitone, Kim Readmond and Tom Rollins

Edited by Kim Readmond

Book design/typography by Trimensions

Printed by Mira Digital Publishing

Contents

I am often asked to describe the experience of raising a child with a disability —
to try to help people who have not shared that unique experience
to understand it, to imagine how it would feel.
It's like this . . .

When you're going to have a baby, it's like planning a fabulous vacation trip — to Italy.
You buy a bunch of guide books and make your wonderful plans.
The Coliseum. Michelangelo's David. The gondolas in Venice. You may learn
some handy phrases in Italian. It's all very exciting.

After months of eager anticipation, the day finally arrives.
You pack your bags and off you go.
Several hours later, the plane lands.
The stewardess comes in and says "Welcome to Holland."

"Holland?!?" you say. "What do you mean, *Holland?*
I signed up for Italy! I'm supposed to be in Italy.
All my life I've dreamed of going to Italy."

But there's been a change in the flight plan.
They've landed in Holland and there you must stay.

The important thing is that they haven't taken you to a horrible, disgusting, filthy
place, full of pestilence, famine and disease. It's just a different place.

So you must go and buy new guide books. And you must learn a whole new language.
And you will meet a whole new group of people you would never have met.

It's just a different place. It's slower-paced than Italy, less flashy than Italy. But after you've
been there for a while and you catch your breath, you look around . . . and you begin to
notice that Holland has windmills . . . Holland has tulips. Holland even has Rembrandts.

But everyone you know is busy coming and going from Italy . . . and they're all
bragging about what a wonderful time they had there. And for the rest of
your life, you will say "Yes, that's where I was supposed to go.
That's what I had planned."

And the pain of that will never, ever, ever, ever go away because the loss of that dream
is a very significant loss.

But . . . if you spend your life mourning the fact that you didn't get to Italy, you may
never be free to enjoy the very special, the very lovely things about Holland.

— Emily Perl Kingsley

Chapter 1

Diagnosis and the Road Ahead

Coming to Terms with Your Child's Hearing Loss

What will I do? What will she do? Will she learn to talk? Will she have friends? Will she go to college? Will she be able to get a job? Will she be an independent person? Will she be able to develop normal relationships? How will we communicate? Will she be happy? Why did this happen? Did I do something wrong?

These questions and thoughts may have gone through your mind or may be going through your mind right now. It's natural to have a lot of questions and many different feelings about your child's hearing loss. The fact that you are doing something to help your child is an important step in the right direction. You are entering into a new area of information you may know very little about. Perhaps you have never known or talked to a child or an adult with hearing loss. Undoubtedly, you will meet some soon. Many very successful adults have hearing loss. Children with hearing loss grow up to be adults with hearing loss who have jobs, families and quality lives, just as people with typical hearing do.

Your child's hearing loss has been verified and, although you may have been hoping there was a mistake or that it could be corrected, the hearing loss is probably here to stay. You may want to seek out a variety of professionals to help you through this difficult time. Talking about your feelings can be helpful. Other parents of children with hearing loss can be particularly good listeners. You might also ask your questions and tell your concerns to your child's doctors, audiologist and teachers. You are going to be learning a lot of information from the professionals who work with you and your child. You might ask each of them questions so you can better understand the implications of your child's hearing loss.

Babies with typical hearing learn to talk by *listening* to others talk, then practicing their own talking. So how do babies with hearing loss learn to talk? Babies with hearing loss learn to talk by listening to others talk, then practicing their own talking.

Any degree of hearing loss will decrease the amount of listening your baby can do. But with the help of hearing aids and/or cochlear implants, it's possible that your baby with hearing loss can now hear your voice and the sounds in your home. Remember! Listening to your voice and all the sounds in your home is key to your baby learning to talk.

Most likely, you have already made a very important decision to help your child learn to talk. To make that possible, your child will need specialized listening devices. It's important for her to gain access to sounds she is currently unable to hear as soon as possible. Initially, you can give her access to those sounds by getting her fit with hearing aids. It isn't always easy to face that your child has to wear special devices each and every day; however, wearing devices at a young age gives your child the best chance of becoming a talking child.

It will take some time for both of you to adjust to using these devices. Know that, over time, it will become easier and you will not feel the same level of frustration you may feel now. Give yourself a pat on the back! You can feel very good about what you have done for your child up to this point. Keep reading and you will continue to learn about the road ahead!

Emotional Impact of Universal Newborn Hearing Screening

You may have first learned about your child's hearing loss through **Universal Newborn Hearing Screening (UNHS)** at the hospital where she was born. UNHS has increased the number of children identified with hearing loss at birth.

Nevertheless, you may be feeling certain emotions you did not expect to have about your new baby. This experience can be very overwhelming. It was most likely not what you had anticipated.

You may even find yourself feeling as though you wish you didn't know about the hearing loss just yet. It may help to consider this early identification a great opportunity for your child. You might occasionally think that not knowing would be better for fostering the relationship between you and your infant. However, later identification can lead to a myriad of uncertainties, tension and emotional distress because of the time lost.

Here's the good news! Early identification resulting from UNHS can lead to some of the following possibilities:

- early diagnosis
- early device use
- early intervention
- healthy attachment with your baby
- milestone development on track with babies who have typical hearing
- success at listening and talking
- success in school, activities, relationships, employment and social groups

For more in-depth information on Universal Newborn Hearing Screening, see Chapter 3.

Some Common Reactions

Some reactions and feelings are typical among people experiencing a crisis. Learning your child has a hearing loss can be a crisis. Some parents experience:

- shock
- denial
- anger
- pain
- regret
- confusion
- fear

- bargaining
- sadness
- recognition that the hearing loss is real
- acceptance that the situation must be handled
- constructive action in helping the child

You may have experienced some of these. Shock is a protective state of mind that helps people block out the intense difficulty of a crisis and focus on mundane details. Denial is another way of coping that involves denying the reality or the severity of the situation. Most parents who experience these feelings do so for a short time. Soon, they experience recognition that their child's hearing loss is real. With acceptance, parents understand and face the difficulty and know they must go forward. Before long, parents begin to help their child learn to listen and talk.

Feeling any or all of these is understandable. You and your family probably have had to change some of your expectations. You may have a different life than you initially expected. You will have to work hard to help your child maximize her potential. So will she.

Feelings are not necessarily good or bad, right or wrong. They are something we all experience. You may wish things were simpler and that this didn't happen to you. You may be confused and overwhelmed about what to do and which advice to follow. You may worry or even have fear about the uncertain future. You may be concerned about expenses related to your child's hearing loss. You may feel guilty because you think you've somehow caused the problem. Try to understand that these are normal reactions. You wouldn't have knowingly caused a problem for your child. With time, hard work and support from others, you'll begin to see your child's successes. As you begin to see these successes, new and different feelings may arise.

Grief

Parents feel a wide range of emotions at the time of diagnosis and beyond (Meadow-Orlans, 1980; Jackson, Traub & Turnbull, 2008; Jackson & Turnbull, 2004). Be aware that the feelings and states associated with grief are often experienced in stages rather than in a sequence (Kurtzer-White & Luterman, 2003; Moses, 1987). Conditions associated with grief include shock, denial, pain, anger, depression, acceptance and advocacy (Kubler-Ross, 2009, 2011; English, 2000; Moses, 1987; Sexton, 2009). It may be useful to know these conditions as you process the idea of your child's hearing loss. They are common and to be expected as you come to terms with the identification of your child's hearing loss. These emotions might vary from day to day, from minute to minute. You may find you experience a certain feeling at one time, then move on to another feeling, then maybe back to the first one, then on to yet another one. This is normal and important. It may help to let yourself feel these emotions so you can appropriately grieve.

States of Grief

SHOCK feeling traumatized, stunned, upset, hysterical or numb	**DENIAL** rejecting the truth	**PAIN** experiencing physical discomfort in certain area(s) of the body	**ANGER** feeling irritated, furious or outraged

DEPRESSION experiencing hopelessness and gloom	**ACCEPTANCE** acknowledging the truth and finding peace with it	**ADVOCACY** moving forward to ensure both child and family have what they need

You may come to a time when you have accepted your child's hearing loss and you're actually in a good place with all you're doing to help your child. But then a life milestone arrives (your child goes to school, gets invited to her first birthday party, gets her driver's license, goes on a first date or graduates from college) and you find yourself moving through a particular state of grief again. Just by being aware of your feelings, you're taking a first step back to being in a good place.

Some Ways to Deal with Feelings

Every person is different, but each one needs to find ways of coping with feelings and moving forward. Here are some suggestions:

■ **Acknowledge your feelings.**
Sometimes acknowledging feelings is really difficult, but it's a great place to start. Feelings are what they are. Don't try to change them. The situation is challenging and it's reasonable to be upset. As you work through this situation, it may help you to acknowledge and accept your own feelings.

■ **Talk to others.**
Find someone to talk to — a spouse, parent, friend or parent of another child with a challenge. You could start by telling him or her how you feel. Some people might help by temporarily distracting you from what's happening in your life. Others might listen and offer advice. Some might just give you a hug when you need it. Tell people what you need and what would help you.

Write in a journal.

Sometimes, thinking and feeling are not enough to help, but talking is too much for you. Other times, you can't find the right listener. If this happens, you might try writing some notes about your feelings in a journal, notebook, letter or online in the form of a blog. You may decide to keep a journal or blog with dated entries about your feelings, thoughts, questions, ideas, successes or challenges. At some time in the future, you might be glad you did.

Find people to support you.

You may benefit from this type of interaction and can use the opportunity to learn about services other parents have obtained for their children. Such groups include:

- □ *Other parents of children with hearing loss*
  Having a child with hearing loss will lead you to new situations, places and people. Meet others when you can. Try to be open to learning from them and sharing with them.
- □ *Parents of children with other special challenges*
- □ *Online chat rooms*
- □ *Discussion groups*
  You may want to consider joining one of these support groups. If you don't find one with which you feel a connection, you can start a group without much more than a few phone calls and a pot of coffee.

Find other ways.

Some parents turn to their neighbors, their friends, their faith community or their spiritual beliefs to help themselves feel better. Often these resources can offer support in a number of ways, sometimes supporting you so you're able to focus on the needs of your child and family. This kind of support can include listening while you say what's on your mind, watching your kids while you take some time for yourself or taking you out to lunch when you just need a distraction. You might occasionally prefer this kind of support that doesn't include advice, suggestions or "what you should do next." Think about what's most helpful to *you*. When you find the kind of support you really need, you'll just know it!

If it doesn't feel right to join a support group now, that's okay. Perhaps you will in the future. You may not be ready for a group at first, but soon you will have a lot to offer other parents and families. Most parents of children with challenges say that other parents provided the most important help they received in the early years. This kind of support may help you feel less alone and move forward with your feelings.

Sometimes your feelings may be so overwhelming, the support of a professional counselor becomes beneficial. At some point, a trained counselor may be just what you need to help you deal with your feelings.

■ **Meanwhile, give yourself a break.**
During the time when you have so many feelings and so much to do and learn, be sure to take care of your own health. You have a real need for sleep, exercise and good nutrition. These are essential to keeping you healthy. Taking care of yourself is not selfish.

Be realistic about what you expect of yourself. Pat yourself on the back for doing what you've already done to help your child. Ask someone who cares about you for some words of encouragement. Get a hug from your child and give back a kiss. Have a good cry to release some stress and pain. Do something good for yourself, even if it's only taking time to watch the quiet beauty of a sunrise or sunset. Be thankful for your child. Don't expect yourself to do every job perfectly. Take time to acknowledge the progress you've already made since your child's hearing loss was identified. Counting the "baby steps" helps you realize how far you've already come!

Getting the Family Involved

When a family unit is faced with a difficult situation, it's typical for all members to be affected. Sometimes it doesn't seem so because people may react differently from one another. Remember that some family members share your feelings and point of view and some have different feelings. Even two people feeling similarly may not have the same feelings at the same time. Since family members may be feeling emotions differently, realize that it's okay to let another family member take the lead until you are ready to join back in.

Parents

For children with two involved parents, it's not uncommon for each parent to react quite differently in times of stress. Parents can try to understand and support each other's feelings and ways of coping. Sometimes one parent shows his or her feelings much more than another, but this parent shouldn't assume the other isn't feeling anything. Parents may want to buffer each other from difficult people or situations for a while. They can encourage each other and agree to share some responsibility for meeting the child's needs. For single-parent families, help from extended family and friends is especially valuable. Although your child's needs are always on your mind, some days you need more support from your family than other days.

Siblings

In a family with a child with hearing loss, siblings are an important resource. Remember that siblings have their own unique reactions to changes in the family dynamic during stressful

times. Even though your child with hearing loss needs a lot of your time and attention, her siblings still need you just as much.

Early intervention and all the related services involve every member of your family. In family sessions with an early interventionist, siblings are just as important as your child with hearing loss. Siblings are great motivators! Family sessions can most certainly include your other children. Siblings often make great play and communication partners and offer a certain level of comfort and ease to your child with hearing loss.

Grandparents

The level of involvement of grandparents varies greatly. Some live out of town and visit for holidays and special occasions. Some live nearby and visit often for play dates. Some live under the same roof with you and your children. And some grandparents are raising grandchildren on their own. No matter what the grandparents' level of involvement, reactions to a grandchild's diagnosis of hearing loss vary. Some are supportive, some are distant, some take over and help and some just don't know what to do.

Some grandparents desire information. Some want to give advice. Some need to find a friendly listener so they can cry it out. Some are drawn to providing love and care for your other children. Some need time alone to process what's happening. Grandparents are certainly in a position to feel strongly about the situation, but not all are able to act on their feelings. Depending on your family's relationship with your child's grandparents, you as the parent can choose what role is suitable for the grandparents to play. Consider when and how you'd like to invite them to participate.

Extended family and friends

This group is likely large and may include your one best supporter. Some people in this group can be consistently supportive, while others might come and go. Try telling loved ones what you feel, know and need. Be grateful for your one best supporter. True supportive friends want to help and will be there when you need help. As you become more comfortable with your child's hearing loss, your friends will follow your lead.

Parents of children with typical hearing can be helpful to you as your child grows and changes. These parents can help you sort out which aspects of your child's development and behavior are typical for any child. You may enjoy sharing this type of information and supporting each other as your children grow up. Although it may be tempting to attribute any difficulty your child has to the hearing loss, you will see this is not always the case.

Explaining Your Child's Hearing Loss to Your Child

As a parent, you choose how to explain your child's hearing loss to her as well as to your other children. Many parents wonder about the best way to do this. Some even wonder if it's okay to talk about it at all — and if so, how to do it. Talking about your child's hearing loss with your child can be difficult, especially when she's an infant and when her language is limited. Yet, even when she's too young to respond, it's still okay to talk about her hearing loss. It's okay to say, in a positive and loving way, "You're deaf. You're wonderful, beautiful and so special to me. You're deaf. Your ears work differently than other people's ears." This doesn't have to be sad. In fact, you can present it to her as factual — just as you would tell her she's tall or brunette or smart or athletic.

If your child has older siblings, consider how to talk with them as well. Some parents choose to be transparent from the start, telling their children their sister is deaf, that she wears hearing aids or cochlear implants and she's learning how to talk. The way you do this is up to you.

Explaining Your Child's Hearing Loss to Others

First, you must learn about hearing and hearing loss. That's what your early interventionists (and this book) are for! Next, think about what you're ready to share. Some families tell everyone in their network about each part of this new journey. Other families prefer to keep the news of their child's hearing loss private until they better understand its implications. There isn't a right or wrong way. Do what feels right for you!

Others — neighbors, people in the grocery store or mall — will see your child's devices. They may notice how you communicate with her, or they may have heard your news. Some families find humor appropriate to curtail unwanted inquiries. Others like to debunk the myth that every child with hearing loss communicates only using sign language. Explaining that your child needs hearing aids or cochlear implants to hear your voice is easier when you yourself understand how this works. It will get easier with time. Meanwhile, here are some one-liners to get you started:

- "Ava has hearing loss."
- "Raymond is hearing-impaired and his hearing aids help him learn to talk."
- "Jada wears hearing aids so she can hear our voices and learn to listen and talk."
- "Billy has cochlear implants because he is deaf. They help him hear."
- "Nia is deaf and that's okay."
- "Those are hearing aids."
- "Someday, I'll be able to describe this to you, but right now, I just can't."

References

English, K. (2000). Personal adjustment counseling: It's an essential skill. *The Hearing Journal*, 53(10), 10, 14–16.

Jackson, C.W., Traub, R.J. & Turnbull, A.P. (2008). Parents' experiences with childhood deafness: Implications for family-centered services. *Communication Disorders Quarterly*, 29(2), 82–98. doi:10.1177/1525740108314865.

Jackson, C.W. & Turnbull, A. (2004). Impact of deafness on family life: A review of the literature. *Topics in Early Childhood Special Education*, 24(1), 15–29. doi:10.1177/02711214040240010201.

Kubler-Ross, E. (2014). *On Death and Dying: What the Dying Have to Teach Doctors, Nurses, Clergy and Their Own Families*. New York: Scribner.

Kubler-Ross, E. (1997). *Questions and Answers on Death and Dying: A Companion Volume to On Death and Dying*. New York: Touchstone.

Kurtzer-White, E. & Luterman, D. (2003). Families and children with hearing loss: Grief and coping. *Mental Retardation and Developmental Disabilities Research Reviews*, 9(4), 232–235. doi:10.1002/mrdd.10085.

Meadow-Orlans, K.P. (1980). *Deafness and Child Development*. Berkeley: University of California Press.

Moses, K. (1987). The impact of childhood disability: The parent's struggle. *WAYS Magazine, 6*, 6–10.

Sexton, J. (2009). The CARE project: Counseling, aural rehabilitation and education. *The Hearing Journal, 62*(7).

Chapter 2

Hearing Loss

Hearing loss can be a tricky and complicated topic. This chapter explains how typical hearing works, including the anatomy and function of the ear, as well as how to characterize when it's impaired.

Anatomy of the Ear

Typical ears have three main parts: the outer ear, the middle ear and the inner ear.

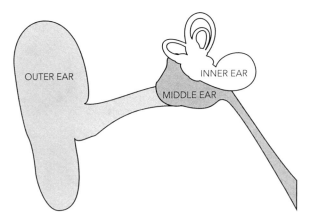

The Outer Ear

Take a look at your child's ears. The **outer ear**, or external ear, is the part of your child's ear you can see. It includes the **pinna**, on the outside of the head. It also includes the **ear canal** (technically called the **external auditory meatus**), the opening that begins to extend into the head. You can see part of the exterior canal; however, it also extends beyond where you can see, into the area that looks like a dark tunnel.

The Middle Ear

You can't see your child's **middle ear** because it's further inside her head. A healthy middle ear is an open, air-filled space that houses the moving bones between the eardrum and the oval window of the **cochlea**, or inner ear. You probably have observed the pediatrician or **audiologist** looking into your child's ear with an instrument called an **otoscope** that magnifies and lights the area. With this instrument, one can see the eardrum, which is the start of the middle ear. The **eardrum,** also called the **tympanic membrane,** is designed to vibrate. Sound causes the eardrum to vibrate somewhat like a drumstick causes the head of a drum to vibrate. Similar to the eardrum, the **oval window** of the cochlea is a membrane that separates two areas of the ear. The oval window is the transition point between the middle ear and inner ear.

The three little bones in the middle ear are called **ossicles**. These bones are the tiniest bones inside the human body! They have both scientific names and common names.

Scientific Name	Also Known As
malleus	hammer
incus	anvil
stapes	stirrup

Can you guess how these bones got their common names? Right! They look like a hammer, an anvil and a stirrup.

Sound waves enter the outer ear, travel through the ear canal and strike the tympanic membrane. This causes the tympanic membrane to move quickly back and forth. The ossicles, which are attached to the tympanic membrane, then vibrate as well. The vibration of the ossicles causes the oval window to vibrate. Think of this like the domino effect. As one structure moves, so do the rest. This process is how sound is "conducted" from the environment through the middle ear. Later, we'll discuss conductive hearing loss, which results from some problem with this process.

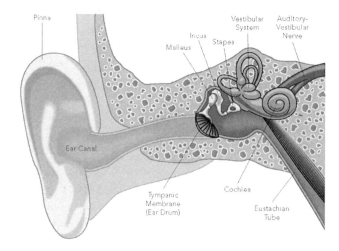

The Inner Ear

The **inner ear** is located just beyond the middle ear, in a section of the skull called the **mastoid bone**. It houses the cochlea, which connects to the auditory nerve. The cochlea is a bony, fluid-filled structure surrounded by the mastoid bone. It contains tens of thousands of tiny hair cells. The **cochlea** looks similar to a sea shell or a snail. It's very tiny — about the size of a pea.

Remember that sounds are received by the outer ear, then conducted through the middle ear. The **oval window** of the cochlea is the point at which the middle ear ends and the inner ear begins. The vibrations of the middle ear bones cause the oval window to vibrate. The vibration of the oval window causes the fluid in the cochlea to move as well. The fluid flows over the tiny hair cells in the cochlea, causing them to sway. The **hair cells** get their name because they're shaped like hairs. Remember that the cochlea is the size of a pea. The hair cells are so tiny, 15,000–18,000 of them fit into that tiny space. The moving hair cells trigger a chemical reaction that results in the stimulation of the **auditory nerve**. The auditory nerve, also called the **eighth cranial nerve**, sends a message to the brain. The brain then determines what sound was heard.

This may seem like a lot of information. It really is! So, to put something very complicated into simpler terms, the process goes like this:

Residual Hearing

You may hear professionals refer to the hearing your child has as residual hearing. **Residual hearing** is the hearing a person with hearing loss does have. People with less hearing loss have *more* residual hearing. People with more hearing loss have *less* residual hearing. Even people with very significant hearing loss typically have some amount of residual hearing. This may explain why you've noticed your child may sometimes respond to your voice when you hold her close, to an airplane overhead or to a barking dog. Your child is using her residual hearing! That's great. Residual hearing is important to keep in mind because it's the starting point for helping your child learn to listen and talk.

The "Simple" Process of Hearing

- The sound enters the ear.
- The eardrum moves.
- The middle ear bones vibrate.
- The fluid in the cochlea moves.
- The hair cells vibrate.
- The auditory nerve reacts.
- The message is sent to the brain.

If you're a person who likes figurative language, think of hearing loss in these terms:

It's not black and it's not white — it's some shade of gray.

In other words, most people with hearing loss have some level of hearing. Their hearing isn't typical, but it isn't completely absent either.

Describing Hearing Loss

Understanding how your child's hearing loss is described and categorized is important so *you* can become the expert on her hearing loss. Experts may have used terms related to hearing loss in one or more of the following ways:

- Your child is *deaf.*
- You have a *child with hearing impairment.*
- Your child is *hearing-impaired.*
- Your child has a *hearing loss.*
- Your child is *hard of hearing.*

Over the years, you may become comfortable with one term more than another. There are many ways to describe hearing loss and it's up to you to decide which term feels best to you. You should know that many people use these terms interchangeably, even though one might sound more appropriate to you than others. This book uses the term "hearing loss" to refer to the physical explanation of your child's hearing ability.

Categorizing Hearing Loss

In the course of this chapter, you can learn to understand more precise ways to describe the extent to which your child can hear. Your child's hearing loss can be described by its type or origin, degree or severity, initiation, shifts, location and cause of loss.

Type (or Origin)	Degree (or Severity)	Initiation (or When)	Shifts	Location (or Where)	Cause (or How)
Conductive	Normal	Congenital	Stable	Unilateral	Known
Sensorineural	Slight	Acquired	Fluctuating	Bilateral	• Environmental
Mixed	Mild	• Prelingual	Progressive	• Asymmetric	• Genetic
	Moderate	• Postlingual		• Symmetric	Unknown
	Moderately severe				• Environmental
	Severe				• Genetic
	Profound				

Types of Hearing Loss

Conductive Hearing Loss

Conductive hearing loss is caused by a problem in the outer or middle ear space. This is a very common type of hearing loss found in children. It has many causes. Some of the causes are temporary and others are permanent.

Although some conductive hearing loss can be permanent, many cases can be managed medically or surgically. Some surgical repairs for conductive hearing loss resulting from craniofacial abnormalities are performed on children only after they are at least five or six years old. This is because some surgical options are available only when your child is older and bigger.

In the case of conductive hearing loss, it's critical to provide an infant or young child access to spoken language through the use of hearing aids. This is particularly important during the first phase of the critical period of language development (birth to 3 years old). It is important even if, at a later time, the family opts to investigate medical intervention with a surgeon.

Temporary Causes of Conductive Hearing Loss

- ear infection (otitis media)
- build-up of fluid in the middle ear
- foreign object in the ear canal
- damage to the eardrum

Permanent Causes of Conductive Hearing Loss

Permanent causes of conductive hearing loss are usually physical abnormalities of the face and/or skull such as:
- malformation or absence of the pinna (The pinna is the visible part of the ear on the head.)
- narrowing or complete closure of the ear canal
- problems with the bones in the middle ear

Sensorineural Hearing Loss

Sensorineural hearing loss occurs when there is a problem in the inner ear, the cochlea or the auditory nerve. One cannot see sensorineural hearing loss by examining the outer or middle ear because those parts of the ear are functioning and may appear normal. Sensorineural hearing loss is permanent. The majority of children with sensorineural hearing loss, even those with profound hearing loss, can benefit from hearing devices such as hearing aids or cochlear implants.

Mixed Hearing Loss

Mixed hearing loss occurs when one has both conductive and sensorineural hearing losses. This can be temporary, such as when a child who has sensorineural hearing loss gets an ear infection. Or it can be permanent, such as when a child who has sensorineural hearing loss also has no outer ear.

Degree (or Severity) of Hearing Loss

You may have heard someone describe hearing loss in terms of percentage (as in "75 percent deaf in my right ear" or "100 percent deaf in both ears"). This is inaccurate. It is far more meaningful to describe hearing loss in a different way. Hearing loss is divided into different categories, or ranges, representing the **degree** of hearing loss. The most often used terms are:

- normal
- slight
- mild
- moderate
- moderately severe
- severe
- profound

The specific levels that make up these degrees are neither exact nor absolute. Think of them more as ranges. When you hear your own child's hearing loss described, you may find the terms are combined to most accurately describe the levels of hearing. In children, degree of hearing loss is commonly described using these measurements:

- normal   0–15   dB HL   the sound of a whisper
- slight   15–25   dB HL
- mild   25–40   dB HL
- moderate   40–55   dB HL
- moderately severe   55–70   dB HL
- severe   70–90   dB HL
- profound   90+   dB HL   the sound of an airplane

If you'd like to see a chart with these numbers, turn to Chapter 4. Notice the degrees of hearing loss listed along the right side of the *Familiar Sounds Audiogram.*

Decibels

You may have heard a professional talk about decibels or you may have seen it written on some of your child's paperwork. The unit of measure used to describe sound for hearing testing is called a **decibel (dB)**. More formally, it is a unit of measurement describing the power or intensity of sound. HL stands for **hearing level**. The unit of measure for hearing loss on most audiograms is dB HL, decibels hearing level.

Understanding decibels can be tricky. What's important to know is that 0 decibels doesn't mean there is no sound. Instead, 0 decibels refers to a really soft sound for a healthy human ear. This is important to know as you talk with your audiologist about your child's hearing loss.

Why Not Use Percentages (%)?

The human ear is a complex organ and sound measurement is also complex. Percentages are relatively simple. To *meaningfully* describe hearing loss, we need a more descriptive unit of measure, which is the decibel. Decibels are the most meaningful way to describe the loudness of sound. It would be far less meaningful to describe hearing loss using simple percentages or ratios.

For example, hearing loss could be *meaningfully* described in the following ways:

- My child has a moderate hearing loss at the right ear and moderate sloping to profound hearing loss at the left ear.
- My child has bilateral profound sensorineural hearing loss.

It would be far less meaningful to describe hearing loss in either of the following ways:

- I have only 50 percent hearing at my left ear.
- My child has 90 percent hearing at one ear and 40 percent hearing at the other.

Hertz

Hertz is the other commonly used term when referring to hearing loss. **Hertz (Hz)** is a measure of frequency or pitch. Like a piano, the inner ear is organized by pitch. One end is low pitch and the other end is high pitch. More formally, Hertz is the number of cycles per second in a sound wave. More cycles per second makes for a higher frequency sound. Fewer cycles per second, and therefore a smaller number of Hertz, makes for lower frequency sounds.

Don't worry if this new terminology sounds overwhelming. Your audiologist understands these measures. With time, so will you. If you have questions about your child's degree of hearing loss, ask the audiologist at your next appointment or talk with your early interventionist. The more times you have the conversation, the more comfortable you'll become with the information.

Onset of Hearing Loss

The onset of your child's hearing loss is either congenital or acquired. Acquired hearing loss is further categorized as either prelingual or postlingual. Read on for more information describing these terms.

More About Decibels (dB)

The decibel scale is logarithmic, which means it's not linear. Here's how it works: For every 3 dB increase, sound is actually twice as intense.

Have we lost you? Take, for example, a 50 dB sound. To make that sound twice as intense, you would need to make it 53 dB (not 100 dB).

Now, think about a 60 dB sound. A 60 dB sound is *not* twice as intense as a 30 dB sound. A 60 dB sound is actually twice as intense as a 57 dB sound.

So why does this matter? As you learn about your child's hearing loss and the way her hearing is tested and measured, this will be important. Small changes in decibel level are significant when talking about hearing ability.

As always, your audiologist will be able to answer specific questions you have about decibels and your child's hearing. For now, see Chapter 4 for more information on describing your child's hearing ability in terms of decibels.

Congenital vs. Acquired Hearing Loss

It's important to recognize when a hearing loss first begins. Some children are born with hearing loss, while others are born with typical hearing and acquire hearing loss as they age. When a child is born with hearing loss, it's considered congenital in nature. With the advent of universal newborn hearing screening, children with **congenital hearing loss** can be referred for follow-up testing as early as 24 hours old!

Acquired hearing loss describes any kind of hearing loss that wasn't present at birth. Noise-induced hearing loss, like that which elderly people or rock stars often have, is acquired hearing loss. Acquired hearing loss in the birth to 3 population can result from trauma, disease (for example, meningitis, measles, encephalitis, chicken pox, influenza, mumps) or the use of ototoxic medications (Cone et al., 2011).

Aminoglycoside antibiotics, such as gentamicin, are examples of **ototoxic medications** (Cone et al., 2011). This means they may cause permanent damage to the hearing system. Physicians should be aware of the side effects of this class of drugs and administer them only when the potential benefit to a child's health outweighs the risk of hearing loss.

Prelingual vs. Postlingual Hearing Loss

If the hearing loss is acquired, it's usually also described as *prelingual* or *postlingual*. These categories are used to describe the time frame when the hearing loss begins in relation to when a child learns to talk. **Prelingual hearing loss** refers to loss that occurs before a child has learned to listen and talk. **Postlingual hearing loss** refers to hearing that becomes impaired after a person has already learned to listen and talk.

Shifts in Hearing

Hearing loss can also be described by changes that may occur in the degree of hearing loss over periods of time. Hearing loss that does not change is called **stable hearing loss**. A child with a stable hearing loss does not show any changes in hearing levels over time.

A hearing loss is described as fluctuating when the degree of loss regularly improves and worsens over time. A child might have a **fluctuating hearing loss** that seems to get better one week, then worse a few weeks later, then better the next day, then worse the next month. Fluctuating loss can be very tricky because hearing levels can change on any given day. This can make accurately programming hearing aids difficult. Sometimes parents are able to perceive these changes readily and report them to their audiologist. Don't worry if you aren't able to see these changes right away. Your early interventionist can help you recognize behaviors that may be signs of fluctuating hearing levels. Additionally, some changes may be so subtle that they are hard to recognize.

With **progressive hearing loss,** the degree of hearing loss worsens over time. Sometimes the degree of loss is minimal; other times the degree of loss is significant. This is often referred to as a "drop in hearing." Children with some causes of hearing loss and some syndromes (for example, cytomegalovirus, unilateral hearing loss, Enlarged Vestibular Aqueduct Syndrome, Usher Syndrome and Pendred Syndrome) are at greater risk for progressive hearing loss. Children whose ears have two very different degrees of hearing loss (that is, one ear responds to sound much better than the other) may be at greater risk for progressive hearing loss as well.

Location of Hearing Loss
Unilateral vs. Bilateral Hearing Loss

A child with **unilateral hearing loss** has typical hearing at one ear and hearing loss at the other ear. Children with unilateral hearing loss often appear to learn language with ease, but may struggle in noisy situations, including classroom environments. Some research indicates that unilateral hearing loss negatively affects language development and school success — most specifically, social language.

A child with **bilateral hearing loss** has loss that affects both ears. If the child has bilateral hearing loss, it also will be categorized as symmetric or asymmetric. **Symmetric hearing loss** occurs when the degree of loss in both ears is the same. **Asymmetric hearing loss** occurs when the ears have different degrees of loss. (Unilateral hearing loss is inherently asymmetric, as it affects only one ear.)

Auditory Neuropathy Spectrum Disorder

Some children with hearing loss have a disorder called **Auditory Neuropathy Spectrum Disorder (ANSD)**. ANSD is characterized by normal cochlear function yet a problem with how sound is transmitted or carried from the auditory nerve to the brain. Children with ANSD encounter problems with the overall clarity of speech that are not necessarily related to the degree of hearing loss. ANSD is diagnosed using a combination of results from Otoacoustic Emissions (OAE) testing and Auditory Brainstem Response (ABR) testing. (More information on these tests can be found in Chapter 3.)

ANSD characteristics may differ for each child. For example, some children experience mild problems related specifically to understanding speech in noisy environments, while others experience significant problems understanding speech in all types of listening environments (quiet or noisy). Degree of hearing loss varies among children and can range from mild to profound. The threshold levels and the symptoms may fluctuate from month to month, day to day or within hours. Because the thresholds and the symptoms vary, a child with ANSD needs to see a pediatric audiologist frequently for monitoring.

Causes of Hearing Loss

Some parents feel they can better accept the diagnosis of hearing loss if they know the cause. It may be important to know the cause of hearing loss because it could be relevant at some later point in your life, such as when considering having another child or when your child wants to have children of her own. It's your choice as a parent to look into the cause of your child's hearing loss — or not. Knowing the cause of your child's hearing loss may or may not affect your decisions about her medical, audiologic or educational needs. For some parents, finding the cause provides a certain peace of mind. For others, it does not. In the end, the choice is yours.

Sometimes you can look for the cause and not find it. In some cases, the cause of hearing loss may be undeterminable or unknown. However, hearing loss with an unknown cause has either a genetic cause or an environmental cause. It's just that sometimes the type and specific nature of the cause cannot be determined by current test methods.

Whether known or unknown, causes of hearing loss can be divided into two main categories:

- environmental causes
- genetic (or hereditary) causes

Environmental Causes

Hearing loss caused by environmental factors may occur in utero while the fetus is developing, during delivery, soon after birth or in childhood and beyond. Doctors continue to study environmental causes of hearing loss and to discover new causes. Environmental causes of hearing loss in children might involve one or more of the following:

During pregnancy

- toxemia
- maternal diabetes
- maternal infections such as cytomegalovirus (CMV), syphilis or toxoplasmosis
- other maternal viral or bacterial illnesses
- maternal use of alcohol
- maternal exposure to radiation

At or after birth

- prematurity, including low birth weight, lack of oxygen and use of mechanical oxygen
- birth trauma
- childhood illnesses such as rubella, meningitis, encephalitis, infantile measles or mumps
- severe injury to the head and/or ears
- exposure to radiation
- continual, untreated otitis media
- ototoxic medications (some types/doses of antibiotics)
- lead poisoning
- excessive noise for an extended duration

Genetic Causes

Genetic hearing loss is the result of some hereditary, or inherited, disorder. There are hundreds of different known genetic types of hearing loss, and new types are continually being discovered. Although some of these numerous types have been identified through genetic research, some children have types of hereditary hearing loss that have not yet been identified. Many of these children have hearing loss without other medical problems.

To get a better understanding of the causes, it's helpful to know how **geneticists** describe genetic hearing loss. Geneticists are medical professionals who study genes and conduct research to learn more about them. Any genetic disorder, including hearing loss, can be classified in one of the following ways:

- dominant trait
- recessive trait
- X-linked
- other rare types

With **dominant trait hearing loss**, typically one parent of the child has hearing loss. The family history shows many family members with hearing loss in successive generations on one side of the family. With this type of hearing loss, there is a 50 percent chance that any one child of these parents will inherit hearing loss.

With **recessive trait hearing loss**, both parents have typical hearing, but both are carriers of a hidden trait for hearing loss. There may be no family members with hearing loss or there may be a distant family member, such as a third cousin, with hearing loss. For many people, it's difficult to believe a child can inherit hearing loss if both parents have typical hearing, but it's true. With this type of hereditary condition, the parents have typical hearing and may have no idea they carry a recessive gene for hearing loss. Recessive trait hearing loss is often discovered after parents have one child with hearing loss and then another child with hearing loss. This can also be investigated through genetic testing.

All of us carry recessive traits for various illnesses or disorders. In most cases, we do not become aware of it because we do not produce a child with a partner who has the same recessive traits we carry. If your child's cause of hearing loss is unknown, heredity could be a cause. When two parents are both carriers of a recessive trait associated with hearing loss, there is a 25 percent chance that any one child of these two parents will inherit a hearing loss.

With **X-linked hearing loss** (which is rare), one parent is a carrier. Inheritance varies based on the gender of the child and on which parent passed along the affected gene. This type of inherited hearing loss is related to the gender-linked chromosomes, for which females have XX chromosomes and males have XY chromosomes.

Sometimes geneticists can determine the cause of a child's hearing loss. In addition to dominant, recessive and X-linked, other genetic conditions can occur. These additional conditions are relatively rare. Some children show a collection of various differences or disorders that suggest their hearing loss may be part of a syndrome. If you or any professional working with your child suspects this, you might choose to look into genetic evaluation. You can find a geneticist at most major children's hospitals and university hospitals.

About the Cause of Your Child's Hearing Loss

Whether it's known or unknown, it can be upsetting to think about the cause of your child's hearing loss. If you want help with this issue, talk to your child's doctor, pediatric audiologist, early interventionist, teacher or therapist. Ask whether a geneticist could help you. Remember: *You are not to blame.* It's not uncommon for parents to feel guilty at times. Try to invest your energy in helping your child. Or try to uncover the cause if you or others feel this is important. You will want to carefully consider a genetic evaluation if a physician or speech and hearing professional suggests one for your child.

The reason a hearing health professional would encourage genetic testing is to provide information that might help personalize and individualize your child's care. Genetic testing should never be encouraged as a method for placing blame or assigning guilt. In the end, the pursuit of genetic testing is a decision for you to make as a family.

Genetic Testing: Is It for You?

Your child's ear nose and throat doctor (ENT) or pediatrician may encourage you to pursue genetic testing. You may wonder if the information obtained will be valuable to your family. Genetic testing may help you understand the cause of your child's hearing loss and help predict if your child's hearing loss could progress (or get worse). The results may allow your child to forgo other clinical tests that can be used to find the cause of hearing loss.

How is genetic testing used?
- to diagnose a disease or syndrome
- to determine if a parent carries a gene mutation that can lead to a disorder in the child
- to predict if a disease may occur in the future

You are not alone!
You may find that your child's pediatrician, ENT doctor, pediatric audiologist or early interventionist can help you through this decision-making process; however, you may chose to seek the guidance of a geneticist to understand the most up-to-date information about how genetic testing is advised related to hearing loss.

How do they test my child's genes?
Most genetic tests are performed on a DNA sample taken from a cheek swab or a blood sample.

Who will do the test and how will we pay for it?
The cost and availability of testing varies depending on where you live. If you need help finding a lab, you can ask your medical team or check out this site: www.genetests.org. The cost may range depending on the extent of testing. Be sure to check with your insurance provider because many companies pay for these tests.

Will the results harm my child?
Some families worry that the results of a genetic test will lead to discrimination from insurance companies or future employers. There are many laws protecting individuals from such discrimination. You can learn about the laws in your state at genome.gov/10002077.

Write down your thoughts and discuss them with your child's pediatrician, ENT doctor, pediatric audiologist or early interventionist. Ultimately, this is your decision!

(Adapted from: http://hearing.harvard.edu/tests.htm. See also Rehm, 2003.)

As of the publication date of this book, the two most commonly tested genetic markers for hearing loss are **Connexin 26** and **Connexin 30**.

References

Cone, B., Dorn, P., Konrad-Martin, D., Lister, J. & Ortiz, C. (2011). *Ototoxic Medications.*
Audiology Information Series. American Speech-Language-Hearing Association. Retrieved from
http://www.asha.org/uploadedFiles/AIS-Ototoxic-Medications.pdf#search=%22ototoxic%22.

Harvard Medical School Center for Hereditary Deafness (n.d.). Retrieved May 28, 2013 from
http://hearing.harvard.edu/tests.htm.

Rehm, H.L. (2003). Genetics and the genome project. *Ear and Hearing, 24*(4), 270–274.

Chapter 3

Hearing Tests

How Did You Get Here?
Universal Newborn Hearing Screening

You may be wondering what started you on this new journey with your baby. For most families, your child may have had a quick hearing screening shortly after she was born during your stay in the hospital. This hearing screening is part of the battery of newborn screenings all babies born in U.S. hospitals receive shortly after birth.

Universal Newborn Hearing Screening (UNHS), mandated in most U.S. states, requires birthing centers and hospitals to provide hearing screenings within the first few days of life. Babies born at home should also receive hearing screenings. UNHS is extremely important because it can give you information about your child's hearing very early on. If your child's hearing loss is diagnosed early, you will be able to start receiving early intervention services while she is still an infant. Early intervention is extremely important for a baby with hearing loss. One reason for this is because it allows you to obtain hearing devices (hearing aids and sometimes a cochlear implant) right away. Another reason early intervention is important is that you can begin a program that helps you understand and learn how to support your baby's development. Early diagnosis through UNHS allows for early intervention right from the start. (For more information on early intervention, see Chapter 19.)

The actual method used for UNHS can vary by hospital. Most use auditory brainstem response (ABR) testing or otoacoustic emissions (OAE) testing. Initially, these tests are used to screen the infant's hearing. If the infant passes the screening, the parents are informed that she has passed. If the infant does not pass the screening, an audiologist (or other professional) informs the parents and makes a referral for diagnostic testing.

Where Do You Go from Here?

Now that you've sought information about your child's hearing and found that it may not be typical, you can expect that your child's hearing will need to be tested regularly by a pediatric audiologist. To feel comfortable about your child's **audiology** appointments, you probably want to know what to expect. Many kinds of hearing tests are available. Your child's hearing may be tested in several ways. Keep reading to learn about characteristics of hearing tests.

Hearing Screenings and Diagnostic Hearing Testing: What's the Difference?

Before getting into the many types of possible hearing tests your child might receive, it's important to know the purpose of each test. Some tests are for screening, while others are for diagnosing. Some tests are objective, while others are subjective. Knowing these variables will give you a better understanding of the hearing tests your child has already had and help you feel more comfortable with future testing.

Hearing Screenings

Screenings determine whether a child needs further testing. Screenings are usually quick and simple. There are many ways to perform hearing screenings.

Tests used for **screenings** can be performed by many people. Below is a list of tests used for screenings and the most likely person to perform each test:

Automated Auditory Brainstem Response Test (ABR)
performed by a trained technician or audiologist
(For more information, see page 30.)

Automated Otoacoustic Emissions Test (OAE)
performed by a trained technician or audiologist
(For more information, see page 31.)

Behavioral Hearing Tests
performed by an audiologist
(For more information, see page 35.)

Gross Hearing Tests
performed by parents or anyone
(For more information, see page 44.)

Hearing screening results: Pass vs. refer

In the United States, approximately three in 1,000 babies are born with permanent hearing loss (Ross et al., 2008). Most states legislate that every newborn is required to have a hearing screening during the first few days of life. To save parents time and money, all children are given a quick hearing screening at birth while in the hospital. Most screenings performed in a hospital use equipment that is automated, so the results appear to the technician or audiologist as "pass" or "refer." Only those who do not pass the screening are referred for further testing.

If your child is referred for further testing, it's very important to know the reason. A child who is referred simply requires additional testing. It is not uncommon for a child to "refer" because of something relatively simple like wax in the ears, a cold or congestion — or even from making noise and being active during the test. Knowing the reason for referral can help you feel informed and empowered.

Pass

If the newborn "passes" the screening, further hearing testing would not be done unless either the parent or physician has a concern, or until the child reaches the age where she begins formal school. Once a child begins formal schooling, hearing screenings are done on a regular basis either at school or possibly in a doctor's office. Children who "pass" the newborn hearing screening, but have one or more high risk factors should also be referred for follow-up hearing testing. Some high risk factors identified by the **Joint Committee on Infant Hearing** are listed below.

Refer

If the newborn *does not pass* the screening, the result will be to "refer." "Refer" means the child needs further testing. Sometimes a child is referred for another screening, and sometimes a child is referred for diagnostic testing. A pediatric audiologist or other professional should refer the parents for further testing by giving them information about where to go and what to do.

Joint Committee on Infant Hearing

The JCIH (Joint Committee on Infant Hearing) is a national organization that addresses issues "important to the early identification, intervention and follow-up care of infants and young children with hearing loss."

The following are recommendations from the JCIH 2007 Position Statement:

When testing should occur
- All infants should have hearing screening at birth.
- If your infant stayed in the hospital Neonatal Intensive Care Unit (NICU) for more than five days, she should have an ABR test after being discharged.
- If your infant did not pass the ABR test, either at birth or after discharge from the NICU, she should be directly referred to an audiologist for rescreening.
- If your infant needs rescreening, a complete test should be done on both ears during the rescreening.
- If your infant was admitted into the hospital within one month of birth and had conditions that could be associated with hearing loss, she should have rescreening before discharge from the hospital or soon after.

Joint Committee on Infant Hearing *(continued)*

Conditions for diagnostic testing

- If your infant needs diagnostic testing and treatment services (such as selection and fitting of hearing devices), this should be done by an audiologist with expertise in evaluating newborns and infants with hearing loss.
- Your infant should have at least one ABR test as part of a complete diagnostic test (for children younger than 3 years old).

Risk factors for hearing loss

Some children have risk factors that make them more likely to have or develop hearing loss. Some risk factors are:

- caregiver concern regarding hearing, speech, language or developmental delay
- family history of permanent childhood hearing loss
- more than five days spent in the NICU
- some treatments given to the infant such as extracorporeal membrane oxygenation (ECMO), assistive ventilation, exposure to ototoxic medications, loop diuretics or hyperbilirubinemia with exchange transfusion
- infections the mother had during pregnancy such as cytomegalovirus (CMV), herpes, rubella, syphilis or toxoplasmosis
- craniofacial anomalies
- physical characteristics associated with hearing loss
- syndromes associated with hearing loss such as neurofibromatosis, osteopetrosis, Usher, Waardenburg, Alport, Pendred or Jervell and Lange-Nielson
- neurodegenerative disorders such as Hunter syndrome
- sensory motor neuropathies such as Friedreich Ataxia or Charcot-Marie-Tooth Syndrome
- infections such as bacterial or viral meningitis
- head trauma
- chemotherapy

Testing children with risk factors for hearing loss

- The timing and number of hearing tests should be individualized for your child if she shows one or more risk factors.
- If your infant passes the hearing screening at birth but has one or more risk factors, she should have at least one diagnostic audiology assessment by 30 months of age.
- If your child has certain conditions such as cytomegalovirus (CMV), syndromes associated with progressive hearing loss, neurodegenerative disorders, head trauma, infections associated with hearing loss, extracorporeal membrane oxygenation (ECMO), exposure to chemotherapy or family history of hearing loss — or if you are concerned about hearing loss — she should have early and frequent hearing tests.
- If your child is diagnosed with hearing loss and you choose for her to wear a hearing device, she should be fit with that device within one month of the diagnosis.

Diagnostic Hearing Testing

Diagnostic testing is done to determine a **diagnosis**, the formal indication of impairment or disability that may affect your child's development. Screenings are quicker and simpler; diagnostic testing is more time-consuming and elaborate.

You may have noticed that OAEs and ABRs are tests used for both screenings and diagnostic testing. You may also have noticed that different individuals can perform these tests. OAE diagnostic testing uses technology similar to OAE screening. The difference between the two is that *the screening* is automated. It works the same with ABR. ABR hearing screening is automated and ABR diagnostic testing is not. As is the case with all diagnostic hearing testing, a skilled pediatric audiologist performs the testing and draws conclusions about potential hearing loss.

ABR testing, OAE testing, tympanometry and behavioral testing are all considered objective hearing tests. **Objective hearing tests** give a valid report of hearing ability based on reliable indicators. Objective tests are not affected by the tester's bias, opinions or beliefs. Because children are involved, behavioral testing involves some element of subjectivity. Yet all objective testing, including behavioral testing, follows systematic and specific protocol so that those performing the testing can feel confident the results are legitimate.

Tests used for diagnosis (diagnostic testing) are listed below with the person most likely to conduct each test:

Auditory Brainstem Response Test (ABR)
performed by an audiologist
(For more information, see page 30.)

Otoacoustic Emissions Test (OAE)
performed by an audiologist
(For more information, see page 31.)

Tympanometry
performed by an audiologist or ENT doctor
(For more information, see page 33.)

Behavioral Hearing Tests
performed by an audiologist
(For more information, see page 35.)

Why Not Start with Diagnostic Testing?

In both the medical and educational fields, screenings are a cost-effective way to look at a large group of people and identify a small number of them who may need additional medical or educational support. It would not be time-efficient or cost-effective for the hospital or birthing center to perform detailed diagnostic testing on every individual when it's likely only a small percentage would truly need additional support.

For example, remember when you had a vision screening in elementary school? The school nurse performed a quick and simple screening on every child in your school. Then, he or she identified those who did not pass the screening. The families of those children were notified and asked to have their children evaluated by an eye specialist. The testing that takes place at an optometrist's office is diagnostic. As a method of saving parents' time and money, only children who did not pass the vision screening were referred to optometrists for diagnostic testing. The same is true with hearing screening. A quick test is done to determine if further testing is needed. Only those who do not pass the screening are referred for further testing.

Types of Hearing Tests

It's important to be familiar with these tests so you understand why a certain method of testing is used, recognize how your child's hearing is evaluated and know what to expect during testing.

Auditory Brainstem Response (ABR) Test

Auditory brainstem response (ABR) is a way to test auditory brainstem function in response to sound. ABR is used to estimate hearing levels in babies or children who cannot give behavioral responses, or with children who give inconsistent responses to sound. The ABR test shows how effectively sound progresses from the inner ear to the brain, how long it takes sound to get to the brain and how loud sounds need to be for your child to hear them. Movement can affect the test results, so this type of testing requires the child to be very still, preferably sleeping. Infants and very young children can have what is called a sleep-deprived ABR. The parents are asked to keep the baby awake for an extended period before the test. The parents then arrive with the baby at the ABR appointment, feed the baby and allow her to sleep. The test begins once she is soundly asleep. For infants around six months old, another option is the sedated ABR. While parents and professionals certainly do not take sedation lightly, it allows for the most accurate test response for some children, particularly active ones. Your pediatric audiologist or physician will determine whether your child will benefit more from a sleep-deprived ABR test or sedated ABR test.

ABR testing is noninvasive and painless. It is usually conducted by a pediatric audiologist who places electrodes on your child's head and small insert earphones in her ears. **Elec-**

trodes look like little wires with sticky pads on the ends that adhere to your child's face and head. They are used to record electrical activity in the brain. **Insert earphones** are little pieces of foam material (similar to disposable earplugs) that connect by a wire to a sound system in an audiology testing area. By putting an earphone in each ear, your pediatric audiologist is able to test each of your child's ears separately. Your child's hearing loss might not be identical at each ear, so it's important to know the specific levels individually. Insert earphones are also nice for babies and small children because they come in a variety of sizes that fit nicely into their little ears. When your pediatric audiologist places earphones in your child's ears, you won't be able to hear the sounds presented. Your pediatric audiologist presents a series of tones or clicks through the earphones. The tones range from low-frequency to mid-frequency to high-frequency. The clicks represent a broad band of frequencies from approximately 1000 to 4000 Hz. Wires carry the information from the electrodes to the computer. The computer then produces a reading of the brain's activity in response to the sounds. After the test, your pediatric audiologist explains the results and any further action to take, which may include seeing a doctor while you're there.

ABR testing can be used for screening or for diagnostic testing. ABR screening lasts about 20 minutes and at the end, the results are presented to the parents as "pass" or "refer." If your child passes, the technician will tell you she passed. If your child refers, the technician will consult with you about what further action you should take. This may involve either a visit to an ear, nose and throat (ENT) doctor or pediatric audiologist for behavioral testing or diagnostic ABR — either sleep-deprived or sedated.

Conversely, diagnostic ABR testing usually lasts a couple of hours. Diagnostic ABR testing is used to determine your child's type of hearing loss (sensorineural, conductive or mixed) and estimate the degree of hearing loss (normal, slight, mild, moderate, moderately-severe, severe or profound). Unlike an ABR screening resulting in a "pass" or "refer," diagnostic ABR testing results in a comprehensive report of specific details about your child's hearing status at each ear. If necessary, for example if the test was not completed during the initial session, an audiologist will schedule a follow-up appointment to repeat the ABR. This is usually because the child woke up before testing was complete. More information about categories of hearing loss, including types and degrees, can be found in Chapter 2.

Otoacoustic Emissions (OAE) Test

When a sound is sent into a typically functioning ear, the ear produces its own sound in response. Did you know that? You can think of these as a kind of echo, but they're actually called an **otoacoustic emissions** (OAEs). OAE testing is a way to check inner ear structures — mainly hair cell function — of babies or children who cannot give behavioral responses. It can be used for screening or for diagnostic testing.

The purpose of the OAE test is to determine the presence or absence of hair cell responses. During this test, your child should experience no pain or discomfort. Typically, you hold her or she sits on your lap. A **probe tip** is a soft, comfortable plastic device that fits into your child's ear and is attached by a long cord to a small machine. Probe tips come in a variety of sizes to ensure a good fit. A combination of soft sounds is presented through the probe tip. The OAE from your child's ear returns to the probe tip. The machine measures the "echo" and provides a reading.

Since the machine measures these very soft OAEs, any noise your child makes can interfere with the result. Therefore, it's necessary for her to be very quiet during the test. This can be difficult, particularly for an active child. It can be helpful to schedule this test around nap time, after you have fed her. It usually takes less than 15 minutes, but it could take longer if she is active and making some noise.

OAE testing is most often used for screening. If your child refers (does not pass) an OAE screening, the technician will consult with you about what further action to take. OAE testing can also be diagnostic. Often a pediatric audiologist will use diagnostic OAE testing during the first diagnostic appointment to obtain baseline data about your child's hearing loss. This is a normal part of the diagnostic process.

Ongoing monitoring of OAEs is needed for children whose pediatric audiologist and/or ENT doctor suspect auditory neuropathy spectrum disorder (ANSD). If any professional working with your child has mentioned this condition, ask him or her for the specifics on how it might affect your child's development. For more information on ANSD, see Chapter 9.

Otoscopy and Visual Examination

Otoscopy is a visual examination of the ear performed by an audiologist. The examination is done with an instrument called an **otoscope**, which is just a lighted magnifier. The purpose of otoscopy is to enable your pediatric audiologist to see if there is excessive wax in the ear canal, a foreign object your curious little person tried to stick in there or any other blockage. This is particularly important before a hearing test because if something is blocking the canal, sound will not pass through appropriately. If your child's ear canals are open and clear, your pediatric audiologist can usually get a good look at the tympanic membrane or eardrum. A good, healthy eardrum looks pearly and is reflective when the light shines on it. An unhealthy eardrum can appear dull, cloudy, red or inflamed. If your pediatric audiologist observes these characteristics, she might suggest an appointment with the ENT doctor before proceeding with audiologic testing.

Tympanometry

Tympanometry is a quick test that measures the movement of the eardrum to determine if there is any abnormality with the eardrum or middle ear. The middle ear is an open space behind the eardrum that should be filled only with air. Tympanometry shows whether sound is impeded, or held back, when moving from the middle ear to the inner ear. Because it measures impedance, it is considered a type of audiometry called **impedance audiometry**. Tympanometry is fast and easy (it takes less than one minute) and helps determine if your child's eardrum movement and middle ear function are normal.

To perform tympanometry, your pediatric audiologist or physician places a soft probe tip into your child's ear canal. The different colored tips represent different sizes and ensure a tight-fitting seal when the tip is placed in the ear. At the push of a button, air flows from a machine called a **tympanometer** through the probe into your child's ear. The tympanometer mechanically alters the amount of air pressure in the ear canal. While this procedure does not hurt, it might feel a little unusual to your child as pressure builds in the ear canal. As the pressure changes, the machine records the movement of the eardrum. If the eardrum is intact and normal and the middle ear space is clear and free from fluid and infection, the eardrum moves freely. A **tympanogram**, or printout with information about the eardrum's response, is produced by the tympanometer.

Tympanogram tracing

A tympanogram includes a graph with a line on it called a tracing. A normal tracing looks like a mountain. An abnormal tracing appears as a flat line, an almost flat line like a molehill or no line at all. This tracing is referred to as a flat tracing and indicates the eardrum is not moving as it should. A flat tracing is often caused by negative pressure in the middle ear. Reasons for an abnormal tracing include:

- excessive wax obstructing the ear canal
- a punctured or torn eardrum
- fluid in the middle ear
- infection in the middle ear
- a blocked or inflamed Eustachian tube
- pressure-equalizing tubes

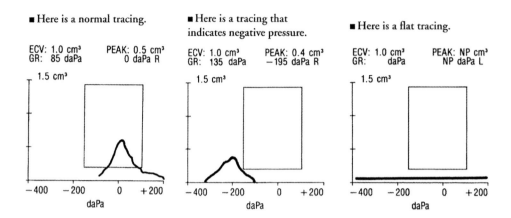

■ Here is a normal tracing.

ECV: 1.0 cm³
GR: 85 daPa
PEAK: 0.5 cm³
0 daPa R

1.5 cm³

−400 −200 0 +200
daPa

■ Here is a tracing that indicates negative pressure.

ECV: 1.0 cm³
GR: 135 daPa
PEAK: 0.4 cm³
−195 daPa R

1.5 cm³

−400 −200 0 +200
daPa

■ Here is a flat tracing.

ECV: 1.0 cm³
GR: daPa
PEAK: NP cm³
NP daPa L

1.5 cm³

−400 −200 0 +200
daPa

The three tympanograms above illustrate a normal tracing, a flat tracing and a tracing indicating negative pressure.

A flat tracing means your child is probably not receiving quality auditory information. Problems with the eardrum or middle ear can detrimentally affect your child's hearing by limiting eardrum movement or blocking sound from moving through the ear normally. This may cause a conductive hearing loss. It's essential for children, even those with typical hearing, to maintain quality auditory input most of the time so listening, language and speech skills can develop optimally.

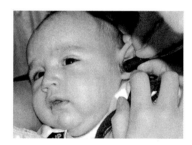

If your child has a flat tracing, your pediatric audiologist may suggest you see a pediatrician or ENT doctor for medical treatment. The physician may treat and/or monitor your child to see that the fluid decreases and/or the infection clears up. Treatment might include antibiotics or even placement of **pressure equalizing tubes**. (For more information on tubes, see Chapter 5.) It's particularly important for problems in the middle ear to be medically treated (if possible) because problems in the middle ear create an additional conductive loss. Skilled pediatricians and ENT doctors recognize the importance of clearing up treatable middle ear issues, particularly for children with hearing loss, and often choose continued medical treatment to eliminate middle ear issues.

Specific Tympanometry Measurements

Your pediatric audiologist might look at several measures recorded on the tympanogram. These include canal volume, static admittance and peak pressure. These measures are used to describe the overall function of the tympanic membrane. The computer uses these measures to create the tracing on the tympanogram.

Canal volume describes the actual amount of space in the ear canal. It is directly related to the shape and size of the ear canal and, as a result, varies from person to person. The numbers that represent canal volume are interpreted by a pediatric audiologist who is familiar with the child being tested. An abnormally large number may indicate a problem. Your pediatric audiologist can tell you what range of numbers is considered typical for your child depending on her age, size and circumstances such as pressure equalizing tubes, which alter the canal volume measurement.

Static admittance is a measure of the energy in the middle ear system.

Peak pressure is the point at which the eardrum is moving at its best, or is demonstrating optimal mobility. The pressure required to move the tympanic membrane typically ranges from −100 to +100, so this range is considered normal. In most cases, abnormal ear pressure is found to be negative pressure and is represented by a negative number. In general, a peak pressure reading of −150 or less (such as −160, −170, etc.) indicates a problem that may need medical treatment.

Behavioral Hearing Tests

Behavioral testing is a kind of subjective testing that may be done in a clinic, hospital, school or doctor's office. Behavioral hearing tests are performed by an audiologist. Children are typically tested by a pediatric audiologist experienced in working with children. Behavioral testing requires the use of an **audiometer**, a machine that produces sound and/or presents sound at varying loudness levels. Your child's responses to sound are determined by her reactions to a variety of sounds produced in a quiet room or sound-treated booth. Her responses or changes in her behavior give information about what sounds she hears. These behavioral responses may be either subtle or overt. Your pediatric audiologist may also use fun objects for reinforcement such as simple toys or specially designed boxes that light up and have moving toys inside them. Skilled pediatric audiologists make the testing experience as child-friendly as possible so your child participates, and perhaps even enjoys it!

Again, behavioral tests can be used for screening or for diagnosing. As is true for ABR and OAE testing, screenings result in a determination of either *pass* or *refer*. If your child refers on a behavioral screening, your pediatric audiologist who did the testing talks with you about what further action you should take to obtain diagnostic testing.

For diagnostic behavioral testing, the purpose is to determine the type (sensorineural, conductive or mixed) and degree of hearing loss (slight, mild, moderate, moderately-severe, severe or profound) in each ear. This will define how the inner ear and middle ear respond together. Read more about types and degrees of hearing loss in Chapter 2.

Types of Behavioral Hearing Tests

Behavioral testing relies upon a person's actions in response to sound. As you can imagine, testing children can be difficult because they may not understand specific tasks, may not follow directions well or may simply refuse to participate. To compensate for the fact that babies and children need special testing situations to obtain useful testing results, there are different types of behavioral testing. The kind of testing your pediatric audiologist uses largely depends upon your child's age and abilities. Kinds of testing include:

- behavioral observational audiometry
- visual reinforcement audiometry
- conditioned play audiometry
- simple behavioral testing

The Audiology Suite and Sound-Treated Booth

An audiology suite includes one small sound-treated area called the booth and another area for the audiometer and other equipment. During testing, your child will spend most of the time inside the booth. You may be seated either inside the booth with your child on your lap or outside the booth with the pediatric audiologist working the audiometer. Often, another pediatric audiologist or your early interventionist stays in the booth with your child to assist with testing. The booth is equipped with headphones, speakers and toys. A window allows the pediatric audiologist to see your child while operating the audiometer. The pediatric audiologist might turn the lights low outside the booth so your child cannot see her. This helps eliminate distractions. If you and other family members are observing from outside the booth, you too must be cautious about eliminating distractions so testing can go as quickly and smoothly as possible.

During behavioral testing, you will be asked to hold or sit nearby your child. Your pediatric audiologist will also ask you to sit quietly, without letting your own response to sound or your anticipation cue your child to respond. Sitting with your child during testing is reassuring for your child, but it can be nerve-wracking for you. Try to remember to stay calm and reassure your child so your pediatric audiologist has the best possible chance of obtaining accurate test results. After the test, your pediatric audiologist will take time to describe the results, make recommendations and answer your questions.

Behavioral Observation Audiometry

For babies and for young children with limited body or head control, pediatric audiologists use a type of testing called **behavioral observation audiometry** (BOA). During BOA, your pediatric audiologist uses an audiometer to present a controlled sound to your baby's ear through an insert earphone or a speaker. Your baby or young child listens to sounds while

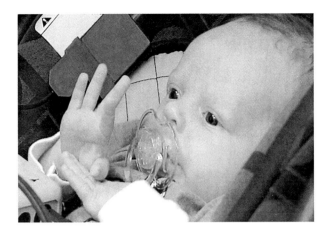

you and your pediatric audiologist look for and interpret behavioral changes. For example, your child might stop sucking the pacifier, start sucking, become wiggly, get very still, blink rapidly, stare, turn her head to search for something or quickly look over to you. There isn't a right or wrong response in this form of testing, just very close observation of what are often subtle changes in behavior. When the behavioral responses remain consistent throughout the test session, your pediatric audiologist reasonably concludes the information gathered during the test is valid and reliable.

Visual Reinforcement Audiometry

Older babies and toddlers are often tested with **visual reinforcement audiometry** (VRA). VRA can be done reliably only when a child is able to sit upright and independently turn her head from side to side. This testing involves the use of an audiometer and reinforcers — special boxes that light up and contain toys that can move. These light-up boxes serve as the reinforcement; they are presented to your child as a reward when she gives an obvious response to hearing a sound. Your child is taught through repetition that each time a sound is heard, the box lights up and the toy moves. At first, your child is exposed to louder sounds your pediatric audiologist knows she will hear (or feel through vibration). Then, gradually, your pediatric audiologist presents quieter sounds. Each time your baby or toddler hears the sound presented, she learns to turn and look at the box, located beside and slightly behind her. Your pediatric audiologist wants to determine the quietest level of sounds your child hears. During this type of testing, you may be asked to hold your child or to sit close to her. As in BOA testing, it's important that you don't give any physical reaction yourself (such as head-turning, shifting your child in your lap, etc.) so the test remains reliable and valid. If you accidentally give your child any clue about when the sound comes on, the test will be inaccurate.

VRA requires some sort of visual reinforcement to motivate your child. A reinforcer is usually a darkened box that lights up during testing. Common reinforcers include a bear that plays a drum and a cow that walks and moos. A computer displaying an animated cartoon video could also be used as a reinforcer. While the types of reinforcers used at pediatric audiology centers vary, the idea behind them is the same: When your child hears something, she looks toward the reinforcer.

Conditioned Play Audiometry

Between about 2 and 3 years old, many children are able to play a game to let the pediatric audiologist know they heard the sound. This is called **conditioned play audiometry (CPA)**. Your pediatric audiologist's goal is the same as with all types of behavioral audiometry. She wants to observe behavioral changes that indicate your child's response to sound. For play audiometry, your child may sit at a small table with you near her or behind her. What distinguishes play audiometry from other testing is the use of fun and interesting toys. Your child may be asked to manipulate a toy each time she hears a sound — place a peg in a pegboard, place rings on a ring stand or put pieces in a container or puzzle. The toy may vary, but in play audiometry your child is taught to listen, wait for the sound and then place the toy as demonstrated. Children are often motivated by fun and colorful toys, which make this type of testing particularly successful. Sometimes early interventionists help parents find ways to practice play audiometry at home before audiology appointments so your child is prepared and you get the most out of the testing session.

Your pediatric audiologist teaches a task by presenting a loud sound she is confident your child will hear, by pairing the sound with an action and then by slowly providing less demonstration of that action until your child seems to understand. Sometimes it's difficult for a child to wait to do the task until she actually hears the sound, so the pediatric audiologist is always watching for false positive responses.

Simple Behavioral Testing

When your child is older, the pediatric audiologist will teach her to raise her hand or press a button when she hears a sound. This type of **simple behavioral testing**, also referred to as **conventional behavioral testing**, is for children and adults who can understand the task of raising a hand or pushing a button in response to hearing a sound.

Behavioral hearing test equipment

All types of hearing tests, other than gross tests, require special equipment and sound-treated areas. The equipment used to test your child's hearing depends on which type of test your child is having. Except for screenings and gross tests, hearing tests typically take place in a **sound-treated booth**. A sound-treated booth used to test children most likely contains a variety of toys and other fun materials for motivation. Some are typical toys like cars, little people or dolls, puzzles, rings and wind-up toys. There may also be toys you don't recognize, like a box with a teddy bear in it. The box lights up and the bear dances to reinforce and motivate your child. Unless she is able to sit unsupported in a small chair, you will likely hold her. Your pediatric audiologist will remain outside the booth to control the other testing equipment. Another pediatric audiologist, technician or sometimes an early interventionist will accompany you in the booth and sit across from you facing your child.

Your pediatric audiologist will sit outside the booth, but will be able to see you and your child through a window. She will give you instructions by talking into a microphone and you will hear her voice through high quality, stereo-like speakers in the booth. When the testing begins, your pediatric audiologist will use an audiometer. An audiometer is a machine that produces sound or presents recorded sound at varying loudness levels. You may hear a series of sounds, including your pediatric audiologist's live voice, recorded speech, tones, music or noise that sounds like static from a radio or TV. Generally speaking, young children respond best to a live voice, so your pediatric audiologist may begin by calling your child's name. She may make an excited statement like "Look, look. Over here!" or she may ask a silly question, like "Woof, woof. Where's the puppy?"

Your pediatric audiologist wants your child to be comfortable and willing to participate in the session. To get going, she may use the speakers to help your child get used to the booth and testing tasks. **Soundfield testing** is performed through a speaker system in the booth. It gives information on what your child hears with both ears. The speaker system transfers your pediatric audiologist's voice, recorded speech, tones and noise into the booth. If your child won't allow earphones in her ears, your pediatric audiologist might also choose to use the soundfield. You likely will be able to hear the sounds coming from big speakers surrounding you. It's important to avoid showing any response to the sound. Your child could pick up on the slightest movement you make. You are aiming for the most reliable responses, so try your best not to help your little one during this time.

Eventually, your pediatric audiologist will need to use insert earphones to gain ear-specific information. So keep in mind that she might do soundfield testing at first, but will work up to using earphones to gain more specific information about your child's hearing.

Is behavioral testing reliable?

You may be wondering if this kind of testing is actually reliable. After all, it could be difficult for a pediatric audiologist who doesn't really know your child to "read" her behaviors well enough to determine accurate hearing levels. So how do you know you can trust these test results?

First, it's important to find an audiologist with pediatric expertise. This is crucial. Pediatric audiologists are specially trained and practiced in the art of "reading" the behaviors of infants and young children, so they can obtain accurate information about hearing levels. Audiologists who work primarily with adults may lack the experience and equipment necessary to elicit and interpret responses from infants and young children. A skilled pediatric audiologist can make all the difference in the world for your child. Be sure you're aware of your pediatric audiologist's areas of expertise.

Audio-Lingo

Audiologist

the person who
does the testing

Audiogram

the graph that
describes your
child's test results

Audiometer

the machine
used to test
hearing

Audiology

the study of
hearing and
balance

During behavioral observational audiometry, your pediatric audiologist obtains estimates of your child's **minimal responses** to sounds. A minimal response is the quietest sound to which your child responds. This is not the same thing as a threshold. **Thresholds** are the lowest levels of sounds your child can hear at different frequencies 50 percent of the time. In time, your child will be able to give your pediatric audiologist accurate information about thresholds. Before that, your pediatric audiologist will use behavioral observational audiometry to estimate minimal responses. Babies can be expected to respond to sounds at certain levels, but they won't respond to some really quiet sounds even though they can hear them. This is normal for babies. Behavioral observational audiometry is a way for a pediatric audiologist to confirm results from previous ABR testing by observing a baby's minimal responses to sounds.

It's also important to consider whether or not your child has developmental disabilities or delays. If so, behavioral testing may be less accurate and therefore less reliable. For these children, testing should be more frequent so test results can be monitored and compared over time. In addition, these responses will be compared to ABR responses.

Finally, remember that as your child grows and matures, her ability to accurately report what she is hearing will improve. If your child has already had hearing tests and you continue to test regularly, she'll be an old pro by the time she is 3! But remember, even if your child is so young that precise results are difficult to obtain, it's very important to have ongoing testing start as early as possible. Some information is better than none, and the sooner you get started gathering information on your child's hearing loss, the quicker you can get her hearing optimally with listening devices.

Sounds used during behavioral testing

During a hearing evaluation, your child may listen through headphones or insert earphones, or she may listen through stereo-like speakers. Your pediatric audiologist has many options for what kind of sound to present through the audiometer:

Speech audiometry

- live voice — your pediatric audiologist will say your child's name and some other words and phrases
- recorded speech — a recorded version of words

Live voice and recorded speech fall under the category of **speech audiometry,** which is behavioral hearing testing using speech instead of other sounds. The purpose of speech audiometry is to measure how loud speech has to be for your child to hear and/or understand it. There are three kinds of speech audiometry. **Speech detection** measures indicate how loud speech must be for your child to hear it. **Speech reception** measures indicate how loud speech has to be for your child to understand it. **Speech perception** measures indicate how well your child understands speech when it's at a conversational level/loudness. Sometimes speech is loud enough for your child to know someone is talking, but not loud or clear enough for her to know what's being said.

Babies and young children are usually more interested in listening to a real voice than any tone or static sound. For this reason, a pediatric audiologist will start a testing session by using live voice to teach your child to listen. While live voice and recorded speech testing does not give information about specific pitches, it does let your pediatric audiologist know your child is able to respond to sound. Remember that behavioral testing is based on your child's responses — no matter how subtle or elaborate. Pediatric audiologists use live voice to determine your child's ability to respond and to teach your child to show some response to sound.

Uh-Oh!
The pediatric audiologist isn't finished testing . . . but my child sure is!

Don't be discouraged if your child is not interested in participating. This is typical behavior for young children. Small children are often able to participate only for short periods of time. It's not uncommon to stop testing before fully completing it. The audiologist will guide you through this process. Remember, a skilled pediatric audiologist is an expert at working with young children during testing — and this includes knowing when enough is enough.

You can expect a skilled pediatric audiologist to be:
- prepared with many motivating activities for your child
- okay with snack breaks
- patient with small children
- patient with parents
- willing to sing lots of kids' songs
- willing to schedule another appointment to finish at a later date

During speech audiometry, the speech is usually presented through the audiometer and can be either your pediatric audiologist's live voice or a recording of someone talking. Speech can be single sounds like *ahhh, mmm* or *buh*, or single words, phrases or sentences. Speech audiometry testing can be done while your child is not wearing her hearing devices, as well as when she is wearing them. These measures help your pediatric audiologist determine your child's ability to understand the spoken language going on around her, both with and without her devices. Once your child learns to respond to a live voice, your pediatric audiologist switches to tones at specific frequencies so she can more precisely determine the level of hearing.

Pure tone audiometry

- single pure tone — an individual sound at a specific frequency that lasts about one second, similar to a single beep sound
- repeated pure tone — an individual sound at a specific frequency that lasts about one second, which is then repeated a couple of times, similar to a beep-beep-beep sound

Pure tones are frequency-specific. That means a single pure tone represents one frequency. Frequency is most simply explained as pitch and can be thought of as high or low. A pure tone is a sound that has only one frequency, as opposed to a sound that contains more than one frequency. Pure tone testing is used to determine how loud a sound at a specific frequency needs to be for your child to hear it. To better understand this concept, think of a pure tone roughly as hitting one single key on a piano as opposed to a chord with a few keys at once. This will become clearer as you learn to read and interpret an audiogram (See Chapter 4).

Warble tone

A **warble tone** is a sound similar to a whistle or birdie sound. More technically, it's a modulated pure tone, which is caused by fluctuating a tone's pitch within a range slightly higher to slightly lower than the pure tone. Warble tone is used in soundfield testing because it has less reverberation than pure tone. It is often more interesting for children to listen to than pure tone and it can be used effectively with people who have specific hearing issues such as ringing in the ear.

Narrowband noise

Narrowband noise, which sounds like the static on a radio, is also frequency-specific. It's different from a pure tone because narrowband noise focuses on a range of frequencies rather than on one single frequency. This will also become clearer as you learn to read and interpret an audiogram (See Chapter 4).

Unaided and Aided Testing

Pediatric audiologists use additional procedures to test children who already have a diagnosis of hearing loss and who already have one or two hearing devices (hearing aids and/or cochlear implants). Your pediatric audiologist will test your child without devices (**unaided**) to determine whether the diagnosis is still accurate. Your pediatric audiologist will also test your child with her devices (**aided**) to determine what kind of access to sound your child is getting and to make adjustments to the levels of sound your child receives through the devices. She will adjust the hearing devices to the levels most beneficial to your child.

Determining Which Test Your Child Needs

The type of tests your child receives depends on the following:

- age
- ability to participate or ability to complete the task
- which test or tests were previously successful or unsuccessful
- what information is needed
- pediatric audiologist and doctor recommendations
- where your pediatric audiologist left off in a previous testing session

One-Time Tests vs. Ongoing Testing

Some hearing tests need to be done only once to obtain a sufficient amount of reliable information. Typically, ABR tests and OAE tests do not need to be done more than once.

Gross Hearing Tests

Don't worry! These tests are not gross, as in disgusting or yucky! Instead, they're quick, easy and require no formal testing equipment.

Gross tests are informal, subjective tests using simple, everyday, sound-making items. They may be done by your pediatrician, by your pediatric audiologist or anyone. They can be done anytime and anywhere. A gross test involves making a sound or sounds and observing the child's response. Gross tests may be done by jangling keys, banging a spoon on a pan, shaking a rattle, hitting a tuning fork and so on.

Gross tests can be both helpful and misleading. Sometimes, the observer is quite knowledgeable about the loudness of the sound and about what the child's response might mean. In this case, special calibrated toys (such as selected bells and rattles) may be used that are known to produce sounds at certain loudness levels. At other times, it's possible the observer may be misled if the child actually sees movement or feels vibration instead of responding to sound. Although sometimes useful, this type of testing cannot give complete or specific information.

Even so, there are certain circumstances in which your pediatric audiologist or ENT doctor could request that the ABR or OAE be repeated to gather more specific information about your child's hearing loss. Children who have had a screening, who were referred for further diagnostic testing and who were diagnosed with hearing loss do not need further screenings. Children without a diagnosed hearing loss should have routine screenings, usually once a year, often performed at school or annually by a pediatrician.

After a child is diagnosed with a hearing loss, it's necessary to continue testing her hearing over time. Ongoing testing includes behavioral tests and tympanometry. In most cases, several tests or test sessions will be needed to obtain complete results. Generally speaking:

- Children from birth to 3 years old with a diagnosed hearing loss should have a complete evaluation every three months. This can vary in some situations.
- Children in particular need lots of ongoing testing for a variety of reasons:
  - to condition them to respond appropriately during testing
  - to allow them time to practice the testing tasks
  - to appropriately test, treat and monitor children with fluctuating hearing loss
  - to appropriately test, treat and monitor children with progressive hearing loss
  - to make earmold impressions, as children grow quickly and frequently require new earmolds
- Children 3 or older with a diagnosed hearing loss should have a complete evaluation every 6 months to a year if no other problems exist — or every 1–3 months if there's evidence or history of significant shifts in hearing levels.

Children with a history of significant middle ear problems should have a tympanometry test approximately monthly. You may recall that tympanometry measures the movement of the eardrum to identify possible issues within the middle ear.

Your child's pediatric audiologist will suggest when to return for more testing. You may want to ask how far in advance to schedule the next appointment for the appropriate time. This can help ensure your child's testing schedule is set up optimally for her.

Between appointments, you may observe changes in your child's response to sound — either with or without her hearing devices. If this happens, promptly call to schedule an appointment. Your pediatric audiologist can retest your child's hearing, make adjustments to her hearing devices and make a medical referral if needed.

Walking Through a Typical Audiology Appointment

After the initial battery of diagnostic tests, you will come to find that the agenda at each and every audiology visit from infancy through toddlerhood looks about the same. A skilled team of pediatric audiologists, and sometimes your early interventionist, will pull out all the stops to entertain your child, while assessing her hearing along the way.

Family and Child Updates

The visit will usually start with a brief conversation about the plan for this appointment as well as an opportunity for you to share your observations about your child's responsiveness to sounds at home and elsewhere. Share any observation you make — none is too small or too silly. If your baby startles only at loud noises, that's good for your pediatric audiologist to know. If your baby babbles way more without any hearing devices on, she'll want to know that too. While pediatric audiologists are skilled in hearing science, there's no substitute for the expert observations of parents. Trust your "mommy or daddy instincts" and speak up with questions and comments.

Otoscopy/Visual Examination

Who: Your pediatric audiologist

Where: In the audiology suite, with your child sitting on your lap

Why: To check your child's outer ear, ear canal and eardrum at each ear

More information: Page 32

Tympanometry

Who: Your pediatric audiologist

Where: Next to the typanometer in the audiology suite, with your child sitting on your lap
Why: To check your child's middle ear at each ear

More information: Page 33

Unaided or Aided Behavioral Hearing Testing

Who: Your pediatric audiologist, possibly another pediatric audiologist

Where: Your child and possibly a pediatric audiologist sit in the booth. Another pediatric audiologist sits just outside of the booth operating the audiometer. You may be either in the booth with your child or just outside the booth with your pediatric audiologist.

Why: To chart how loud sounds must be at certain frequencies for your child to hear them

More information on behavioral hearing testing: Page 35

More information on unaided and aided testing: Page 44

Hearing Devices

Who: The pediatric audiologist and sometimes your early interventionist

Where: In the audiology suite and in the booth

Why: Your pediatric audiologist recommends the type and brand of hearing devices and explains how to work and use the devices. This includes putting devices on your child, adjusting settings, changing batteries, keeping devices clean and dry and troubleshooting. There may be some time that your child wears her devices during testing. Your child's hearing will be tested both without devices (unaided) and with devices (aided). If needed, your pediatric audiologist will take an impression of your child's ear so she can order an earmold to attach to each hearing aid or cochlear implant.

More information: Chapters 6–9

Follow-Up

The time to schedule your next appointment is at the end of your current appointment. Remember to schedule a time when your child will be rested but alert. Try to avoid nap or feeding times. If you need more batteries or other supplies for your hearing devices, remember to ask before you leave. This is your chance to ask questions! Take your pediatric audiologist's business card in case you forget to ask something during the appointment. That way, you can always call!

References

Joint Committee on Infant Hearing. (2007). *Year 2007 Position Statement: Principles and Guidelines for Early Hearing Detection and Intervention Programs.* Retrieved on February 4, 2009 from www.asha.org/policy.

Ross, D., Holstrum, W.J., Gaffney, M., Green, D., Oyler, R. & Gravel, J. (2008). Hearing screening and diagnostic evaluation of children with unilateral and mild bilateral hearing loss. *Trends in Amplification, 12*(1), 27.

Chapter 4

What *Can* Your Child Hear?

Access to Sound

As a parent of a child learning to listen and talk despite her hearing loss, you're likely to learn a lot of new terminology. You may have already read about some of this terminology in this book. One phrase you will hear occasionally is "access to sound."

A child's **access to sound** refers to the sound available to her in the environment. Children with typical hearing have full access to all of the many sounds people typically hear — a door opening, a car driving, a dog barking, feet walking across a floor, a doorbell ringing, sirens blaring and, most importantly, *people talking*. Children with hearing loss have less access to these sounds. Hearing loss isn't typically "all or nothing." Your child likely has access to some amount of sound — maybe high frequencies or low frequencies, for example. Your child's specific hearing loss determines what access she has to the sounds around her.

So how do you improve your child's access to sound? Children with hearing loss can wear **hearing devices**, such as hearing aids or cochlear implants. The devices your child's pediatric audiologist recommends are intended to give her better access to sound.

Remember: To learn how to talk the way people with typical hearing do, your child needs to hear at or close to typical hearing levels as much as possible. Even with hearing aids or cochlear implants, her hearing will never be normal; however, hearing devices can improve her access to sound. Better access to sound and specialized instruction are the keys for your child to successfully learn how to talk. Providing your child with the best hearing device technology available is a great first step in helping her become a talking child.

What Can Your Child Hear Without Hearing Devices?

Although every child is different, there are some ways to describe what children with certain degrees of hearing loss might hear without hearing devices.

Without hearing devices, a child with **mild hearing loss** may have difficulty hearing quiet or distant speech. The family of this child may not even notice that her hearing loss interferes with her becoming a listening and talking child. Yet, once a child is in a school setting, her challenges with hearing and/or understanding become more obvious. This is because, even with a hearing aid, it can be difficult to hear speech that is distant or when there is background noise. Before universal newborn hearing screening became so prevalent, mild hearing loss was diagnosed later (between ages 3 and 6). Because children seemed to be developing so typically, no one noticed a problem in infancy or very early childhood.

Without hearing devices, a child with **moderate hearing loss** may clearly hear speech produced very close to her only if the room is relatively quiet. Without hearing devices, this child will likely have difficulty understanding language, as well as learning to use it. This is because a child with moderate hearing loss doesn't have access to all the sounds we use in spoken language. If a child can't hear a sound, she won't know that it exists in words; therefore, she won't know to use it in her own speech. For example, if a child never hears the "s" sound, she will say "buh" for bus and "oop" for soup. This child will likely experience limitations in vocabulary development. This happens because she doesn't have access to enough sounds to distinguish between two different words, so those two words can sound the same to her. For example, she might not hear the differences between words like "eye" and "light" or "boat" and "nose."

Without hearing devices, a child with **severe hearing loss** may be able to hear a loud voice only about one foot from her ear. This access to sound is so limited that a child without hearing devices would have great difficulty developing spoken language without intervention.

Without hearing devices, a child with **profound hearing loss** may be able to hear only very loud sounds, or she may not respond to any sounds at all. A child with profound hearing loss might be aware of vibrations caused by loud sounds because she actually feels the vibrations rather than hearing the sound. This child would have such limited access to sound, she wouldn't likely learn to talk successfully without hearing devices.

So That's Why Your Child Hears Some Sounds!

Some children with hearing loss actually respond to some sounds even when they aren't wearing hearing devices. If this is true for your child, it may seem surprising that she has a hearing loss since, after all, she does respond to some sounds. She is able to respond because of her residual hearing. **Residual hearing** is the hearing that your child with hearing loss does have. Remember, hearing loss is usually not "all or nothing." Many people with hearing loss *are* able to hear at least some sounds. Your child's residual hearing enables her to hear some sounds while her hearing loss makes her miss other sounds. Some parents report that their child hears them, so they conclude it's impossible for her to have hearing loss; however, it really is very possible.

Understanding an Audiogram

An **audiogram** is a graph. It is a visual representation of the loudness (or intensity) of sounds a person can hear at different pitches (or frequencies). An audiogram is the end product of a hearing test. It's part of the report you receive after your child has her hearing tested. You definitely want to develop an understanding of an audiogram. The pediatric

C I D CID C E N T R A L   I N S T I T U T E   F O R   T H E   D E A F

Name _____ DOB _____ Gender   M / F   Evaluation Date _____

LEGEND	Left	Right
Air Conduction (AC)	X	O
AC Masked	□	Δ
Bone Conduction (BC)	> ∧	<
BC Masked	]	[
No Response	↘	↙
Soundfield	S	
Hearing Aid	L	R
Binaural Aided or BAHA	B	
Cochlear Implant	CI	

ABBREVIATIONS
MLV = Monitored Live Voice
NR = No Response
SRT = Speech Recognition Threshold
SDT= Speech Detection Threshold
WNL = Within Normal Limits
BOA = Behavioral Observation Audiometry
CPA = Conditioned Play Audiometry
VRA = Visual Reinforcement Audiometry
CONV = Conventional Audiometry
NBN (ᵗ) = Narrow Band Noise
CNT = Could Not Test
VT= Vibrotactile

SPEECH AUDIOMETRY SRT / SDT in dB HL

	Unaided	Aided
Right Ear:	_____	_____
Left Ear:	_____	_____
Binaural:	_____	_____

Source: Earphones / Inserts / Soundfield / Bone Oscillator
Response Mode: CONV / BOA / VRA / CPA
Reliability: Good / Fair / Poor
Validity: Acceptable / Questionable

Threshold (dB HL)

250   500   1000   2000   4000   8000
-10
0
10
20
30
40
50
60
70
80
90
100
110
120

750   1500   3000   6000

Frequency in Hertz (Hz)

OTOSCOPY	
Left Ear	Right Ear
_____	_____

Tympanometry	Left Ear	Right Ear
Canal Volume (ml)		
Static Admittance (mmhos)		
Peak Pressure (daPa)		

DEVICE: Left: _____   Right: _____

COMMENTS: _____
_____
_____
_____
_____
_____
_____
_____

cc _____   Audiologist _____

audiologist will refer to your child's audiogram during every visit! While each audiology center's audiogram looks slightly different, there are some standard markings. Ideally, all of the information described in this chapter will be included on your child's audiogram, but since each center's form looks different, you might notice that some information is not there. That's okay! Just ask your pediatric audiologist if you would like information that is not on the actual audiogram.

The vertical lines represent pitches or frequencies of sound (labeled on the audiogram as 250–8000 Hz). Think of these lines like the keys on a piano, with the lowest pitches represented by the lines toward the left and the highest pitches represented by the lines toward the right.

The horizontal lines represent intensity or volume of sound. The softest sounds are at the top and the loudest sounds are at the bottom. If this seems backward to you, you're not alone! People often think the louder sounds should be at the top, but that's not the way a typical audiogram is designed. The more you see this, the more you'll understand it. It's not uncommon for it to take some time to get used to this.

Standard Audiogram Symbols

LEGEND	Left		Right
Air Conduction (AC)	X		O
AC Masked	□		Δ
Bone Conduction (BC)	>	∧	<
BC Masked	]		[
No Response	↘		↙
Soundfield		S	
Hearing Aid	L		R
Binaural Aided or BAHA		B	
Cochlear Implant		CI	

Air Conduction Symbols

Air conduction (AC) means that the sound is traveling to your child's ear through the outer ear, then into the middle ear and on to the inner ear. During air conduction testing, sound is presented through earphones that insert into your child's ears or speakers. On the audiogram, an O is used to represent the right ear responses through air conduction. An X is used to represent left ear responses through air conduction.

Masking Symbols

Masking is a technique used by the pediatric audiologist to verify what one ear is able to hear without the help of the other ear. This technique is used when one ear hears significantly better than the other. Masking with air conduction is done by inserting an earphone into each ear. The ear being tested listens to beeps and tones. The non test ear listens to noise that sounds like static. When the right ear is given beeps and tones and the left ear is given masking, the pediatric audiologist marks those right ear responses on the audiogram with a triangle (Δ). When the left ear is given beeps and tones and the right ear is given masking, the pediatric audiologist marks those left ear responses on the audiogram with a box (□).

Bone Conduction Symbols

An audiogram also has a marking for **bone conduction** (BC). Many people don't realize that the cochlea actually responds to the vibrations of the skull caused by sounds. So when sound waves collide with the skull, the bones of the skull vibrate. That vibration causes the fluid in the cochlea to move. Remember that when the cochlear fluid moves, a signal is sent to the brain. The brain interprets the signal as something being heard. Bone conduction is another way to get sounds to the cochlea; however, unlike air conduction, bone conduction does not need the outer ear and middle ear. For people whose hearing loss is caused by a problem with the outer ear or middle ear, bone conduction testing is an important way to determine the ability of the cochlea and auditory nerve to send information to the brain. (For more information on the process of hearing, see Chapter 2.)

Bone conduction testing can be done by putting an **oscillator**, a vibrating bone conduction device, on either the right mastoid bone, the left mastoid bone or the forehead. (The mastoid bone is one of the skull bones that houses the ear system. If you put your hand on your head just behind either ear, the bone you feel is your mastoid bone.) Because the vibrating device can be placed at different points on the head, a pediatric audiologist has different markings to indicate the location of the device during testing. The less-than symbol (<) is used to indicate bone conduction results when the vibrating device is placed on the right side of the skull. The greater-than symbol (>) is used to indicate bone conduction results when the vibrating device is placed on the left side of the skull. The caret symbol (^) is used to indicate bone conduction results when the device is placed on the forehead or any placement that is not nearer to one ear than the other.

No matter where the vibrating device is placed on the head, the amount of vibration is nearly always the same. So, for example, just because the vibrating device is placed on the right doesn't mean that the right ear is going to hear the sound better. Because of this, any unmasked bone conduction marking (<, > or ^) indicates the combined ability of the cochlea and auditory nerve on both the left and the right sides of the head.

Remember the term *masking*? It's a technique used by the pediatric audiologist to verify what one ear is able to hear without the help of the other ear. It can be done with bone conduction testing, too. Masking with bone conduction is done by placing the oscillator on the ear being tested and an earphone into the non test ear. The ear being tested listens to beeps and tones. The non test ear listens to noise that sounds like static. When the right ear is given beeps and tones and the left ear is masked, the pediatric audiologist marks those right ear responses on the audiogram with an open bracket ([ ). When the left ear is given beeps and tones and the right ear is masked, the pediatric audiologist marks those left ear responses on the audiogram with a close bracket ( ]).

No Response Symbol

The **no response symbol** indicates that the child does not respond to sounds at a particular frequency until testing reaches the limits of the testing equipment. $\wp$ indicates no response at the unaided right ear during air conduction testing. χ indicates no response at the unaided left ear during air conduction testing. ς indicates no response during soundfield testing with both ears unaided.

Soundfield Symbol

When the pediatric audiologist presents sound to your child through speakers in a sound-treated audiology booth, she is presenting in the soundfield. The sound plays out into the entire booth, not just into earphones through which your child hears. Because the sound is presented to the entire booth, the sound is presented equally to both ears. The pediatric audiologist marks your child's responses to sounds presented in the soundfield with an S. Because in this case the sound is presented to both ears, the S marking doesn't provide any information about specific hearing ability at each ear, just at the better hearing ear.

Device Symbols

Unaided testing involves testing your child without hearing aids or cochlear implants. **Aided testing** involves testing your child with devices. The pediatric audiologist marks an R on the audiogram to indicate the level at which your child hears at each frequency at her right ear while wearing her hearing device at her right ear. The pediatric audiologist marks an L on the audiogram to indicate the level at which your child hears at each frequency at her left ear while wearing her hearing device at her left ear.

Bilateral Devices Symbol

The pediatric audiologist marks a B on the audiogram to indicate the level at which your child hears at each frequency when using her devices at both ears. Some children have hearing aids at both ears, collectively called **bilateral hearing aids** (which allows for **binaural listening).** Others have a cochlear implant at each ear, collectively called **bilateral cochlear implants**. Other children have a cochlear implant at one ear and a hearing aid at the other. This combination is referred to as **bimodal**.

More About Audiograms

Page 51 contains an example of a blank audiogram. Besides the actual graph containing your child's hearing levels at certain frequencies, the audiogram typically contains a lot more information, so it might look very overwhelming. Don't worry! It will take time to get comfortable looking at audiograms. That's normal. The notes below might help you dissect the parts of the audiogram so it becomes a little easier to understand.

Although all audiograms look different, your child's audiogram will ideally have all of the following information on it. If not, ask your pediatric audiologist for any additional information you'd like.

At the top of the audiogram on page 51, there is a place for your child's name, birth date and gender. Next, there is a line to indicate the date of the hearing test (the same date on which the audiogram is completed).

Notice in the example that just under the line for the evaluation date is a graph to plot your child's responses to sounds. This is the actual audiogram. Notice the numbers across the top and bottom of the graph that indicate frequency. Frequency is measured in Hertz (Hz). The frequency range common for audiograms is 250 Hz (a low-pitched sound) to 8000 Hz (a high-pitched sound). This range of frequencies (250–8000 Hz) is the typical frequency range of human speech. That's why pediatric audiologists measure hearing at and between those levels. For more information about frequency and Hertz, turn to page 18.

The numbers listed down the vertical side of the example audiogram indicate the intensity or loudness of sound. The word "threshold" is written on the side of this graph. During testing, the pediatric audiologist determines your child's threshold for each ear. **Threshold** describes how loud a sound at a certain frequency (or pitch) needs to be for your child to hear it. In other words, threshold is the quietest a sound can be at a certain frequency for your child to hear it. Threshold is measured in decibels (dB). A decibel is the loudness of sound. More formally, it is a unit of measurement describing the power or intensity of sound. On any audiogram, you will see dB followed by other letters, such as HL, SPL or SL. These letters represent different ways to describe the sound presented during a hearing test. HL is most common and stands for hearing level. For more information on intensity, threshold and decibels, turn to page 17.

To the left of the example audiogram on page 51 is a legend containing the standard audiogram markings along with the abbreviations pediatric audiologists typically use on an audiogram. Under the abbreviations is a box for speech audiometry. This test is given to children and adults who have at least some ability to understand and use language. Find more information about speech audiometry in Chapter 3.

The box under speech audiometry has four components. The first is the **source**. This describes which tools are used to provide your child with sound during testing. Pediatric audiologists might use earphones that cover the ears, insert earphones (soft foam tips that fit into the ear canal) or a soundfield (sound played through speakers into the testing booth). The pediatric audiologist circles the source(s) used during testing on this particular audiogram. Sometimes she uses more than one source of sound.

Next is the component called **response mode**. The response mode describes the way the pediatric audiologist determines your child's responses to sounds during testing. The pediatric audiologist circles the type of response mode used. This particular audiogram has the following four choices. These choices are described in detail in Chapter 3 — Hearing Tests.

- conventional audiometry, also known as simple behavioral testing
- behavioral observation audiometry
- visual reinforcement audiometry
- conditioned play audiometry

The next two components in this box are reliability and validity. **Reliability** describes the consistency of your child's responses. Before the pediatric audiologist marks the audiogram, she wants to be sure she has seen your child *consistently* respond to each sound. Usually, a pediatric audiologist checks and rechecks each marking on the graph to make sure each response is consistent. She marks the reliability as good, fair or poor so anyone reading the audiogram can understand how confident she was about your child's responses during testing. This is important because children can have good days and not-so-good days. A fair or poor rating might lead the pediatric audiologist to double-check those responses at a future appointment. The reliability rating gives good insight for future testing. **Validity** refers to the accuracy of the test. Think about validity as how convinced the pediatric audiologist is that the test is accurate. In a nutshell, reliability refers to the consistency of your child's responses. Validity refers to the accuracy of the test during that appointment.

The box directly under the example audiogram (to the right) is for otoscopy. **Otoscopy** is a physical examination of the ear. The purpose of otoscopy is to examine the outer ear, the ear canal and the eardrum. **Tympanometry** is a test that measures how the middle ear functions. More information about otoscopy and tympanometry is provided in Chapter 3.

The device section is where the pediatric audiologist indicates which hearing devices your child wore during the aided portion of testing. (During unaided testing, your child does not wear hearing devices.)

The comments section is for additional notes and information. It's particularly important to read these notes when considering the reliability and validity of the testing. The pe-

Scenarios for Reliability and Validity

Scenario 1:
Your child had a great morning nap, her tummy is full and she's in a great mood. Throughout the test session, she turned her head every time she heard a sound. The pediatric audiologist feels confident that the responses she was giving at all levels accurately represent what your child is able to hear.

Reliability: (Good) / Fair / Poor

Validity: (Acceptable) / Questionable

Scenario 2:
It's nearing nap time. Your child is a little cranky and just wants to crawl up into your arms and sleep. You have only a couple more minutes of testing. You and the pediatric audiologist notice that your child doesn't consistently respond to sounds you think she should hear. But when she does respond, the pediatric audiologist feels as though the responses are accurate.

Reliability: Good / (Fair) / Poor

Validity: (Acceptable) / Questionable

Scenario 3:
Your child has had a rough morning. She's really showing off those terrible twos. She repeatedly pulls out the insert earphones and has no interest in the toys the pediatric audiologist is offering. Sometimes she responds to sounds that you think she should hear. Other times, she responds when no sound is presented. Her responses seem totally inconsistent. Because of these circumstances, the pediatric audiologist doesn't believe the testing was accurate.

Reliability: Good / Fair / (Poor)

Validity: Acceptable / (Questionable)

diatric audiologist may put comments here if she suspects the testing was somehow compromised. Remember that testing can be difficult with babies and little children. A pediatric audiologist often writes notes or comments in this section to clarify what happened during testing. In addition, this might be where she includes information about the type and degree of hearing loss.

Audiology Overload?

Understanding an audiogram can certainly be overwhelming! It's a lot of information. But don't worry — you'll get it. The more time you spend looking at your child's audiogram, the more comfortable you'll become with it. Also, a big part of the job of any pediatric audiologist is to help you feel comfortable with your child's hearing levels and testing. Although it can be intimidating, try to ask questions when you have them. It's important for you to ask. A good pediatric audiologist will be happy to answer all of your questions.

Your Child's Audiogram

Now that you have a basic understanding of the standard markings on an audiogram, take a look at your child's audiogram specifically. If you don't already have a copy of your child's latest audiogram, be sure to ask for one. Locate the different sections. Again, the marks on the audiogram indicate how loud sounds must be at certain frequencies for your child to hear them. Pediatric audiologists may vary somewhat in the way they mark audiograms, but a legend or key will help you make sense of it all.

The audiogram can also give you an idea of your child's degree of hearing loss. Your pediatric audiologist may have drawn a line connecting all the Os and then another line connecting all the Xs. This is a good visual for you to use to determine your child's degree of hearing loss. For more information on degree of hearing loss, turn to Chapter 2.

Familiar Sounds Audiogram

Another helpful visual tool is a **familiar sounds audiogram**. This shows common sounds — such as birds chirping, people talking, a dog barking, etc. — plotted on an audiogram using the same markings as a regular audiogram (pitch across the top and loudness down the side). The familiar sounds are depicted to give you an idea of their average pitch (frequency) and loudness (intensity). This is particularly useful if you want to see what familiar sounds your child is able, or unable, to hear. You can plot your child's audiogram right on the familiar sounds audiogram on the next page. This will show you what she can hear without hearing devices. If you take a colored pencil or crayon and shade in the area on the audiogram beneath those lines, you can see the sounds your child is able to hear.

You can also plot the level of sound your child can hear *with* her hearing devices. This is your child's aided test result. On an aided audiogram, instead of Xs and Os, you will see:

- **R** for right ear aided responses
- **L** for left ear aided responses
- **B** for binaural (or both) ears aided responses
  and/or
- **CI** for responses with one cochlear implant

This is a good way for you to see how much access to sound hearing devices are giving your child.

familiar sounds AUDIOGRAM

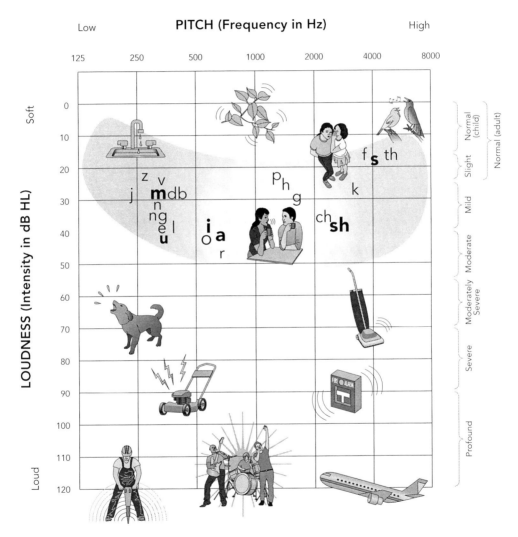

Adapted from the American Academy of Audiology and Northern, J. and Downs, M. (2002).
Hearing in Children (5th ed.). Lippincott Williams and Wilkins, Baltimore, Maryland.

CID 🆔 CENTRAL INSTITUTE FOR THE DEAF

Speech Banana

The shaded area (on the familiar sounds audiogram) that sort of looks like a banana is actually called the **speech banana**. It shows the average level of loudness of various speech sounds, including vowels and consonants. The goal of wearing hearing devices is to gain access to all the sounds that fall within the speech banana. Notice that speech ranges in loudness between 20 dB and 55 dB and average conversational speech varies between 40 dB and 55 dB. *Remember*: To learn how to talk the way people with typical hearing do, your child needs to hear as close to normally as possible. Ideally, your child will be able to hear soft speech sounds while wearing her devices. If your child is hearing unclear sounds, she will produce unclear speech. That's why the pediatric audiologist wants to help provide her with the access to the sound she needs to hear spoken language.

Although your child may have some unaided responses (responses while not using hearing devices) between 40 dB and 55 dB, these responses might represent your child's ability only to *detect* sound (to know that sound is present) and not her ability to *discriminate* sounds (to distinguish one sound from another). If your child has aided responses (responses while using hearing devices) in this range, she could be hearing speech that sounds distorted or unclear.

Recipe for Success

A pediatric audiologist and fancy equipment can give your child access to sound, but this doesn't mean the work is finished. In fact, it's just getting started! To develop listening and spoken language skills, children must have access to sound — but that's not the only ingredient in this recipe. Specially trained early interventionists, teachers of the deaf, auditory-verbal practitioners, pediatric audiologists and speech-language pathologists are some of the other ingredients. You will learn more about all of these other ingredients in the following chapters. But for now, just remember: The most important ingredient in helping your child learn to talk is *you!*

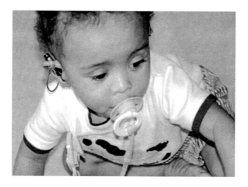

Chapter 5

Your Child's Health and Development

Keeping Your Child Healthy All Over

While this book focuses on issues related to your child's hearing and ears, it's also important to keep in mind that your child's overall health is critically important to her learning how to listen and talk. Think about when you don't feel well. You may be tired and crabby. You probably want to lie around, relax and not think about anything. When your child doesn't feel well, she also wants to do this. She needs lots of energy to learn to talk successfully. It's hard work! You're also working really hard to help your child learn to talk. You will get even more benefit if you help to keep her whole body healthy and strong. Good nutrition, good sleep habits and regular visits to the pediatrician are all critically important to your child's well being — and to her ability to learn to listen and talk.

Pediatrician

A pediatrician is a doctor who specializes in working with babies and children. Your pediatrician will be important as you work to keep your child well and healthy. If you have older children, you most likely already have an established pediatrician. Or you may have just recently chosen a pediatrician to see your new baby. It's likely that you will really get to know this person as your child grows and develops. Be sure you are comfortable with your pediatrician's approach to your child's hearing loss. If you have a good relationship with him or her, your pediatrician will be a good ally in helping you feel confident about medical decisions you make for your child.

Ear, Nose and Throat (ENT) Doctor

In medicine, the study of the ear, nose and throat is called otolaryngology; therefore, an ENT doctor is also called an **otolaryngologist** or **otorhinolaryngologist**. Hearing health is important for any child. But in the case of a child with hearing loss, it's crucial. Any level of additional hearing loss caused by temporary illness reduces the quantity and quality of sound your child can hear. In other words, if your child's hearing aids have been programmed to her specific hearing loss, any additional temporary hearing loss due to illness will make that program less optimal. For example, if she has an ear infection, she will not likely hear at the same level as when she doesn't have an ear infection. In addition, when your child needs to be seen quickly, having an established relationship with an ENT doctor may reduce the amount of time it takes to get an appointment. (Appointments for new patients require a longer block of time so they can be scheduled only for certain times in a doctor's week. This may make it more difficult to quickly get an appointment.) Because hearing health is so incredibly important for a child with hearing loss, it's very worthwhile for you to develop a positive, friendly relationship with your ENT doctor.

Most likely, you will have some choice among ENT doctors in your area. It can be overwhelming to decide which one is best for your family. The first step is to ask trusted friends, family, your pediatric audiologist or your pediatrician for recommendations. Once you have the names of some recommended ENT doctors, feel free to meet with a few of them to help make a choice.

Before the initial visit with an ENT doctor, consider the following:

- Research the doctor and the facility where he or she works. The Internet can be a great source of information, but be sure you look at sites that are valid and trustworthy.
- Make sure the ENT doctor is a provider for the type of medical insurance you have.
- Learn what days the ENT doctor is in the clinic/office for appointments and if he or she sees patients at multiple locations.
- Take note of the office staff, how easy they are to contact, how friendly they are and whether they seem organized. You will probably interact more with them than with the doctor.

At the initial visit with an ENT doctor, ask lots of questions. Below is a list of suggestions. You might want to ask just a few, all of them or none at all. These questions don't have right or wrong answers. They are just a way for you to get information about the ENT doctor so you can decide if he or she is right for you.

- Do you specialize in pediatrics? Do you also treat adults?
- Do you specialize in a certain area such as hearing loss?
- Have you worked much with children who have hearing loss?
- Have you worked with other children who have hearing loss similar to my child's?
- What's your experience with genetic causes for hearing loss?
- What's your experience with syndromes related to hearing loss?
- Do you work with children who wear hearing aids, cochlear implants or both?
- With which audiology and/or cochlear implant teams do you work?
- What's your policy on treatment with antibiotics?
- Who will address my concerns when I call the office?
- Will my child always see you, or will she see a nurse practitioner, resident or fellow?
- Who covers your cases when you're out of the office or otherwise unavailable?

Remember this: When it comes to choosing doctors, you *do* have options. There are many reputable ENT doctors and the choice is yours. So be prepared with the tools you need to make a decision with which you will be satisfied.

Remember this, too: If you choose a doctor whom you later learn isn't right for you and your child, you have the choice to look into changing doctors. You are your child's advocate. Certainly, you want to do what's right for her. If you feel a particular doctor is not meeting your needs, it is your right and obligation to make a change.

Pediatric Audiologist

An **audiologist** is a professional who usually works in a clinic, hospital or school. An audiologist tests hearing, counsels patients and parents about hearing devices and fits hearing devices. A **pediatric audiologist** is an audiologist who specializes in working with children. This is of the utmost importance because conducting hearing tests with adults is a lot different than with children. Your pediatric audiologist is going to be a big part of your life. Your family's relationship with your pediatric audiologist begins with your first audiology appointment and continues to grow from there. Your pediatric audiologist will help determine your child's degree of hearing loss, then recommend and fit appropriate hearing devices. He or she will also show you how to put your child's devices on, how to keep them on and how to take care of them. A pediatric audiologist is responsible for helping to educate and support you all along the way. This includes following your child, making adjustments to devices and device programs as necessary and recommending changes in devices when needed.

It's important to find an audiologist who has not only experience working with children with hearing loss, but also the understanding and patience necessary to work with small children. Specifically, you need to find a skilled pediatric audiologist. You should choose someone with whom you feel comfortable — someone who listens and will help you understand — someone with whom you feel like you can connect.

Many hospitals and some schools have **audiology centers** that employ a group of audiologists. If you live in an area with many options for pediatric audiology services, you may be faced with making a decision between audiology centers. You might find it convenient to take your child to the audiology center at her school or school district. Alternatively, you might prefer to use the audiology center affiliated with your ENT doctor. When you choose an audiology center, you might see the same pediatric audiologist each visit, but you also might see several pediatric audiologists over time. If this is the case, all of the pediatric audiologists will get to know you and your child, and you will have the benefit of all of their expertise.

Ideally, you have a choice in which pediatric audiologist you see. More likely, depending on where you live, only one pediatric audiologist may be available to you. If so, don't hesitate to set up your first appointment and begin establishing a good relationship. Some families find it worthwhile to travel farther to find a more appropriate pediatric audiologist. These families might see one audiologist in their hometown for more frequent appointments, but make annual appointments with one located further away who has more experience working with children.

Keeping Your Child's Ears Healthy

One of the most common ear issues for babies and children is the ear infection. Many children with typical hearing are prone to ear infections, and so are many children with hearing loss. The most common and problematic kind of ear infection for hearing loss is located in the middle ear. The formal name for a middle ear infection is **otitis media,** which literally translates to "inflammation of the middle ear." **Ear infections** are characteristic of red or inflamed tissue and infected fluid and/or mucus.

Ear infections are very common in young children primarily because of the specific anatomy of their middle ears and specifically of the eustachian tubes. In older children and adults, the **Eustachian tube**, a tube-like structure connecting the middle ear to the back of the throat, is angled downward to promote fluid drainage. In young children, however, the eustachian tube lies nearly flat or horizontally in the head, so fluid doesn't always drain well. Even though children have similar anatomy, some are just more prone to fluid problems than others.

Sometimes ear infections don't hurt at all and other times they do. At the most extreme, an ear infection is incredibly painful, causes fever, causes the eardrum to rupture and/or leads to other more serious infections. For children with typical hearing, an ear infection causes some level of conductive hearing loss. For children who already have permanent hearing loss, an ear infection makes the hearing loss more significant. Some physicians prefer not to treat every ear infection because the current trend is for more conservative use of antibiotics. When you have a trusted relationship with your pediatrician or ENT doctor, you can discuss more aggressive management of your child's hearing health.

Your child may have an ear infection if you see the following behaviors:

- tugging or rubbing the ear
- irritability
- unwillingness to lie down
- fever
- change in appetite
- change in sleeping patterns
- drainage from the ear
- unwillingness to wear hearing devices

If you suspect your child has an ear infection, contact your pediatrician or ENT doctor. Be prepared to explain your child's symptoms so the doctor can accurately make a recommendation. He may ask that you either bring the child in to be seen or follow his advice at home. If your doctor suspects an infection, he might prescribe oral antibiotics. If your child seems to repeatedly have ear infections, your doctor might suggest the placement of tubes as the next course of treatment.

Tubes

"Tubes" is an easy way to refer to something with a much longer name. Below is a list of the many formal names for tubes, yet all these names refer to the same thing . . . tubes:

- pressure equalizing tubes (or PE tubes)
- ventilation tubes
- tympanostomy tubes
- myringotomy tubes
- tympanoplasty tubes
- transtympanic tubes
- grommets

Tubes are tiny structures, typically made out of plastic, that are surgically inserted into the eardrum. A child who has frequent and/or continual middle ear problems, such as fluid or infection, may be a candidate for tubes. Tubes are intended to help release fluid or mucus from the middle ear and keep the middle ear ventilated. These tiny tubes, about the size of a pencil lead, are placed through the eardrum to allow air to enter the middle ear space to reduce the risk of continued middle ear fluid, mucus or infection. Tubes are placed in the ear during outpatient surgery by an ENT doctor. The surgery lasts only five to 15 minutes but requires the child to be completely still, so sedation with anesthesia is needed for children.

Remember that a healthy middle ear doesn't contain any fluid at all. Tubes help maintain an air-filled middle ear in two ways:

1. Tubes allow fluid or mucus to drain from the middle ear into the outer ear so the drainage can be wiped away. You may notice some fluid or mucus draining out of your child's ear after the tubes are inserted. This is good!
2. A sort of draft is created between the tube and the Eustachian tube. The **Eustachian tube** connects the middle ear to the back of the throat. Think about when you open a door on one side of the room and a window on the other. This causes a draft that allows air to flow through the room. Tubes can allow for that same kind of airflow through the middle ear and Eustachian tube, helping to release fluid and mucus and allowing it to drain down the back of the throat.

If tubes work properly — that is, if they don't become blocked or fall out — they should allow the middle ear to stay healthy. It's likely there will be a decrease in fluid, a decrease in infections and/or a better and faster response to treatment with antibiotic medication. When a child no longer needs tubes, they can be removed by your ENT doctor. As your child grows, it's actually more likely that the tubes will fall out on their own. Don't worry! The tubes are so tiny, you might not even notice.

Sounds complicated, doesn't it? Don't be shy about asking your pediatric audiologist and doctor to explain this and answer all your questions. Usually, the placement of tubes works well by reducing fluid and infection and helps parents breathe a sigh of relief.

If your child had no hearing loss at all, issues with the outer or middle ear such as middle ear infection could create hearing loss. For children who already have a diagnosed conductive or sensorineural hearing loss, an additional temporary hearing loss due to ear infection makes her hearing loss even more significant. Remember that your child's hearing aids are programmed for her permanent hearing loss. Additional hearing loss could reduce the quantity and quality of sound provided by her hearing aids. Remember that to learn to listen and to talk, she needs as much quality access to sound as possible. This will be an important time for you to ask lots of questions and obtain the recommended treatment.

Sensory Integration and Sensory Processing

A child with hearing loss may show some difficulty organizing information that comes to her through her senses. Because one of her senses is impaired — the sense of hearing — and because of a delay in obtaining access to sound, a child's brain can be affected. It's possible that this can result in the brain having difficulty using all the information it receives through any of the senses. This difficulty can hinder the child's ability to react appropriately to the environment.

What Is Sensory Integration?

The term sensory integration, or sensory processing, describes a child's ability to take in, understand and use information around her. The dictionary describes *integration* as the process of coordinating into a functioning and unified whole (Merriam-Webster, 2013). So sensory integration is the process of coordinating all of the information gathered by the senses so a person can function normally.

Most of us are familiar with the common five senses — hearing, vision, taste, smell and touch. But two other senses are less commonly known. They are proprioception and vestibular sense. Proprioception is the ability to know where one's body parts are in relation to each other. This can also be thought of as body positioning. Vestibular sense is related to movement and the ability to understand the body's own movements within the environment. Balance is an important part of vestibular sense.

As a child senses sounds, sights, movement, touch, tastes and smells, the brain processes each sensation, determines if it's something the child needs to react to and tells the child how to respond. This all happens in a split second. The brain uses all the information it receives through the senses to help the child react appropriately to stimuli within the environment.

What Is Sensory Processing Dysfunction?

Sensory processing dysfunction (SPD) refers to the body's inability to properly take in and use sensory information. A child with SPD has difficulty organizing sensory information to carry out everyday tasks, such as dressing, eating or playing. For instance, a child may dislike fingerpainting because she doesn't like to get her hands wet or sticky. Large crowds may overwhelm a child with SPD because of the noise level and number of people around. Often, children with SPD have difficulty paying attention because they're unable to filter out the sensations around them. Children with SPD might also have outbursts or tantrums when something unexpected happens.

A child with hearing loss may experience more difficulty with sensory processing. Likely, this is due to one or both of the following reasons:

- Because the sense of hearing is not as strong, the brain makes other senses more sensitive to compensate.
- A child's sense of movement is controlled by structures within the **vestibular system**. That system is located very near the hearing structures of the ear. It's not uncommon for a child with atypical hearing structures to also have an atypical vestibular system. In other words, if your child has hearing loss, her ability to process movement sensations may be impaired as well (Bharadwaj, Daniel & Matzke, 2009).

Although a child with hearing loss may have difficulty using sensory information, she doesn't automatically have sensory processing dysfunction. Some children have mild sensory processing issues, while others have more severe cases.

Your Child and Sensory Integration

Currently there is no formal diagnosis for sensory processing dysfunction, yet many children receive treatment to help lessen the effects of sensory issues on their lives. Even as early as infancy or toddlerhood, you may notice some behaviors that seem unusual or atypical. Those could be behaviors related to issues with sensory integration and could include the following characteristics:

Over-responsiveness to sensory input

A child who is over-responsive to sensations may be referred to as sensory defensive. A child who is over-responsive to senses feels something much more significant than what it actually might be. For example, a simple pat on the back feels to her more like a slug on the back. The child can be defensive of one or many types of sensations (movement, touch, lights, textures, etc.).

Sensory defensive behaviors include but are not limited to the following:

- The child really dislikes being touched.
- The child really dislikes people standing close.
- The child really dislikes having dirty hands or being messy.
- The child really dislikes tipping her head back.
- The child likes only a few certain foods.
- The child often shows fear or lack of movement.
- The child shows fear of feet leaving the ground.
- The child often seems lethargic or extremely sluggish.

Under-responsiveness to sensory input

A child who is under-responsive often seeks more intense sensory input than children with typical sensory processing. This is called sensory-seeking behavior. This child is likely to perceive something as much more minor than what it actually might be. She might seem unaware of something significant that she should have responded to. For example, a child might bump her head really hard but have no reaction at all. Since this child might not sense the information as readily, the input must be much more intense for her to perceive it. This child often prefers big movements, strong tastes and smells and loud sounds.

Sensory seeking behaviors include but are not limited to the following:

- The child frequently demonstrates repetitive movements such as:
    - spinning
    - jumping
    - falling
    - crashing
    - rocking
    - hand flapping
    - turning head from side to side
- The child constantly touches other people and objects.
- The child shows little reaction to pain.
- The child is a messy eater.
- The child often chews on inedible objects.
- The child seems indifferent to environmental temperatures.

How Are Sensory Integration Issues Treated?

If you suspect your child has difficulty processing sensory information, you can ask your early interventionist or your child's teacher for information on what steps to take next. Your child most likely will need to be evaluated by an occupational therapist (OT) so a determination can be made about whether she will need OT services.

An OT is likely to use a specific kind of checklist, called a sensory profile, to determine whether your child would benefit from interventions related to sensory processing needs. Many quality OTs would hesitate to officially label an infant younger than 18 months with sensory processing dysfunction, but they may go ahead with implementing some sensory-based strategies as a part of the IFSP and, eventually, the IEP.

If it's determined your child needs OT services related to sensory needs, you can set up a time for regular therapy sessions. During those therapy sessions, the OT can show you many strategies to help your child at home, in school and out in the community. The strategies are intended to help your child process sensory information more typically and therefore reduce sensory-seeking or sensory–defensive behaviors. The strategies depend upon your child's specific sensory behaviors and the degree to which the behaviors affect her.

References

"Integration" Definition and More from the *Free Merriam-Webster Dictionary.* (2013). Retrieved May 28, 2013 from http://www.merriam-webster.com/dictionary/integration.

Bharadwaj, S.V., Daniel, L.L. & Matzke, P.L. (2009). Brief Report — Sensory-processing disorder in children with cochlear implants. *American Journal of Occupational Therapy, 63,* 208–213. Doi:10.5014/ajot.63.2.208.

Chapter 6

Hearing Devices and Assistive Listening Devices

What's the Difference?

You will be hearing a lot about two categories of devices people with hearing loss might use. One category is hearing devices. **Hearing devices** include hearing aids, bone conduction hearing systems and cochlear implants. **Assistive listening devices** include tools your child might use in conjunction with her hearings aids, bone conduction hearing devices and/or cochlear implants. They are tools to make life easier for people who are unable to hear some typical environmental sounds — particularly sounds around the house. Hearing devices and assistive listening devices can be used together or separately.

Hearing devices
- hearing aids
- bone conduction hearing devices
- cochlear implants

Assistive listening devices
- personal FM/DM systems
- soundfield systems
- alarm clocks
- doorbells
- safety alarms
- phones

Hearing Devices: Does Your Child Need Them?

This is a really important question. As you read through the next few chapters, you will learn what certain hearing devices do. Remember that, ultimately, the purpose of all hearing devices is to deliver sound to an ear that doesn't pick up the sound on its own. Your child needs that sound to be audible in order for her to be aware of her surroundings and to learn to listen and talk.

In Chapter 11, you will learn that, for any child to learn how to talk, she has to listen to others talk. She learns to monitor and adjust her own voice according to what she hears. Because your child's ears are unable to take in sound typically, she needs hearing devices to help her gain *better* access to sound. The way she talks will be representative of what she hears, so you want her to hear as optimally as possible.

For many parents getting hearing devices for their child for the first time, the process can be overwhelming and exhausting. This can be because of the complexity of some hearing devices and/or the perceptions associated with wearing such devices. Or maybe it's just because there's a lot to handle.

Where to Begin

Something helpful you can do for your child and yourself during the process of getting hearing devices is to understand the following:

- what hearing devices do
- how to work the devices
- how to keep the devices working properly
- what to do if the devices don't work properly

Your pediatric audiologist and early interventionist can support you as you learn the ins and outs of using devices. Knowing where to begin doesn't take away the emotions you may experience, but it can reduce stress and difficulty, resulting in greater comfort and ease for you and your child.

The Importance of Full-Time Device Use (During All Waking Hours)

Accomplishing consistent use of hearing devices is an extremely important part of helping your child learn to talk. No matter what hearing devices your child uses, she should be using them as often as possible. We live in a very noisy world with lots of sound surrounding us almost all the time. Learning to talk requires hearing these sounds as well as possible every day. One of the most important challenges you have as your child's advocate is to ensure she wears her devices during **all waking hours**. What does "all waking hours" mean? Well, your

Interesting Facts About Listening and Learning to Talk

A baby with typical hearing listens for about 10 waking hours each day, 365 days each year. That is 3,650 listening hours each year.

If a baby with hearing loss wears her devices for only three hours each day, that's only 1,095 hours of listening in a year! It would take another seven years just to have the same amount of listening experience.

A toddler with typical hearing listens for about 12 waking hours each day, 365 days each year. That is 4,380 listening hours each year!

If a toddler with hearing loss wears her devices for only three hours each day, that's only 1,095 hours of listening in a year! It would take another nine years to have the same amount of listening experience.

(adapted from *Learn to Talk Around the Clock,* Rossi, 2003.)

child should wear her devices any time she is awake. Depending on the water resistance of her devices, you may need to remove the devices if there's a chance they could get really wet or submerged in water (such as when bathing or swimming). "All waking hours" might not happen right away, but it's a reasonable and necessary goal.

Hearing Devices

A **hearing device** is a piece of equipment designed to deliver sound to an impaired ear. There are three main types — hearing aids, bone conduction hearing devices and cochlear implants. Some children use only one of these devices. Others use two. *None* of these devices restores hearing, but they can give your child increased access to sound so she can hear the sounds going on around her.

Hearing Aids

A hearing aid is a relatively small electronic device that amplifies sound, or makes it louder. The hearing aid is the most commonly used device for children. Many children with hearing loss use hearing aids early on. Some of these children continue to use hearing aids. Other children, usually those with severe or profound hearing loss, might go on to use a cochlear implant, or even two. Specific and detailed information about hearing aids, specifically air conduction, behind the ear hearing aids, can be found in Chapter 7.

Bone Conduction Hearing Devices

Bone conduction hearing devices are small electronic devices containing hearing aid components as well as a vibrating mechanism. They are generally used by people who are unable to wear air conduction behind the ear hearing aids because of an atypical physical structure of the outer or middle ear. Specific and detailed information about bone conduction hearing devices can be found in Chapter 8.

Cochlear Implants

A cochlear implant is a surgically implanted device designed to provide sound for children with severe to profound hearing loss who do not receive much benefit from one or two hearing aids. A cochlear implant has two main components. One component is surgically implanted; the other is worn externally, behind the ear and on the head behind the ear. Specific detailed information about cochlear implants can be found in Chapter 9.

What Are the Best Hearing Devices for Your Child?

Determining which hearing devices are best for your child may not be easy. You can work with a qualified pediatric audiologist to help you make the decision. Your child needs time, training and evaluation. Remember if your goal is a talking child, she needs to consistently hear speech well enough to understand it. Your child's aided responses during audiologic testing will help provide information on which devices best meet her needs.

Consistent use of hearing devices is absolutely necessary. If your child has worn hearing aids consistently for six months or more, your pediatric audiologist can help determine if those hearing aids are most beneficial for your child or if other devices might be more appropriate. If you have unanswered questions about the hearing devices most appropriate for your child, you might want to obtain a second opinion. For this, you may want to consult an additional pediatric audiologist. Currently, children as young as 12 months (and occasionally even younger) are able to receive cochlear implants. Because the ear-level hearing aid and the cochlear implant are the most common devices used by young children, you will likely have some additional questions about these.

Assistive Listening Devices

Assistive listening devices are tools your child might eventually use in conjunction with her hearing aids and/or cochlear implants. When children begin attending school regularly and find themselves needing to listen in classrooms or other noisy settings, they may benefit from assistive listening devices. It's best for the parents, audiologists and educators to determine which type of device is best suited to meet the child's needs in a particular educational setting.

Personal Systems

A **personal FM/DM system** is an assistive listening device used to deliver quality auditory information to your child's hearing aid or cochlear implant. A personal FM/DM system can improve the clarity and loudness of sound going to your child's ear so she is able to hear better in noisy situations like the classroom when the teacher is at a distance. It is most commonly used in the classroom setting.

A personal FM/DM system has two main parts — a microphone and transmitter the teacher wears and a receiver embedded in or attached to your child's hearing aid or cochlear implant. As the teacher talks, the microphone picks up the sound of her voice. That sound is then transmitted to your child's device through the receiver. Personal FM/DM systems transmit the sound in a way similar to how a radio or streamer works. The system is wireless, so nothing physically connects the teacher's microphone to the child's device.

Some parents like to use a personal system in noisier situations outside of school. Driving is one such situation. Riding in the car can be noisy for people who wear hearing aids or cochlear implants. Parents might use the system to talk while driving so the child in the back seat receives a higher quality auditory signal than she would without the FM/DM system.

Classroom Soundfield Systems

Soundfield systems are another way of improving listening conditions in a classroom. Soundfield systems have been reported as beneficial to all students in a classroom — not just to those with hearing loss. To transmit a signal, a soundfield system can use infrared (IR) or line-of-sight, radio frequency modulation (FM) or digital modulation (DM). Regardless of the mode of transmission, and similar to personal systems, the teacher wears or holds a microphone near her mouth. Her voice is sent directly to the system's receiver. Unlike personal systems, though, the sound is not just delivered to a single student. Instead, the sound is delivered to a speaker system in the classroom. The system increases the volume of the teacher's voice so it's slightly louder than her speaking voice and ideally louder than the level of noise generated in a typical classroom. Many teachers find the use of a soundfield system increases attentiveness for the majority of students and reduces teacher voice fatigue.

Other Assistive Listening Devices

In addition to some of the more common assistive listening devices like FM/DM and soundfield systems, it may be helpful for you to know about other products available to people with hearing loss. Even though your child may be too young to use any of these right now, these tools might be of interest to you as she gets older. Your pediatric audiologist can provide information on these devices, and a simple online search can provide tons of information, too.

Alarm clocks

Many alarm clocks use alternative methods, such as vibrations or flashing lights, to wake a person with hearing loss.

Doorbells, phones and safety alarms

Devices are available to alert people with hearing loss to sounds they might not hear. These devices can be set up in the home according to personal preference. When someone rings the doorbell, a certain lamp or light flashes. When the home phone rings, another lamp or light flashes. Fire, security and other safety alarms can be set up, too. These alarms might use flashing lights, or they might use vibrations to alert a person who is sleeping.

TTYs/TDDs

TTY stands for teletypewriter. TDD stands for telecommunications device for the deaf. These devices may be used to communicate through a phone line. A person with a TTY/TDD can call another person with a TTY/TDD and communicate by typing messages across a small screen on the device. In addition, relay services exist so a person without a TTY/TDD can call a person with one, and vice versa. At the time these products were invented, they were state-of-the-art. Now, with the common use of e-mail, video conferencing and text messaging, TTY/TDD systems are not often used.

Reference

Rossi, K. (2003). *Learn to Talk Around the Clock: A Professional's Early Intervention Toolbox. Level B.* Washington, DC: Alexander Graham Bell Association for the Deaf and Hard of Hearing.

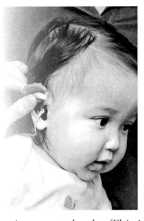

Chapter 7

Behind the Ear (BTE) Hearing Aids

What Is a Hearing Aid?

Ahearing aid is an electronic device that amplifies sound. In other words, a hearing aid makes all sounds in the nearby environment louder. This includes talking, environmental sounds and noise. It's important to remember that hearing aids make sound louder but not necessarily clearer. Many children have a specific type of hearing loss that allows them to hear some sound, but because of the damage present in the impaired ear or ears, it is experienced as muffled, distorted or unclear. Even so, amplification can help many children have much better access to sound than they would without hearing aids.

Skilled Pediatric Audiologists and Hearing Aids

Before getting more in-depth with hearing aids, it is essential to note the importance of having a skilled pediatric audiologist work with you and your child. Your child's access to sound literally depends on it! Audiology appointments can be very busy. With hearing tests, hearing aid choices, hearing aid fittings, audiologic support and counseling, you can imagine how important it is to work with professionals who have expertise in the field as well as experience working with children. You might want to ask your pediatrician and/or ENT doctor to recommend a skilled pediatric audiologist or audiology team near you. Audiology is a complicated and detailed field. The better your audiology services, the better off your child will be as she learns to listen and talk.

Hearing Aids for Kids

Many kinds of hearing aids are available, but only certain types are used for young children. Each hearing aid contains internal controls set by a pediatric audiologist to provide optimal sound for the child. This can be thought of as a prescription setting, which means that hearing aids are not interchangeable from one child to another.

The most high-tech kind of hearing aid is a **digital hearing aid**. Your child should be fit with a digital hearing aid, which your pediatric audiologist programs according to your child's hearing loss. A digital hearing aid uses sophisticated digital signal technology to emphasize some sounds while minimizing others, such as background noise. This allows your child better access to important sounds — particularly to the sounds of speech.

Two main categories of hearing aids are **air conduction hearing aids** and **bone conduction hearing aids**. Most often, air conduction hearing aids are used by children who have typically-formed outer and middle ears. Air conduction hearing aids are the more common hearing aids. A behind the ear hearing aid is the most common kind of air conduction hearing aid used with children. This hearing aid sits on the outer ear and is anchored into the ear by an earmold. (See the photo.)

Bone conduction hearing aids are used for people who have physical malformation of the outer ear or middle ear that precludes them from using an air conduction hearing aid. They can also be used for people with single-sided hearing loss to transmit sound over to the normal-hearing cochlea.

Behind the Ear (BTE) Hearing Aids

The most commonly used hearing aid for children is an air conduction hearing aid called the **behind the ear (BTE) hearing aid**, also referred to as an ear-level hearing aid. As you can guess by its name, the BTE hearing aid rests comfortably just behind the ear. The remainder of this chapter is dedicated to information on the BTE hearing aid. BTE hearing aids are custom-fit to your child by the use of an earmold. The earmold fits into the part of the outer ear you can see. (Find more information on earmolds on pages 82–85.)

Each hearing aid has special parts in a small case, smaller than your little finger. You can order the plastic case in your child's skin color, hair color or in a variety of fun, bright, opaque or see-through colors. There may be buttons or switches on the case, which connects to a hook, tubing and your child's earmold.

BTE Hearing Aid Components

■ **Battery**

The **hearing aid battery,** which is about the size of a pea, provides the power to operate the hearing aid. Batteries come in several sizes, and each hearing aid requires a specific size. Batteries can last about one to two weeks, but they need daily checking to

A Tour of a BTE Hearing Aid

A hearing aid is powered by a small battery located inside the hearing aid case. Sound enters the microphone on the case of the hearing aid, and the sound is converted into an electrical signal. An amplifier inside the case increases the signal and sends it to a receiver, also inside the case. The receiver changes the electrical signal back into sound. This amplified (louder) sound is sent from the receiver, through a plastic hook attached to the hearing aid case, through some plastic tubing, through the earmold and into your child's ear.

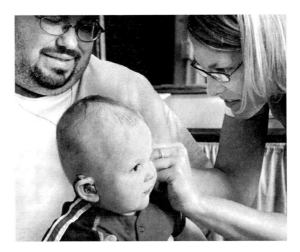

verify that they still have power. The life of batteries varies based on the power of the hearing aid and how long it is used each day.

The battery sits in a small compartment inside the case. Learn to recognize the positive side, marked with a +, and insert it as indicated in the compartment. If it's in backwards, the hearing aid won't work. Keep a fresh supply of batteries on hand so you can change the battery when needed. Since it's important for your child to have consistent access to sound, it's essential that you always have working batteries available. To avoid ever having to go without the hearing aids because of a dead battery, provide batteries for all caregivers. Because batteries can be a choking hazard to young children, consider removing, checking and reinserting them out of the view of your little one.

■ On/off switch

The parts of your child's BTE hearing aid depend on the brand you and your pediatric audiologist choose for your child. Some BTE hearing aids have an actual on/off switch on the outside of the case. Other hearing aids are turned on or off by adjusting the battery door — slightly open is "off" and all the way closed is "on." Your pediatric audiologist will show you what the markings on your child's hearing aid mean.

Because children often like to "adjust" their own hearing aids, many hearing aids have a feature that disables those switches. This prevents your child from being able to turn the hearing aids "on" or "off" and gives you a little more peace of mind knowing she is not secretly adjusting them when you're not looking. Your pediatric audiologist will describe all of these features to you when your child is fit with her hearing aid.

■ **Program switch**

Digital hearing aids are capable of being programmed to suit your child's specific hearing loss. The pediatric audiologist uses a computer to set the programs inside the hearing aid. Typically, a hearing aid is capable of holding more than one program. When your child gets older, she will need to access sound in various listening environments such as the classroom, cafeteria, auditorium, parties, etc. She will be able to use the program switch to help her hear better in those particular situations.

If a hearing aid is capable of having more than one program, it must also have a switch for changing programs. You may notice a little switch or button on the case of the hearing aid. (Some hearing aids have a switch cover or optional faceplate so the switch is then covered.) The program switch enables a change of program according to the listening situation. At first, while your child gets used to wearing a hearing aid and listening with it, it's important for it to be set to a level appropriate for all situations.

For very young children, the pediatric audiologist might disable the program switch so it stays on the appropriate setting at all times. This feature is designed for children who might decide to "adjust" their hearing aids when parents aren't looking. If the pediatric audiologist cannot disable the program switch on the hearing aid, she will likely set the hearing aid with only one program. This ensures your young child is getting appropriate access to sound at all times while wearing the hearing aid.

■ **Microphone**

A tiny microphone is located beneath a small opening in the case. The microphone brings in sound. More formally, the microphone picks up sound from the air and changes it into electrical impulses. The microphone has to stay clean and free from debris so it can pick up sound effectively. It's the most sensitive and delicate part of the hearing aid. Some hearing aids have a microphone cover for protection but still allow sound to enter. Try to keep food, dirt, soap, hair oil, hair spray, creams and anything similar away from this opening.

■ **Amplifier**

The **amplifier** increases the level of the electrical impulses or electrical signal and sends the signal on to the receiver. Essentially, the amplifier makes sound louder. Your pediatric audiologist will set the appropriate amount of amplification using special software at audiology appointments.

■ **Receiver**

The **hearing aid receiver** is the part of the hearing aid that changes the electrical signal back into sound. It sends the amplified (louder) sound through the hook, tubing and earmold and then into your child's ear. Basically, the receiver takes sound from the hearing aid and delivers it into your child's ear.

▦ **Ear hook**

The **ear hook,** or hook, is usually made of clear, hard plastic. It is curved and is attached to the top of the BTE hearing aid on one end and to soft tubing (connected to the earmold) on the other end. A hook used by a young child is about the size of a piece of thin elbow macaroni. It is designed to help get the sound from one place to another — specifically from the hearing aid to the earmold. The hook snaps or screws onto the hearing aid and should be connected to it tightly. The curve of the hook is important. Your pediatric audiologist will choose a hook with a curve that fits nicely to your child's ear to ensure that the hearing aid sits on the ear appropriately.

▦ **Tubing**

The **tubing** is a short length of plastic that feels soft or pliable. It attaches to the tip of the hook on one end and to your child's earmold on the other end. The tubing is cut to the length that allows your child's hearing aid to sit comfortably *on* the ear while the earmold sits comfortably *in* the ear. Your pediatric audiologist can cut this tubing to an appropriate length for your child's ear.

Special Hearing Aid Features for Older Children

When your child is a little older, you can teach her how to change the program depending on the situation and her listening needs. Most digital hearing aids have the ability to hold several programs, but the exact number of programs varies by specific device and manufacturer. Your child distinguishes between programs by listening for beeps the hearing aid produces when the program is changed. If she pushes the program switch, she may hear one beep, indicating the hearing aid is on Program 1. If she pushes that same program button again, she may hear two beeps, indicating the hearing aid is on Program 2. Another push of the button and she may hear three beeps, and so on. Say your child's hearing aid has the capability of holding four programs. They might be as follows:

Program 1: For use in the classroom when she wants to hear both the teacher and other students

Program 2: For use in the classroom with an FM, infrared system or soundfield system so she can focus on the teacher's voice

Program 3: For use in noisy settings such as the school cafeteria, restaurant or a party when your child wants her hearing aid to pick up only the sound of the voices within a few feet and to decrease the sound of background noise

Program 4: For use while talking on the telephone

In addition to manually switching programs, several brands of hearing aids can be programmed to switch automatically to the program that will help your child hear best in her current listening environment.

Some models of hearing aids are water resistant, which really helps children who have wet hair and skin after bathing, swimming or perspiring. Other models are not water resistant; this means they should be kept dry. If your child perspires a lot, moisture may collect in the tubing and hook, and this could interfere with the transmission of sound. Your pediatric audiologist may sell you a dehumidifier and may have additional suggestions or solutions for moisture problems. (For more information on dehumidifiers for hearing aids, see page 86.)

Earmolds

Children who use BTE hearing aids need **earmolds**. An earmold is a small piece of soft silicon or vinyl material that fits snugly into your child's ear. Its purpose is two-fold: It holds the hearing aid comfortably at the ear and it funnels amplified sound from the hearing aid into the ear canal.

The earmold is custom-made to fit your child's external ear. It's first molded out of a temporary material, then made into a more permanent material. (See the next page for a complete description of the earmold process.) An earmold is usually soft and comfortable, yet it needs to fit very snugly. A snug fit should eliminate or minimize feedback, immediately recognizable as a high-pitched whistling sound. Feedback occurs when sound leaks out of the earmold and is re-amplified by the microphone.

Earmolds are available in a variety of materials, some of which are hypoallergenic for sensitive skin. The earmold may be clear or skin-colored, or it may be a bright, vibrant color. Some are even made with swirls of color, glitter or stars. Once your child is old enough, she may ask for these! Pediatric audiologists often have sample earmold colors and styles from which you and your child can choose. Having a choice in the matter often helps children who would otherwise be not so willing to wear the hearing aids. Bright pink glittery earmolds, for example, can be pretty exciting to show off.

Just as little feet grow and shoes no longer fit, little ears grow and earmolds no longer fit. As your child grows, new earmolds must be made. This occurs often in a child who is constantly growing — about once a month for babies and every few months for young children. You know your child is starting to outgrow an earmold when it feels loose when you put it in — or when you hear feedback even when it's in the ear correctly.

When you hear feedback, you know your child's hearing aid is not working optimally. The feedback may indicate only that the earmold has been bumped or loosened. Adjust it to see if you can eliminate the sound or determine if there's another problem. If it's really time for a new earmold, contact your pediatric audiologist for an appointment to have it made. Meanwhile, you can use a special hearing aid cream to hold you over until your child gets the new earmolds, which could take a couple weeks. The sticky cream makes a seal between your child's ear and the earmold. Your pediatric audiologist can sell you this product. It's just a temporary solution, so be sure to make an appointment for new earmolds as soon as you believe they're too small.

Audiology Appointments for Children with BTE Hearing Aids

If your child wears BTE hearing aids, you will have regular appointments with your pediatric audiologist. Your pediatric audiologist will give you a lot of information about the devices. She will also adjust the hearing aids to fit your child's hearing loss and her little ears.

Your pediatric audiologist needs to test your child's hearing, both without the device and while wearing the device. For more information about a typical audiology appointment, see the section called Walking Through a Typical Audiology Appointment in Chapter 3.

Earmold Impressions

To ensure the earmold fits properly in your child's ear, your pediatric audiologist makes an impression of your child's ear. This is called an **earmold impression**. It is made in your pediatric audiologist's office and then sent to a lab where it is used to make an earmold. Taking an earmold impression involves a few steps:

1. You hold your child comfortably, but firmly, on your lap.
2. Your pediatric audiologist inserts a dam — a little piece of cotton or foam — into your child's ear so the impression material cannot go too far into her ear canal.
3. The earmold impression material looks like goop. It's often pink. Your pediatric audiologist squirts the soft material into your child's ear. This doesn't hurt but may feel a little strange and cold to the skin.
4. After several minutes, the material firms.
5. Your pediatric audiologist removes a fully formed impression of your child's ear.
6. Your pediatric audiologist asks you to choose from an assortment of colors and designs, including every color of the rainbow, opaque, translucent, sparkly, swirled, etc. Some of the choices are limited by the size of your child's ear.
7. Your pediatric audiologist sends your child's impression to a specialized lab.
8. After about two weeks, your child's new earmold comes back in the color of her choice.
9. Lastly, you'll need another appointment for the pediatric audiologist to fit the earmold to your child's hearing aid and ear, adjust the tubing and hook and perform some tests on the hearing aid and earmold to ensure they are working properly.

Real Ear to Coupler Difference (RECD)

Even after your child has a custom-fit earmold, there are ways to make her access to sound optimal. To ensure the settings on your child's hearing aid are as precise as possible, skilled pediatric audiologists use certain measures to program the hearing aid even more accurately after inserting new earmolds. Your pediatric audiologist will adjust your child's hearing aid settings so the sound is precisely what she needs — not too much sound and not too little sound. This is done by obtaining a measurement called Real Ear to Coupler Difference (RECD). Every time your child receives new earmolds, your pediatric audiologist should attempt to obtain RECDs.

The process of obtaining RECDs is painless and simple for your child. Your pediatric audiologist takes a measure of your child's ear with the earmold in place. She uses a special computer and a thin probe tube (basically a flexible, hollow, skinny, plastic tube).

These measurements may not be obtainable at every audiology visit. This might be because your child is simply "finished" cooperating with testing. That's okay! Your pediatric audiologist can use the average measurements for your child's size and age.

When Should Your Child Wear the Hearing Aids?

The best answer to this is *always*. One exception is when your child is sleeping. The small parts could be a potential choking hazard for a waking child who decides to explore the hearing aids in bed. If the hearing aids are not water-resistant, you will also need to remove them while your child bathes or swims. You want to accomplish full-time use as quickly as

How to Wash Your Child's Earmold

Earmolds work best when they're clean. Yet they often collect perspiration, wax, dirt and cream, which can collect on the surface and inside the canal opening. For most children, washing the earmold once a week is enough. For children who develop a lot of ear wax that is noticeable daily, you may need to wash the earmold more often.

Try to get into the good habit of selecting one night a week when you're usually home for washing the earmolds. Set aside a few minutes on that night every week for this routine. It's best to wash the earmold after your child is in bed for two reasons. First, you don't want to do it during her wearing time. Second, you don't want a young child to see you do this and get the idea that she should try it on her own!

Supplies for cleaning an earmold
- two clean cups or bowls
- some mild liquid soap, such as dishwashing liquid or baby shampoo
- warm tap water
- clean wash cloth or paper towel
- hearing aid pick

Steps for cleaning an earmold
1. Take hold of the hook of your child's hearing aid with one hand and the tube of the earmold with the other. Gently tug (don't yank) until the two come apart.
2. Put the hearing aid away in its designated place.
3. Gently remove any visible wax, dirt or cream from the canal opening of the earmold with a hearing aid pick.
4. Put one or two drops of liquid soap into one cup or bowl. Add warm tap water to produce some bubbles. Agitate the earmold in the soapy water and rub all surfaces of the earmold with your soapy fingers. Drop the earmold into the cup or bowl and let it soak for a few minutes.

How to Wash Your Child's Earmold *continued*

5. Return and plug up the sink drain. Don't forget this! You don't want to learn the hard way how slippery earmolds are when they're wet! Remove the earmold and hold it under warm running tap water until the soap has rinsed away.

6. Give the earmold a good hard shake at least 10 times to remove the water. You might also use a special tool called an earmold blower to blow water and debris out of the earmold and tubing. For more information on the earmold blower, accessories and related equipment, see pages 86–87.

7. Put a clean washcloth or paper towel inside the other bowl. Set the earmold in the bowl and move the bowl to a safe place (away from a heat source). Let the earmold dry overnight.

8. In the morning, the earmold will be dry, and you can reattach it to the hearing aid hook. Expect to do a bit of pushing in order to attach the more pliable tube of the earmold to the harder plastic ear hook connected to the hearing aid.

9. If you notice the earmold is dirty at a time other than your scheduled weekly washing, or if you're in a hurry on your usual day, you can take some shortcuts. Substitute the time soaking in bubbly water with a good, minute-long rubbing of the earmold in the soapy water. Next, with the drain plugged, hold the earmold under warm running water for a minute or two. After the rinse, shake the earmold or use the blower to force air through and the water out. When you've done this several times, the earmold should appear dry, and you can reattach it to the hearing aid and put it back on your child.

possible so your child doesn't continue to miss important talk around her. Full-time hearing aid use is considered to be *all waking hours,* with the exception of bathing or water play for hearing aids that aren't water-resistant.

Children vary in response to new hearing aids. Some wear them happily from day one, and some try to remove them constantly. Many fall somewhere in between these two extremes. Children who wear hearing aids happily right away might do so because the sound is interesting to them, because they have taken on your positive attitude or because they typically do what's expected anyway. After being in quiet so long, children who start out resistant to hearing aids might not understand the sounds they are hearing. If this is the case, don't be discouraged. There's definitely time to build success!

Introducing BTE Hearing Aids to Your Child

Your child's first introduction to hearing aids is important. Your point of view lays the foundation for hers. The most significant factor determining if a young child wears hearing aids is whether or not the parents have made up their minds that the child will do so. Remember, for your child to learn how to talk, she must be able to listen with hearing aids during all waking hours.

How to Begin

First and foremost, start with a positive attitude. Yes, you might find it difficult to realize that your child needs to wear something visible on her ears. This does make her invisible hearing loss noticeable to others. Remember that your goal is to help her listen so she can talk. With consistent hearing aid use, you are giving her that opportunity. Your positive and determined attitude sets the stage for your child.

What You Need

Start by collecting the materials you need. As you do this, remind yourself that this is the preparation for providing important sound to your child on a regular basis.

You need the following:

- **Hearing aids**

- **Storage location**
  You need a place to store the hearing aids and some related equipment to use each day to check that they're working properly. Choose a location beyond the reach of small children, such as a dresser top or kitchen cabinet. Avoid the bathroom as it can be too humid for storing a hearing aid safely. Decide today that when the hearing aids are not on your child, you will return them to this location. This helps avoid wasted time looking for the hearing aids or related equipment.

- **Sturdy storage container**
  This container holds all of your accessories and related equipment. This could be a decorative tin, a plastic container with a lid or a zip-up pouch. Ideally, you want the container to look nice, interesting or colorful because it helps make a positive statement about the importance of the hearing aids. In some families, it's an advantage if small children are unable to open the container on their own.

- **Accessories and related equipment**
☐	batteries	Your child's hearing aids require a specific size battery. Your pediatric audiologist can help you get packs of batteries or can recommend a place you can buy them. Some health insurance plans cover the cost of children's hearing aid batteries, so be sure to ask.
☐	battery caddy	This small container is used to hold spare batteries. It can be easily attached to a backpack, purse or key ring.
☐	battery tester	This small device is used to determine if hearing aid batteries have full power or if they need to be replaced.
☐	dehumidifier	Your pediatric audiologist can sell you a low-tech, portable kit that can store a hearing aid overnight while eliminating moisture from the hearing aid and earmold. Most kits look like a

small box, cup or jar with a packet of desiccant inside. The desiccant must periodically be reactivated to ensure optimal function. You can also purchase an electronic dehumidifier that disinfects and removes moisture from a hearing aid and earmold using desiccant and sometimes ultraviolet light. It is not portable and the desiccant bricks must be disposed of and replaced instead of reactivated.

☐ earmold blower   This tool is used for removing moisture and debris from the earmold and tubing. It looks similar to a bulb syringe used for nasal suction.

☐ hearing aid brush   This small brush is used to remove debris from an earmold.

☐ hearing aid cover   These are specially designed, flexible covers made for hearing aid moisture protection. They protect the amplifier, case, controls and battery compartment from humidity, sweat, hair products and dirt while leaving an opening for sound to enter the microphone. Hearing aid covers are not necessary for water-resistant hearing aids.

☐ hearing aid pick   Similar in size to the brush, this is a tool used to remove earwax and debris from the opening of the earmold.

☐ hearing aid cream   This white cream is used to temporarily control hearing aid whistling or feedback by creating a seal between your child's ear and the earmold. A dab of this cream can reduce the chance of feedback until your growing child receives better-fitting earmolds.

☐ stethoset   This device is used to test a hearing aid to ensure it's working properly. It looks similar to a stethoscope but has a small rubber cup at the tip used to attach, or couple, the hearing aid.

☐ water-based lubricant   This is a slippery gel that can be used to ease earmold insertion. It is especially helpful for brand new earmolds with a snug fit.

Checking and Testing Hearing Aids

It will take about five minutes each morning to check your child's hearing aids. If you do it first thing every day, you can put them on her as she gets up. Here's a list of the steps you can take for each hearing aid:

1. Remove the battery and insert it into the battery tester. If it has full power, put it back into the hearing aid. If not (even if it's borderline), insert a fresh battery.

2. Take a look at the earmold. Be sure there's no wax or anything else in the canal or on the surface. If clear, proceed to Number 4.

3. If clogged, use a hearing aid pick or brush to gently remove the wax or dirt. If the earmold is really dirty, read How to Wash Your Child's Earmold on page 84 and do so.

4. Turn the hearing aid on and attach the small cup of the hearing aid stethoset to the long, thin canal end of the attached earmold. Put the ear inserts on the stethoset in your ears. **WARNING!** If your child's hearing aid is powerful, be sure to pinch the tube of the stethoset so the amplified sound does not overwhelm your ears. You can also ask your pediatric audiologist about a filtered stethoset designed to muffle the sound for someone with typical hearing to listen safely to a powerful hearing aid.

5. Talk as if you're testing a microphone in an auditorium. You can say "Testing: one, two, three, four" or you can use the Ling test described on the next page. Each time you listen to the hearing aid before putting it on your child, your goal is to be sure the sound is as clear today as it was the first day your child got it. If it is, you're almost ready to put it on your child. If it isn't, read the troubleshooting section on pages 97–98.

Putting on BTE Hearing Aids

1. Turn off the hearing aids. If you insert the hearing aids while turned off, you won't have to listen to feedback they might produce. If you want to use gel or cream, apply it to the earmolds now. Use only a bit and avoid getting any near the hole in the earmolds or on the actual hearing aids.

2. If you're putting the hearing aids on an infant, lay her on the changing table or a blanket on the floor. If you're putting them on a toddler or older child, sit or kneel beside the child so you're at ear level. Aim the tip of the earmold into the canal of the child's ear and downward toward the chin. Turn it so the earmold fits against the child's external ear. Once you've inserted the earmold, tug gently on your child's ear or push in gently on the earmold to make it fit snugly. As soon as she is wearing the hearing aid, turn it on.

3. Repeat Step 2 with the other hearing aid.

4. Say something to your child. You might say:
   - □ "Hello, (her name)."
   - □ "Here's your hearing aid. I love you."
   - □ "bababababa." The advantage of using this nonsense vocalization is that, after daily repetition, your little one might learn to say it to you as soon as you have inserted and turned on the device. This is a clear indication she is hearing the sound of your voice!
   - □ "ah," "oo," "ee," "s," "sh," "m" and silence (Ling test)

   Hooray! You did it! Even if it seems tricky at first, it will certainly get easier over time. The more times you do it, the easier it'll be!

Special Considerations for Infants

Parents often ask about strategies for helping infants optimally use their hearing aids, since common positions for infants can cause feedback. These positions occur when cuddling, nursing and riding in a car seat. For cuddling and nursing, you can choose the "football" hold so the hearing aids are not pressed up against you. When babies are in a car seat, the hearing aids will likely feed back. It's okay for this to happen, but the sound of that feedback can be disturbing. You are encouraged to keep the hearing aids in during short car trips, but give yourself permission to remove the hearing aids during longer trips. The more upright the child is, the less feedback is likely to occur.

Keeping the Hearing Aids on Your Child

Sometimes keeping the hearing aids on your child is a matter of identifying a problem with wearing the hearing aids and finding a solution to that problem. If you feel like you've tried everything and your child is still presenting a challenge, this section might help. See if your child is experiencing any of the following problems and follow the guidelines for making it better. In addition, know that sometimes your child might remove both hearing aids even if only one of them is bothering her. Be sure to check both hearing aids in this case.

The Ling Test

The Ling test is a quick and easy way to ensure that, while wearing her devices, your child has access to the range of speech sounds that we use when we talk.

To perform a standard Ling Test, first put the device on your child. If your child wears two devices, only put one of them on at this moment. Make sure the device is turned on. Place yourself next to or behind your child so she can hear you but can't see your face. Say the following sounds one at a time and teach her to repeat each sound after you say it:

- "ah" (as in hot)
- "oo" (as in boo)
- "ee" (as in bee)
- "s"
- "sh"
- "m"
- silence

Each time you perform this test, say the sounds in a different order.

If your child has two devices, turn the first one off and put the second one on. Make sure this device is on. Repeat the Ling test with that device. Then put the first device back on so she is wearing both and both are turned on.

Note any difficulty your child has repeating these sounds back to you with the device(s) and report any consistent problems to your pediatric audiologist.

For more information on the Ling test, including how to perform a modified version on infants and babies, see page 149. (Pollack et al.,1997; Sindrey, 2002)

Tell Your Child

It's good practice to tell your child what you're going to do before you put her device on and before you take her device off. For example, before you put the device on your child, show her the device and say "I'm going to put your hearing aids on now." Make eye contact, nod your head and wait for her to acknowledge you. Then put each device on.

Similarly, when you take the device off, get in the habit of saying "I'm going to take your hearing aids off now" or "Are you ready for me to take these off?"

Eventually, you'll get to the point where you can ask your child to put on and take off her devices herself. Until that point, it's nice to tell her what you plan to do before you do it. Besides being respectful and mindful of her personal space, this will teach your child that her involvement is important!

Uncomfortable Earmold

See if something about the earmold is causing discomfort. It might have a rough or uncomfortable spot, or it might look and feel like it isn't fitting correctly. If you suspect this problem, make an appointment with your pediatric audiologist to work out any earmold issues. Inserting the hearing aid should not hurt! If it does, work toward a solution right away. (Note: Do not modify the earmold yourself.) Observe your child carefully. Some young children wear the hearing aids happily, yet are annoyed while they're being inserted. If this is true for your child, your progress toward rapid insertion should solve the problem in time.

Red or Sore Ear

Be aware that if your child actually winces upon insertion of the hearing aid, she might have a sore in her ear or an ear that hurts due to an infection. Ask your doctor or pediatric audiologist to help solve any of these problems.

Uncomfortable Hook or Tubing

Ask the pediatric audiologist whether the hook size is optimal for your child and whether the length of the earmold tubing is optimal. Sometimes adjusting one or both of those leads to greater comfort. This may lead to your child wearing the hearing aid more cooperatively.

The Hearing Aid Keeps Falling Off

Sometimes your child's hearing aids may flop off her ears and hang from the earmolds. This could bother her and lead her to take them all the way off. Your child just may need something to hold the hearing aids on and keep her mind off them so she is more likely to leave them on. It's just a matter of time before finding the solution that will work for you and your child. Here are some hearing aid retention devices that may solve this problem:

■ **Huggie or hearing aid ring**
This is a small tubular ring of plastic that fits onto the hearing aid and around the ear. It must be secured on the hearing aid in a way that doesn't block the microphone. Ask your pediatric audiologist where and how to purchase this.

■ **Adhesive**
Certain kinds of tape can help hold the hearing aid in place by sticking the case of the hearing aid directly to the skin behind your child's ear. Your pediatric audiologist should be able to obtain hearing aid tape for you, yet you also can buy wig or toupee tape from a barbershop or beauty supply store.

■ **Hearing aid clips**
Clips with lanyards can be used to secure the BTE hearing aids to the back of your child's shirt or collar. They won't keep her from pulling the hearing aid off, but they can help you avoid losing the hearing aid once she does. In addition, for young children who are very active and mobile, a clip can prevent you from totally losing the hearing aid on a busy playground or in the backyard. These clips are ideal for using with either one or two hearing aids. The cords come in bright colors. Loop the tiny plastic ring at one end of the cord around the hook of the hearing aid. Loop the plastic ring at the other end around the hook of the other hearing aid. Pin the cord to your child's collar or the back of her shirt. Many hearing aid companies have clips for purchase. Your pediatric audiologist can help find what might work best for your child.

■ **Bonnet**
Using a bonnet is the most sure-fire way to keep your child's hands from removing the hearing aid. You can buy, alter or make one for this purpose. Remember, this is a temporary measure; it can help meet your goal of having a listening and talking child! The cloth should be lightweight so  sound can get through. Cloth that is too thick may distort the sound or cause feedback. The fit should be rather snug so little fingers can't creep inside. A mom of a baby boy thought of this strategy! Her words were, "He *will* wear the hearing aids all the time!"— and he did!

■ **Headband**
If your child can tolerate a headband, get a stretchy one and put it on over her ears. Try not to cover the hearing aid's microphone. Boys can wear sweatband-type headbands. Girls can wear headbands with designs or bows on them. Remember, it's only temporary! This can help if the hearing aid falls or flops off the ear and bothers your child.

Weaning Your Child from Bonnets and Headbands

If you need to use a bonnet or headband, you can eventually eliminate its use. After some time, your child will probably forget about tugging on the hearing aids. By then, she will be accustomed to the experience of sound and benefit from listening to it. At first, try brief periods without the extra item, selecting active times when your child's hands are busy. Next, you can try longer periods of time without the bonnet or headband. Eventually she will be so used to leaving her hearing aids alone that you won't need the bonnet or headband at all. Through this whole experience, remember that each step is necessary to help your child develop into a listening, talking child.

Steps to Accomplishing Full-Time Use

Remember that your goal is a talking child, and hearing aid use during all waking hours is necessary to achieve this goal. Now that you know how to put the hearing aids on and keep them on, here are some suggestions for accomplishing full-time use.

1. For the first week or so, expect your child to wear the hearing aids for some short periods each day rather than for the entire day. Select several times when your child is well rested and when you can interact with her, closely supervise her and keep her busy. If you choose an activity in which your child's hands are busy (such as eating, swinging or playing with a favorite toy), she is less likely to touch or remove the hearing aids. Some children enjoy clapping with you as you say "Hooray!" each time you insert the hearing aids.

2. If your child doesn't bother with the hearing aids at all, try leaving them in a while longer than planned; however, if at all possible, you should take care to anticipate and remove them before she thinks to do so. This teaches her that *you* do the taking out — and she should not.

3. If your child reaches up and tries to remove the hearing aids, tell her "No" in a calm and firm voice. Try to hand her something else to keep her hands occupied or change activities to otherwise distract her. You can also say things like "Leave it in," or "No touching." If you overreact, she may develop the habit of reaching for the hearing aids just to see you get excited, so avoid overacting. At the end of the wearing time, take each hearing aid off by wiggling your index finger behind the earmold itself. Then pinch with your thumb while turning and pulling the earmold out. Note: Don't be a "tube puller!" If you pluck the hearing aid out by pulling on the tube, the tube can detach from the earmold. This keeps the hearing aid from working and fitting properly.

4. Repeat Steps 1–3 several more times during the day. Then increase the wearing time so your child is wearing the hearing aids a little bit longer than on the previous days.

5. Next, try to achieve full-time use. This means keeping the hearing aids on as long as possible between sleep times and bath or water play (for hearing aids that are not water-resistant). This will reinforce the notion that you are in charge of wearing times but are reasonable in your expectations. During these weeks, be sure to include some outings and outside play and keep your eyes on those hearing aids at all times!

6. Congratulate yourself because you and your child have accomplished quite a lot. Full-time hearing aid use is approaching!

If you're unable to accomplish these steps on your first attempt, try not to feel discouraged. It's okay to start over and go through the steps again. You won't be the first parent who has had to try again. Remember that your goal is a talking child, and use this idea to motivate you!

Increasing Hearing Aid Wear Time

Some children are reluctant or stubborn about wearing hearing aids. If this is true for your child, remain calm but determined. If you look frustrated rather than calm, your child will sense this. Your firm, gentle insistence will go further toward success than your appearing ruffled, annoyed or upset.

Set aside a period of 15 minutes when your child is well rested and when you can give undivided attention to her. Set a goal that she will wear the hearing aids for those 15 minutes. Try to arrange things so you can avoid everything else during this time. Select a fun activity that requires your child to use both her hands, and do the activity together. You might try making pudding, floating toys in water, swinging, dusting and sweeping, blowing bubbles she can pop or throwing balloons up in the air.

Gather the materials needed for the activity ahead of time. When you're ready to begin, hand your child two of the items, one for each hand. Put in your child's hearing aids, say "Hooray!" and clap your hands. Be ready to begin the activity quickly. Each and every time she reaches for or removes the hearing aids, calmly say "No" and replace them. Say nothing else and do nothing else about the removal or the attempt. Hand her something else and continue the activity.

When things are going along well and she is fully absorbed in the activity, resist the temptation to just leave the hearing aids in her ears. After your goal is met (about 15 minutes), remove the hearing aids. This builds toward success because your interaction involved you not allowing her to take them out and you being willing to take them out after a reasonably short time. Try a similar activity and repeat these same techniques again later. The more times a day you can do this, the sooner your child will wear the hearing aids all day.

Most children who are busy and happy are distracted from thinking about and touching the hearing aids and will learn to leave them alone during these periods. You should see some improvement in a week or less. Improvement can be measured by a decrease in your child's attempts at removal or actual removal of the hearing device.

When you have noticed improvement, choose another few times a day when you can supervise but not be totally involved with the activity. Giving your child a meal can work well, especially if it's a few minutes past regular meal time and she is truly hungry. Have everything ready ahead of time. If appropriate for your child's age, plan ahead to include some finger foods to keep those hands busy. Once your child is seated, put the hearing aids on, clap and say "Hooray!" Then quickly supply the meal. Sit or stay nearby and follow the same routine of responding calmly with "No" and replacing the hearing aids as needed. Whether your child is still being fed or can feed herself, hand her something or encourage her to try some finger foods.

After two or three weeks, you should have many periods each day when your child is agreeably wearing her hearing aids for about 15 minutes at a time. Congratulations!

Accomplishing Full-Time Hearing Aid Use as a Working Parent

You can see that getting your child comfortable with wearing hearing aids all day might be more easily accomplished if you are with your child all day. While this is true, there are also ways to accomplish full-time hearing aid use even if you are not with her all day. The most

Guess What? She Keeps Taking Off the Hearing Aids!

Just as many young children refuse to wear hats, bows or sunglasses, many also refuse to wear hearing aids. If your child pulls the hearing aids off over and over again, recognize that this isn't a choice for her. When you see this about to happen, try the following:

One last time, put the hearing aids on your child. Do whatever you need to do to distract her and keep her from taking them off.

- Hand her a toy to keep her hands busy.
- Gently hold her hands and sing her a song.
- Hold her close to you and rock her.

Leave the hearing aids on for 30 more seconds. Then, *and this is the most important part,* YOU take the hearing aids off of her so she learns that it's only okay for YOU to take them off — not her.

A short while later, put them back on and try this process again.

It's also important to anticipate the times your child might be likely to take off the hearing aids. When she feels crabby, ill, exhausted or unusually irritable, plan for a "break" and remove the hearing aids, as needed, before your child does.

Part of establishing full-time hearing aid use is helping your child and the rest of your family understand that hearing aid use is a necessity — not an option. This is most easily done by establishing a hearing aid routine and sticking with it.

common approach for working parents is to use morning, evening and weekend hours (or whenever you are with your child) as the initial wearing times.

Once your child is successfully wearing the hearing aids when you're with her, arrange an hour to teach your child care provider how to manage the hearing aids when you're away. You learned how and so will the child care provider. If your child care provider understands that the hearing aids are necessary for your child to learn to listen and talk, she should be willing to work with you. Sometimes parents can arrange for their early interventionist to assist with a hearing aid orientation.

Involving Your Child in Hearing Aid Care

You can increase your expectations just a bit in terms of hearing aid care once your child is about 24 months old, has been wearing the hearing aids cooperatively for six or more months and has the motor control to do so. Yes, even toddlers can start learning!

When it's time to remove the hearing aids, tell your child it's time and reach out your hand for one hearing aid to be placed there. In the beginning, guide your child's hand up to the hearing aid and help her gently take hold of the hook and tubing. Guide her little hand in removing the hearing aid and earmold. Teach her the gentle way to remove her hearing aid without detaching the tubing from the earmold. Repeat this with the other hearing aid. Show her how her hearing aids always go into the special container when she's not wearing them. Once this habit is established, encourage her to remove the hearing aids herself when asked and put them in the appropriate place.

Help her as needed until she can successfully hand you the hearing aids or put them in their special container when you ask her to. She will learn to appreciate your allowing her to do this herself. Your child will benefit by learning independence, and this will help develop her self-esteem. Remember to praise your child for her accomplishment!

Hearing Aid Use in the Car

Because hearing aids can automatically adjust to control for excessive background noise, most adult users don't mind wearing their hearing aids during car travel. However, a car is a small, closed, reverberant area. Amplified sound bounces off the hard surfaces of the car's interior only to be amplified again by the hearing aids. This is certainly a different listening

environment, and a young child may need time getting used to it. If your child seems bothered at first, know that she will become more used to car rides over time.

Since little ones are typically in safety seats in the back seat, situate your child on the opposite side of the vehicle from the adult in the front seat who will watch over the child. This makes it easier for the adult to see and monitor the child. If car rides mostly include you and your child, then put her on the passenger side of the back seat so you can look back at her occasionally.

If your child takes out the hearing aids and puts things in her mouth, remove the hearing aids for car trips until these behaviors have diminished. A loose earmold or battery is a choking hazard. Be sure your child is not putting small parts in her mouth or damaging the hearing aid. Be aware that young children have been known to toss hearing aids out the windows of moving cars. For this reason, travel with the windows up until your child has developed consistent hearing aid use in the car. If you have window locks, this is a good time to use them.

Hearing Aid Insurance

Little children (and family life) can be hard on hearing aids. Most new hearing aids come with a one-year warranty but may last up to five years, so you may want to choose insurance coverage for after the warranty expires. Pediatric audiologists who order and dispense these hearing aids have the option to purchase a manufacturer extended warranty covering parts and labor for up to three years. Companies that offer hearing aid insurance typically offer coverage for repair as well as for replacement. Families should not assume their homeowner's insurance covers their child's hearing aids. Investigate your policy to see if coverage is possible. If not, several private insurance companies cover only assistive listening devices, usually at a reasonable cost. Talk with your pediatric audiologist to determine if the manufacturer's coverage, your homeowner's insurance or private coverage is appropriate.

Insurance coverage for repair usually covers parts and labor. Sometimes manufacturers offer an option to forego the repair insurance until it's needed. Then, if a need arises, a family can pay the repair fee, which may be a couple hundred dollars. Payment of this fee covers the cost of the immediate repairs and extends the warranty for 6–12 additional months.

There are a variety of reasons a hearing aid would need to be replaced instead of just repaired. Some common causes for replacement are being chewed by a dog, run over by a car, thrown from the window of a moving car, ground in a garbage disposal or stepped on and crushed by a sibling. Insurance for replacing a hearing aid is usually good for only one replacement, regardless of the length of coverage. The one-time replacement fee varies in price but may cost up to several hundred dollars.

Whether you, your insurance company or a third party pays for your child's hearing aids, be aware that digital hearing aids may cost several thousands of dollars. You may want to teach your child to treat the hearing aids with extra special care. They should hold up well to the typical rough and tumble life of a young child, but not to abuses such as stomping on them or giving them to the family dog. Your own special care of the hearing aids and your attitude and treatment of them gives your child her first lesson about their importance and value.

Troubleshooting BTE Hearing Aids

Some hearing aid problems are simple and can be solved easily at home. Others have to be solved by your pediatric audiologist. Still others require your pediatric audiologist to return the device to the manufacturer for professional maintenance or replacement of parts. The chart on page 98 shows some common problems you can try to fix. In each case, if you are not successful, contact your pediatric audiologist and ask what to do next.

Now What?

Once your child has accomplished use of her hearing aids during all waking hours, the first thing you should do is give yourself a pat on the back! You are on the right track to having a talking child. The next step for you and your child is to begin developing some important and necessary listening skills. Chapter 10 contains lots of information on listening and auditory development. Your child needs these skills to become a successful talking child. Congratulations on completing this important step!

Problem	Possible Solution
The hearing aid won't turn on.	■ Insert or replace the battery. ■ Check the +/– placement of the battery. ■ Check the battery size and number. ■ Make sure the on/off switch is set to the on position or the battery door is all the way closed. ■ See if the earmold or tube is clogged or damp and remove any debris or moisture. ■ Remove the battery and place it in the dehumidifier overnight.
The hearing aid sounds weak.	■ Replace the battery. ■ See if the earmold or tube is clogged and clean it.
The hearing aid sound is distorted.	■ Replace the battery. ■ Check for moisture or debris. ■ Brush the microphone.
The hearing aid whistles.	■ Adjust the earmold to fit snugly on the tubing. ■ Adjust the earmold to fit snugly in your child's ear. ■ Use hearing aid cream to make a seal between your child's ear and the earmold. Your pediatric audiologist can supply this for you. ■ Schedule an appointment to get new earmold impressions.

References

Pollack, D., Goldberg, D. & Caleffe-Schenck, N. (1997). *Educational Audiology for the Limited-Hearing Infant and Preschooler: An Auditory-Verbal Program* (3rd ed.). Springfield, IL: Charles C Thomas Publisher, Ltd.

Sindrey, D. (2002). *Listening Games for Littles* (2nd ed.). Washington, DC: Alexander Graham Bell Association for the Deaf and Hard of Hearing.

Chapter 8

Bone Conduction Hearing Devices

What Is a Bone Conduction Hearing Device?

Bone **conduction hearing devices** are generally used by children unable to wear behind the ear hearing aids because of the physical structure of their outer and/or middle ears. For these children, the inner ear may work well. The bone conduction hearing device is designed to get sound around the outer and middle ear structures and directly to the inner ear.

A bone conduction hearing device is a processor that contains hearing aid components and a vibrating mechanism. For children under the age of 5, the device is attached to a soft headband and worn over the skin and/or hair on the head. The device is placed on one of the bones of the skull — either on the forehead bone or on the mastoid bone just behind the ear. Sound is transferred through the skin to the bones of the skull. The bones of the skull vibrate, sending sound directly to the inner ear — bypassing the outer and middle ears.

 Remember that children who are typically candidates for bone conduction hearing devices may have completely typical inner ears, but the outer and/or middle ears are unable to conduct sound normally. The bone conduction hearing device delivers sound directly to the inner ear, which is encased in bone.

A bone conduction hearing device is a small sound processor (about the size of a domino) containing both the hearing aid components and vibrating mechanism. Its microphone picks up sound in the environment and makes the device vibrate at different rates according to the loudness (intensity) and pitch (frequency) of the sound coming in. Your pediatric audiologist will discuss with you whether your child will benefit from just one or two devices. A bone conduction hearing device can be worn two ways:

1. **On a soft elastic headband** — The device can be attached to a removable soft headband you can simply put on and take off of your child. The headband comes in several cute designs and colors from which you and your child can choose. You can put either one or two devices on the headband. The device or devices securely snap on so they cannot fall off. The headband is then placed on your child's head so the vibrator is lightly pressing on the bones of the skull over the skin — either at the forehead or just behind the ear on the mastoid bone. Sound is transferred through the skin to the bones

of the skull. These bones vibrate, sending sound to the bony inner ear, bypassing the outer and middle ears. Most children under 6 years old wear the device on a headband until the point at which families and physicians consider implantation.

2. **Implanted** — A bone conduction hearing device can be attached to an abutment connected to a metal screw surgically implanted in the skull. Depending on which brand you choose, the implantation is either at the side of the base of your child's skull or just behind the ear. Your physician and pediatric audiologist will discuss with you whether one or two implanted devices are most beneficial for your child. Implantation is not recommended until a child is at least 5 years old because of the growth and size of the child's head.

Whether or not you plan to pursue surgical implantation, your child may wear a bone conduction hearing device on a headband throughout her early life. The device is the same whether worn on a headband or on a surgically implanted abutment.

Surgical Implantation

Once implanted, a bone conduction hearing device is referred to as **bone anchored hearing device** or bone anchored implant. As with any surgery, you and your child should be in contact with a skilled surgeon — specifically, one experienced with bone anchored hearing device surgery. Your pediatric audiologist can help you find more information and recommend a surgeon near you who can perform the surgery.

Depending on your surgeon's recommendation, the implantation requires either one or two surgeries. A screw is implanted into the skull either at the base of the skull or in the bone just behind the ear. The screw is embedded so the bone heals and grows around it, securing it in place.

For those having only one surgery for implantation, the surgeon will then attach another metal piece, called the abutment, to the implanted piece. The abutment sticks out a little past skin level. The skin is replaced around the abutment, and a small patch of hair in the area right around the abutment is permanently removed.

For those having two surgeries, the surgeon first implants the screw. He or she sews the skin back together at that point so the implant is totally covered. The child goes home and heals for the next six months before having the second surgery. The second surgery involves attaching the abutment. The surgeon opens the skin over the screw and attaches the abutment, which sticks out a little past skin level. The skin is replaced around (but not over) the abutment. The surgeon might permanently remove a very small patch of hair in the area right around the abutment.

A few weeks after the abutment is put in place, the pediatric audiologist will fit the external, removable component. The audiologist can explain the various parts and functions and demonstrate how to snap the hearing device onto the implanted abutment.

The most significant benefit of the implanted device over one worn on a headband is that the implanted device is directly connected to the bone by way of the abutment. This prevents lost vibrations in transmission over the skin.

Keeping the Abutment Area Clean and Healthy

Because the abutment is both under the skin and outside of the skin, certain precautions must be taken to keep the area clean and free from infection. Your pediatric audiologist and surgeon will explain these precautions in advance so you can use this information during the decision-making process. Families must be willing to take the extra steps necessary to ensure the area remains clean and free from infection. The surgeon and pediatric audiologist can provide recommendations, procedures and tools for keeping the area healthy.

Skilled Pediatric Audiologists and Hearing Devices

Audiology is a complicated and detailed field. The better your audiology services, the better off your child will be as she learns to listen and talk. It's essential to note the importance of having a skilled pediatric audiologist work with you and your child. Her access to sound literally depends on it!

Audiology appointments can be very busy. With hearing tests, hearing device choices and fittings, audiologic support and counseling, you can imagine how important it is to work with professionals who have expertise in the field as well as experience working with children. Ask your pediatrician and/or ENT doctor to recommend a skilled pediatric audiologist or audiology team near you.

Bone Conduction Hearing Device Components

■ **Sound processor**

The device that snaps onto either the headband or the surgically implanted abutment is called the **sound processor**. The sound processor is about the size of a small domino. It comes in lots of colors and has the following parts:

■ **On/off switch**

Some processors have an on/off switch or dial. For others, the battery door must be closed to be on, or open to be off. Your audiologist can demonstrate how to turn the device on and off.

■ **Volume control**

Some processors have a separate control for making volume adjustments. Others have a dial that controls power and volume. Your pediatric audiologist can show you how to adjust the device's volume and explain what volume is most beneficial for your child.

■ **Battery door**

Speech processors use a small disposable battery, which provides the power to operate them. Batteries last a while (50–60 hours of use) but need daily checking to verify that they still have power. Battery life varies based on how long they are used each day. The battery sits in a small compartment under the battery door. Learn to recognize the positive side of the battery, marked with a +, and insert it as indicated in the compartment. If it's in upside down, the sound processor won't work. You need to keep a fresh supply of batteries on hand. Batteries can be a choking hazard to young children. If any of your children are under age 5, please remove, check and reinsert the battery out of the child's or children's view.

■ **Microphone**

A tiny microphone is located on the part of the speech processor case that faces out. The microphone picks up sound from the air and sends it to the processor. The microphone has to stay clean and free from debris so it can pick up sound effectively. Your pediatric audiologist can give you tips on how to keep the microphone clean.

■ **Program selector/button**

The **program selector** is a small button on the speech processor. It is used to change the program setting from one program to another. Some devices also contain a mute feature controlled by the same button. During your audiology appointments, your pediatric audiologist sets the programs within the processor to suit your child's specific hearing loss.

■ **Coupling**

The **coupling** (or snap coupling) is the part of the speech processor that attaches to either the soft headband or to the surgically implanted abutment. It is designed to hold the speech processor securely in place.

■ **Safety line**

The **safety line** is an optional component some people choose to use. The safety line connects the speech processor to your child's shirt or other clothing. If the speech processor happens to detach from the abutment, it will not get lost. Instead, it will simply dangle from the safety line. This can give parents extra peace of mind.

Audiology Appointments for a Bone Conduction Hearing Device

If your child wears any type of hearing device, you will have regular appointments with a pediatric audiologist. He or she will give you a lot of information about the device, and will adjust it to meet your child's individual needs.

If your child wears a bone conduction hearing device on a headband, your pediatric audiologist will check the site at which the device vibrates on her head, ensuring the connection is not too tight or too loose. A good rule of thumb for tightness is to be able to insert two fingers under the headband.

If your child has the surgically implanted abutment, your pediatric audiologist will check the site to ensure it is clean and healthy looking and to be sure the abutment is in place as it should be. If the audiologist notices any problems, she will recommend that you see your ENT doctor or surgeon immediately.

Next, your pediatric audiologist will remove the sound processor and test it. She will check to be sure it's working properly and adjust the controls and programs.

Your pediatric audiologist will test your child's hearing, both without the device and while wearing the device. For more information about a typical audiology appointment, see the section called Walking Through a Typical Audiology Appointment in Chapter 3.

When Should Your Child Wear the Hearing Device?

The best answer to this is *always*. The only exceptions are when your child is in water or is sleeping. Many hearing devices can't get wet, and the small parts could be a potential choking hazard for a waking child who decides to explore the hearing device in bed. You need to accomplish full-time use as quickly as possible so your child doesn't continue to miss important talk around her. Full-time hearing device use is considered to be *all waking hours,* except during water play or bathing.

Children vary in response to a hearing device. Some wear it happily from the first day on, and some try to remove it constantly. Many fall somewhere in between these two extremes. Children who wear a hearing device happily right away might do so because the sound is interesting to them, because they have taken on your positive attitude or because they typically do what's expected anyway. After being in quiet so long, children who start out resistant to the hearing device might not understand what sounds they're hearing. If this is the case, don't be discouraged. There's definitely time to build to success!

Introducing a Bone Conduction Hearing Device to Your Child

Your child's first introduction to a hearing device is important. Your point of view lays the foundation for hers. Your resolve is the most significant factor determining whether or not a young child wears her device, so you must have made up your mind that she will do so. Remember: To learn how to talk, your child must be able to listen with her hearing devices during all waking hours.

How to Begin

Start with a positive attitude. Yes, you might find it difficult realizing that your child needs to wear something visible on her head. This does make her invisible hearing loss noticeable to others. Remember that your goal is to help her listen so she can talk. With consistent use of her devices, you are giving her that opportunity. Try to feel good about that, because it's so important! Try telling yourself you want her to have the best possible sound input, and this is the way to begin. Your positive, determined attitude sets the stage for your child.

What You Need

Start out by collecting some materials. You need the following:

- **Bone conduction hearing device(s)**
  This includes either just the sound processor to be attached to the abutment or the sound processor and the headband. You will need both sound processors if your child has two.

- **Storage location**
  Determine a place to store the devices and some related equipment to use each day to be sure they're working. Choose a location above the reach of small children, such as a dresser top or kitchen cabinet. This helps avoid wasted time looking for the devices or related equipment.

- **Sturdy storage container**
  The devices should be stored in a dehumidifier when not in use. Your pediatric audiologist can most likely sell you one. In addition, find a sturdy container to hold all the other equipment. This could be a decorative tin, a plastic container with a lid or a zip-up pouch. Ideally, you want the container to look nice, interesting or colorful because it helps make a positive statement about the importance of the device. In some families, it's an advantage if small children are unable to open the container on their own.

- **Accessories and related equipment**
  - ☐ batteries   Your child's devices require specific size disposable batteries. Your pediatric audiologist can help you get packs of batteries or recommend a place for you to purchase them. In addition, some health insurance covers the cost of children's hearing device batteries, so be sure to ask.

  - ☐ battery caddy   This small container is used to hold spare batteries and easily can be attached to a backpack, purse or key ring.

  - ☐ battery tester   This small device is used to determine if disposable batteries have full power.

☐   dehumidifier   Your pediatric audiologist can sell you a low-tech, portable kit that can store hearing devices overnight while eliminating moisture. Most kits look like a small box, cup or jar with a packet of desiccant inside. The desiccant must be reactivated periodically to ensure optimal function. You also can purchase an electronic dehumidifier that disinfects and removes moisture from a hearing device using desiccant and sometimes ultraviolet light. It is not portable, and the desiccant bricks must be disposed of and replaced instead of reactivated.

Checking and Testing Bone Conduction Hearing Devices

Check each of your child's devices first thing every day so you can put them on as soon as she gets up. For each device, here's a list of the steps you can take:

1. Remove the battery and insert it into the battery tester. If it has full power, put it back into the sound processor. If not (even if it's borderline), insert a fresh battery.
2. To be sure the sound processor is working, turn it on and listen to it. Do this by first turning it on and adjusting the volume to the level recommended by your pediatric audiologist.
3. If your child wears the sound processor on a headband, snap the sound processor onto the headband. Next, put the sound processor up against *your* head so that the vibrator rests on your forehead.

   If your child wears the sound processor on an implanted abutment, snap the sound processor onto the plastic test probe that comes with the device. The **test probe** is made specifically for you to use for checking and testing the device.
4. Plug your ears (with ear plugs if possible) to block sound from going into your outer and middle ears.
5. Talk as if you are testing a microphone in an auditorium. You can say "Testing: one, two, three, four" or you can use the Ling test (see page 107). Each time you listen to the sound processor before putting it on your child, your goal is to ensure the sound is as clear today as it was the first day your child got it. If it is, you're almost ready to put it on your child. If it isn't, read the troubleshooting section on pages 111–112).

Putting on the Headband and Hearing Device

Now it's time to put the device on your child. You can imagine that not all babies and young children are going to let someone put a headband on them and then just happily leave it alone and in place. Many young children — maybe even most — take it off, look at it and perhaps toss it aside before moving on to the next interesting activity. Here are some steps to make that initial introduction a positive experience:

Tell Your Child

It's good practice to tell your child what you're going to do before you put her device on and before you take it off. For example, before you put it on, show it to her and say "I'm going to put your hearing device on now." Make eye contact, nod your head and wait for her to acknowledge you. Then put the device on.

Similarly, when you take the device off, get in the habit of saying "I'm going to take your hearing device off now" or "Are you ready for me to take this off?"

Eventually, you'll be able to ask your child to put on and take off her device. Until that point, it's nice to tell her what you plan to do before you do it. Besides being respectful and mindful of her personal space, this will teach her that her involvement is important!

1. Be sure the device is on and the volume is set to the level recommended by your pediatric audiologist.
2. Place the headband around your child's head so it fits comfortably.
3. Adjust the device to fit snugly against your child's skull — either at the base just above the back of her neck, on the forehead or temple or just behind the ear on the hard bone called the mastoid. For children who crawl and walk, optimal positioning of the device is at the mastoid bone just behind the ear. For children in a seat, car seat or lying down, optimal placement is on the forehead, to reduce the possibility of feedback or whistling.
4. Once your child has the device, say something. You might say:
   - ☐ "Hello (her name)."
   - ☐ "Here's your hearing device. I love you."
   - ☐ "ah," "oo," "ee," "s," "sh," "m" and silence (Ling test)
   - ☐ "babababababa." The advantage of using this nonsense vocalization is that, after daily repetition, your little one might learn to say it to you as soon as you have inserted and turned on the device. This is a clear indication she is hearing the sound of your voice!

Putting the Hearing Device on an Implanted Abutment

Children with implanted abutments often have worn headbands for some period of time before the surgery. They're usually older and more experienced than younger children at using their device. Therefore, they're far less likely to resist. Before placing the device on your child, be sure it's on and the volume is set to the level recommended by your pediatric audiologist. Snap the sound processor onto the abutment. If your child has two devices, repeat this process with the second one. After she has it on, say:

- ■ "Hello (her name)."
- ■ "ah," "oo," "ee," "s," "sh," "m" and silence (Ling test)

The Ling Test

The Ling test is a quick and easy way to ensure that, while wearing her device, your child has access to the range of speech sounds that we use when we talk.

To perform a Ling test, first put the device on your child. If your child wears two devices, put only one of them on at this moment. Make sure the device is turned on. Place yourself next to or behind her so she can hear you but can't see your face. Say the following sounds one at a time and teach her to repeat each sound after you say it:

- "ah" (as in hot)
- "oo" (as in boo)
- "ee" (as in bee)
- "s"
- "sh"
- "m"
- silence

Each time you perform this test, say the sounds in a different order.

If your child has two devices, take the first one off and put the second one on. Make sure this device is turned on. Repeat the Ling test with that device. Then put the first device back on so she is wearing both and both are turned on.

Note any difficulty your child has repeating these sounds back to you with the device. Report any consistent problems to your pediatric audiologist.

For more information on the Ling test, including how to perform a modified version on infants and babies, see page 149.

(Pollack et al., 1997; Sindrey, 2002)

Steps to Accomplishing Full-Time Use

Remember that your goal is a talking child, and hearing device use during all waking hours is necessary to achieve this goal. Now that you know how to put your child's device on and keep it on, here are some suggestions for accomplishing full-time use. Remember that there is no official amount of time in which you *must* accomplish this. All children are different. Some do it in a few days, others take a few months and many fall somewhere in between. You and your child will be able to do it in your own time.

1. For the first week or so, expect your child to wear her hearing device for some short periods each day rather than for the entire day. Select several times when your child is well rested and when you can interact with her, closely supervise her and keep her busy. If you choose an activity in which your child's hands are busy (such as eating, swinging or playing with a favorite toy), she'll be less likely to touch or remove a device. Some children enjoy clapping with you as you say "Hooray!" every time you put the device on.

2. If your child doesn't bother with the device at all, try leaving it in a while longer than planned; however, if at all possible, anticipate and remove it before she thinks to do so. This teaches her that *you* do the taking off — not her.

3. If your child reaches up and tries to remove a device, tell her "No" in a calm and firm voice. Try to hand her something else to keep her hands occupied or change activities to otherwise distract her. You can also say things like "Leave it on" or "No touching." If you overreact, she may develop the habit of reaching for the device just to see you get excited. At the end of the wearing time, take the device off your child.

4. Repeat Steps 1–3 several more times during the day. Then increase the wearing time so she is wearing the device a little bit longer than on the previous days.

5. Next, try to achieve full-time use. This means keeping the device on as long as possible between sleep times and bath or water play. Take care to remove the device before your child gets crabby with exhaustion and tries to do so herself. This will reinforce the notion that you are in charge of wearing times, but are also reasonable in your expectations. During these weeks, be sure to include some outings and outside play and keep your eyes on that device at all times. If your child is ill, exhausted or unusually irritable one day, try to anticipate the need for a "break" and remove the device, as needed, before your child does.

6. Congratulate yourself because you and your child have accomplished quite a lot. Full-time device use is approaching!

If you're unable to accomplish these steps on your first attempt, you may get discouraged. It's okay to start over and go through the steps again. If you have to do this, don't worry. You won't be the first parent who has had to try again. Remember that your goal is a talking child. Use this idea to motivate you!

Increasing Hearing Device Wear Time

Some children are reluctant or stubborn about wearing devices. If this is true for your child, remain calm but determined. If you look frustrated rather than calm, your child may sense this. Your firm, gentle insistence will go further toward success than your appearing ruffled, annoyed or upset.

Set aside a period of 15 minutes when your child is well rested and when you can give her your undivided attention. Set a goal that she will wear her device for those 15 minutes. Try to arrange things so you can avoid everything else during this time. Select a fun activity that requires your child to use both her hands and do the activity together. You might try making pudding, floating toys in water, swinging, dusting and sweeping, blowing bubbles she can pop or throwing balloons up in the air.

Gather the materials for the activity ahead of time. When you're ready to begin, hand your child two of the items, one for each hand. Put the device on her, say "Hooray!" and

Guess What? She Keeps Taking Off the Device!

If your child pulls off her device over and over again, try this: One last time, put it on your child. Do whatever you need to do to distract her and keep her from taking it off.

- Hand her a toy to keep her hands busy.
- Gently hold her hands and sing her a song.
- Hold her close to you and rock her.

Leave the device on for 30 more seconds. Then, *and this is the most important part,* YOU take the device off of her so she learns that it's only okay for YOU to take it off — not her.

A short while later, put the device back on and try this process again.

It's also important to anticipate the times your child might be likely to take off her device. When she feels crabby, ill, exhausted or unusually irritable, plan for a "break" and remove the device before your child does.

clap your hands. Be ready to begin the activity quickly. Each and every time she reaches for or removes the device, say "No" in a calm but firm voice and replace it. Say nothing else and do nothing else about the removal or the attempt. Hand her something else and happily continue the activity.

When things are going along well and she is fully absorbed in the activity, resist the temptation to just leave the device on. After your goal is met (about 15 minutes), remove it. Doing this builds toward success because your interaction involved both you not allowing her to take it off *and* your being willing to take if off after a reasonably short time. Try a similar activity and repeat the same techniques again later. The more times a day you can do this, the sooner your child will wear her hearing device all day.

Most children who are busy and happy are distracted from thinking about and touching their hearing devices and learn to leave them alone during these periods. You should see some improvement in a week or less. Improvement can be measured by a decrease in your child's attempts at removal, or actual removal, of the hearing device.

After you have noticed improvement, choose another few times a day when you can supervise but not be totally involved with the activity. Giving your child a meal can work well, especially if it's a few minutes past regular meal time and she is truly hungry. Have everything ready ahead of time. If appropriate for your child's age, plan ahead to include some finger foods to keep those hands busy. Once your child is seated, put the device on, clap and

 Part of establishing full-time hearing device use is helping your child and the rest of your family understand that hearing device use is a necessity — not an option. This is most easily done by establishing a routine and sticking with it.

say "Hooray!" Then quickly supply the meal. Sit or stay nearby and follow the same routine of responding with "No" and replacing the device if and when she removes it.

After two or three weeks, you should have many periods each day when your child is agreeably wearing her device for about 15 minutes at a time. Congratulations!

Accomplishing Full-Time Hearing Device Use as a Working Parent

You can see that getting your child used to wearing a hearing device all day might be more easily accomplished if you're actually with your child all day. While this is true, for many parents it's just not practical. There are also ways to accomplish full-time hearing device use even if you can't be with her all day. The most common approach for working parents is to use morning, evening and weekend hours (or whenever you're with your child) as the initial wearing times.

Once your child is successfully wearing her hearing device when you're with her, arrange an hour to teach your child care provider how to manage it when you're away. You learned how, and so will the child care provider. If your child care provider understands that the hearing device is necessary for your child to learn to listen and talk, she should be willing to work with you. Sometimes parents can arrange for their early interventionist to assist with a hearing device orientation for the caregiver.

Involving Your Child in Device Care

When your child is ready, is old enough and has been wearing her device cooperatively for six months or more, it's important to increase your expectations just a bit in terms of device care. Now your child is ready to begin helping with this. Yes, even toddlers can start learning!

When it's time to remove the device, tell your child it's time and reach out your hand for it to be placed there. In the beginning, guide your child's hand up to the device and help her take hold of it. Once this habit is established, if your child has the motor coordination, encourage her to remove the device herself when asked. Help her as needed until she can successfully hand you the device when you ask for it. Show her how it always goes into the special container when she's not wearing it. Your child will benefit by learning independence, and this will develop her self-esteem. Remember to praise her for her accomplishment!

If and when your child has a bone conduction device surgically implanted, she will be a little older and perhaps ready to learn more about care. At first, she will need help attaching and detaching the externally worn piece, but over time she will feel confident doing this on her own. She will also need reminders about keeping the area clean and healthy.

Hearing Device Insurance

Little children (and family life) can be hard on hearing devices. Most new devices come with a one-year warranty but may last up to five years, so you may choose insurance coverage for after the warranty expires. Pediatric audiologists who order and dispense these devices have the option to purchase an extended manufacturer warranty covering parts and labor for up to three years. Companies that offer hearing device insurance typically offer coverage for repair as well as for replacement. Families should not assume their homeowner's insurance covers their child's hearing devices. Investigate your policy to see if coverage is possible. If not, several private insurance companies cover only assistive listening devices, usually at a reasonable cost. Talk with your pediatric audiologist to determine if the manufacturer's coverage, your homeowner's insurance or private coverage is most appropriate for you.

Insurance coverage for repair usually covers parts and labor. Sometimes manufacturers offer an option to forego the repair insurance until it's needed. Then, if a need arises, a family can pay the repair fee, which may be a couple hundred dollars. Payment of this fee covers the cost of the immediate repairs and extends the warranty for 6–12 additional months.

There are a variety of reasons a device would need to be replaced instead of just repaired. Some common causes are being chewed by a dog, run over by a car, thrown from the window of a moving car, ground in a garbage disposal and stepped on and crushed by a sibling. Insurance for replacing a hearing device is usually good for only one replacement, regardless of the length of coverage. The one-time replacement fee varies in price but may cost up to several hundred dollars.

Whether you, your insurance company or a third party pays for your child's hearing devices, be aware that they may cost several thousand dollars. You may want to teach your child to treat them with extra special care. They should hold up well to the typical rough and tumble life of a young child, but not to abuses such as stomping on them or giving them to the family dog. Your own special care of the hearing aids and your attitude and treatment of them gives your child her first lesson about their importance and value.

Troubleshooting Bone Conduction Hearing Devices

Some problems are simple and can be solved easily at home. Others have to be solved by your pediatric audiologist. Still others require your pediatric audiologist to return the device to the manufacturer for professional maintenance or replacement of parts. The chart on the next page shows some common problems you can try to fix.

Now What?

Once your child has accomplished full-time hearing device use, the first thing you should do is give yourself a pat on the back! This is huge! You're on the right track to helping her become a talking child. The next step will be to begin developing some important and

Problem	Possible Solution
The sound processor won't turn on.	■ Insert or replace the battery. ■ Check the +/– placement of the battery. ■ Check the battery size and number. ■ Make sure the battery door is all the way closed. ■ Make sure the on/off switch is set to on. ■ Remove the battery and place it in the dehumidifier overnight.
The vibration feels weak.	■ Replace the battery. ■ Check the volume control setting. ■ Check the program switch.
The sound is weak.	■ Replace the battery. ■ Check the volume control setting. ■ Check the program switch.
Soreness or inflammation at the abutment.	■ Contact the ENT doctor/surgeon. You will need to see the doctor as soon as possible.
None of these solutions	■ Contact your pediatric audiologist. Audiologists have only minimal trouble-shooting abilities in office. Often, a device has to be sent to the manufacturer for repair. If this happens, your pediatric audiologist may supply you with a loaner until your child's device is returned in working condition.

necessary listening skills. Chapter 10 contains lots of information on listening and auditory development. Your child needs these skills to become a successful talking child. Congratulations on completing this important step!

References

Pollack, D., Goldberg, D. & Caleffe-Schenck, N. (1997). *Educational Audiology for the Limited-Hearing Infant and Preschooler: An Auditory-Verbal Program* (3rd ed.). Springfield, IL: Charles C Thomas Publisher, Ltd.

Sindrey, D. (2002). *Listening Games for Littles* (2nd ed.). Washington, DC: Alexander Graham Bell Association for the Deaf and Hard of Hearing.

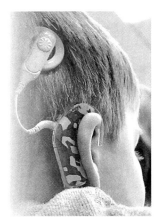

Chapter 9

Cochlear Implants

What Is a Cochlear Implant?

A **cochlear implant** is a surgically implanted device designed for children and adults with severe to profound hearing loss. A cochlear implant might be recommended for a child who does not receive sufficient benefit from one or two hearing aids. Most children with profound hearing loss are considered candidates for a cochlear implant based on their audiograms alone. However, as with all surgically implanted devices, additional factors affect candidacy. A thorough evaluation determines whether a child is a candidate for the device.

Use of a cochlear implant requires surgery. The device consists of external components worn on the outside of the body and internal components that are surgically implanted. The surgery, performed by a specially-trained ear, nose and throat (ENT) doctor, involves electrodes and a stimulator/receiver, which are inserted in the temporal bone area behind the external ear. The external components include a microphone, a speech processor and a transmitter coil that attaches by magnet to the internal components. The external components can be worn a variety of ways depending on the brand of cochlear implant and the age of the child wearing it. To learn how the cochlear implant works, see page 124.

Pros and Cons of Cochlear Implants

If your child is a candidate for a cochlear implant, you may want to consider possible pros and cons. You may choose to add your own to the list below as you consider this important decision.

Pros	Cons
■ Cochlear implants provide an opportunity for a child with severe or profound hearing loss to have quality access to the sounds of speech. ■ Cochlear implants provide an opportunity for a child with severe or profound hearing loss to hear environmental sounds she otherwise would not be able to hear with hearing aids.	■ Cochlear implants do not restore typical hearing. ■ As with any surgery, there are associated risks such as infection. Talk with your surgeon about these risks. ■ Expenses can be an issue for many families, including the expenses of the surgery and cochlear implant external parts. *continues...*

Pros	Cons
▪ Cochlear implants provide an opportunity for a child with severe or profound hearing loss to learn to listen, talk and succeed in a predominantly hearing and talking world. ▪ Cochlear implants provide an opportunity for a child to learn language similarly to the way children with typical hearing learn so she will not need to depend on a visual form of communication.	▪ Equipment wear and tear requires visits with a skilled pediatric audiologist. Upkeep can be expensive. ▪ Depending on the internal device, children with cochlear implants must have the internal piece removed before having an MRI of the head.

Cochlear Implant Candidacy

Cochlear implant candidacy is taken very seriously — by parents, pediatric audiologists, surgeons and the United States Food and Drug Administration (FDA). If you start thinking about a cochlear implant for your child, you might want to know what factors contribute to candidacy.

Sources of Candidacy Information

▪ initial information required for candidacy: age, medical evaluation, audiologic evaluation, level of benefit from hearing aid use, amount of family support and educational placement options
▪ FDA guidelines on cochlear implant candidacy
▪ recommendations and decisions made by a local cochlear implant team

Initial Requirements for Cochlear Implant Candidacy

Age

Most surgeons prefer to wait until a child is at least 12 months old for cochlear implant surgery. Some surgeons are willing to implant earlier if there is a reasonable need to do so, such as **ossification**, or bony growth, in the cochlea resulting from meningitis. Cochlear implant surgeons consider head growth as a factor when considering a child younger than 12 months.

Medical evaluation

Your child must be evaluated by a cochlear implant surgeon. Medical evaluation is necessary so you and the surgeon can be sure your child is ready for this kind of surgery. Some factors to consider during medical evaluation are:

- your child's ability to undergo surgery and anesthesia
- the structure and anatomy of your child's inner ear
- the structure and function of your child's auditory nerve

You also need a scan (MRI and/or CT scan) of your child's head to give the surgeon a look at her specific anatomy and help make a plan for surgery or a recommendation against it. In addition, the surgeon will explain the process for cochlear implantation and the associated risks. The surgeon's explanation can be detailed and overwhelming. Your early interventionist and pediatric audiologist can review the information with you later after you've had time to think about it.

Audiologic evaluation

A qualified pediatric audiologist, or a team of them, tests your child's hearing to determine her degree of hearing loss at each ear. Depending on your child's age, they may also test to determine her speech perception ability. Generally, to be considered for candidacy, your child must have severe or profound sensorineural hearing loss.

Level of benefit from hearing aid use

Your child must show little, if any, benefit from the use of hearing aids. Most children complete a hearing aid trial for at least six months of full-time hearing aid use before being considered for cochlear implant surgery. Information from your child's therapist or educators about progress with hearing aids will help determine what level of benefit she receives from hearing aids.

Family support

Strong family support is an absolute necessity for success with a cochlear implant. The decision to pursue cochlear implantation should not be taken lightly. Children who successfully use cochlear implants almost always have good family support. To provide good family support, you and your family must be willing to do the following:

- help your child wear the device during all waking hours
- keep the device functioning properly
- take your child to many required audiology appointments
- teach your child listening, language and speech skills required while she's at home
- work with professionals in educational or therapy settings to meet your child's needs

Educational placement options

Although some children receive cochlear implants as a way to improve their environmental awareness or their quality of life, other children receive them as the foundation for learning to listen and talk. All children with cochlear implants can benefit from an educational program that focuses on auditory skill development. For children learning to listen and talk, this is essential. For your child to learn to listen and talk, she must qualify for placement in an early intervention and/or educational program that focuses on auditory skill development. As a cochlear implant user, your child will need extensive listening training from experienced early interventionists, teachers, auditory-verbal therapists, audiologists and/or speech-language pathologists in order to learn to understand and use spoken language.

Cochlear Implant Candidacy Guidelines from the Food and Drug Administration (FDA)

In an effort to protect the health of all U.S. citizens, the FDA offers guidelines for many products that we might use. One of those products is the cochlear implant. The FDA recommends use of the following guidelines for determining cochlear implant candidacy. It is important to remember that FDA guidelines are just that — guidelines. They are not law. You and your child's cochlear implant team, including the ENT surgeon, will discuss what's best for your child.

FDA Guidelines for Cochlear Implantation Candidacy in Children

Guidelines	Criteria
Age of eligibility	12 months and older
Onset of hearing loss	**Prelingual hearing loss** refers to loss that occurs before a child has learned to listen and talk.
	Postlingual hearing loss refers to hearing that becomes impaired after a person has already learned to listen and talk.
Degree of sensorineural hearing loss	Severe to profound for children older than age 2
	Profound for children younger than age 2
Other criteria	Lack of auditory progress with hearing aids

Deciding on a Cochlear Implant

To make the best decision regarding a cochlear implant for your child and family, it's important to have all the information you can get. Your pediatric audiologist will be a huge help through this process, as will the ENT surgeon who performs the surgery. Hopefully, you can develop a strong and trusting relationship with these professionals so you feel confident in your decision. If you decide to go ahead with implantation, you can continue these good relationships and rest assured that your child is getting the best care possible.

What's It Like to Listen with a Cochlear Implant?

This is one of the most common questions asked about the cochlear implant. To those of us with typical hearing, it's difficult to imagine what an alternate form of hearing would sound like.

Most reports indicate that cochlear implant users perceive a less natural sound than people with typical hearing do. A child who uses a cochlear implant is not likely to be able to compare the sound she hears using the implant to any other sound we might consider "normal." Her brain will learn to perceive sound through the use of her implant in a way that will eventually sound very typical and right to her.

Some people search the Internet for examples of what a cochlear implant sounds like to those who wear them. Although you might want to find one of the various websites that provide cochlear implant simulations, keep in mind that these simulations are often old, and they most likely represent guesses at what a cochlear implant user might hear.

Parents also often ask how their child's voice will sound if she uses a cochlear implant. Your child will learn to modify her voice based upon listening to others through the implant. Your child's therapist or educator can work with her to modify her voice quality to help her develop speech that sounds "normal." In other words, many children who have successfully used cochlear implants from early on have speech that sounds like that of children with typical hearing.

Many parents find that one of the most reassuring ways to understand what their child might sound like someday is to listen to other children who have used cochlear implants for a few years. You might want to go to the cochlear implant manufacturers' websites to hear children with cochlear implants talking. Your child's audiology center or a school that provides listening and spoken language instruction should be able to provide you with more information about this.

Skilled Pediatric Audiologists and Cochlear Implants

Audiology is a complicated and detailed field. Excellent audiology services are required for your child to have the access to sound she needs to learn to listen and talk. It's essential to have a skilled pediatric audiologist working with you and your child. Your child's access to sound literally depends on it! With so much to do during audiology appointments — hearing tests, device choices, mappings and troubleshooting — you need to work with an audiologist who has expertise with cochlear implants as well as experience working with children. You might want to ask your pediatrician and/or ENT doctor to recommend a good pediatric audiologist near you.

Cochlear Implant Manufacturers

Currently, three manufacturers produce cochlear implant equipment. Each one has specific characteristics that make it different from the others. Your ENT doctor may have a specific recommendation based on your child's anatomy or other issues, but for some parents, the decision is up to them. A lot of information about each product is available online. Because technology continues to improve so quickly, you might check these manufacturers' websites for the most current device details and options. Here is some information to help you start your search.

Cochlear Implant Manufacturer	Website
Advanced Bionics	www.advancedbionics.com
Cochlear Americas	www.cochlearamericas.com
Med-El	www.medel.com

Internal Components of a Cochlear Implant

The internal component of the cochlear implant is made up of a number of parts that together can fit in the palm of your hand. Each part has an important purpose in making the device functional.

■ **Internal magnet**

When implanted, the **internal magnet** is located just under the skin usually above and slightly behind the ear. Its purpose is to allow the coil (on the external device) to stay in place on the skin just over the location of the internal receiver. This is necessary for the transfer of electronic information through the skin from the external device to the internal receiver. In a nutshell, the internal magnet attracts the external magnet to hold the external device in place on the head.

■ **Internal receiver**

The **internal receiver** is located just under the skin near the magnet. Electronic information is delivered from the external component to the internal receiver using FM radio waves. The internal receiver then changes the electronic information into electrical signals or impulses.

■ **Electrode array**

The **electrode array** is a set of electrodes on the internal component contained in a structure that is thin and a few inches long. It is inserted into the cochlea during implantation. The number of electrodes in the array depends on the brand of cochlear implant you choose.

■ **Electrodes**

Electrodes are individual conductors. Electrical signals go from the internal receiver to the electrodes. Each electrode responds to specific information depending on the intensity (or loudness) and the frequency (pitch) of the sound from the environment. Electrodes stimulate certain nerve fibers of the auditory nerve, which then sends the information to the brain, where it is perceived as sound.

External Components of a Cochlear Implant

No matter which manufacturer you choose, certain parts are common among all cochlear implant devices. The different manufacturers have varying ways of configuring these parts, depending on the age and size of the cochlear implant user.

Some configurations are designed so the entire external device is located at ear level. Other configurations are designed to reduce the weight of the components at the ear by relocating some of them to the shoulder or back of the shirt. All devices are designed to grow with your child and can be reconfigured as she gets older and bigger.

Device Configurations

Some brands have an option for wearing the external device at ear or head level. This means the entire external device is worn at or near the ear. Another option is the body-worn configuration. This is designed so the battery and controls are located on a small, compact unit that clips to the back of your child's shirt, on an armband, to a baseball cap or somewhere on the body that's comfortable. With some devices, that unit connects to the ear level unit with a thin cord. With other brands, that unit connects directly to the coil with a thin cord. The benefit of this style is that some of the weight from the battery is taken off your child's little ear and instead clipped somewhere on her clothing, most usually on the back of her shirt. This can be really helpful if the weight of the ear level device seems to be too much for your little one's ear to hold up. Another important benefit is, if the ear level device falls off your child's ear, it is still attached to her shirt by the cord. This helps prevent the device from getting lost during active play or movement. Still, many people prefer the ear-level configuration because it's compact and all in one place. In addition, one cochlear implant company recently began offering a single-unit processor that contains the processor, battery and all other necessary external equipment in a single, compact piece. Likely, this will become more common as cochlear implant technology continues to advance.

Disposable vs. Rechargeable Batteries

Some cochlear implant manufacturers may recommend a specific brand of battery to use in their device. Some pediatric audiologists recommend you use rechargeable instead of disposable batteries, depending on the mapping parameters of your child's device.

■ Batteries

The external component of a cochlear implant is powered by batteries. Cochlear implants can be powered by rechargeable cochlear implant batteries or disposable batteries. Depending on the style of device your child wears, the batteries are located at the ear level or in the body-worn attachment.

The device you choose most likely comes with rechargeable batteries and a special charger for those batteries. Your pediatric audiologist can show you how to change the batteries and use the charger. She also can tell you how long a fully charged battery will last so you can always be prepared with backups. Battery life depends on your child's map (described on page 122) and how often she's using the implant, which is ideally all waking hours. Typically, a rechargeable battery can power your child's device for a full day of listening. Rechargeable batteries are more cost effective than disposable batteries because you can use them over and over. It's important to remember, though, that if you lose the rechargeable batteries, they are expensive to replace.

You may also have the option of using disposable batteries. Most cochlear implant brands take size 675 or AAA. Devices use 1–3 disposable batteries. Some devices need a special adapter in order to use the disposable batteries. That adapter may come with the device, along with the rechargeable batteries and the charger. Disposable batteries may power your child's device longer than rechargeable batteries on a single charge. You might decide to use disposable batteries only as a last resort. Batteries can be a choking hazard to young children, so you may consider removing, checking and reinserting these batteries out of the view of your little one.

■ Microphone

The cochlear implant microphone looks similar to the microphone on a behind the ear hearing aid. It picks up sound from the environment and sends it to the processor. The microphone has to stay clean and free from debris so it can effectively pick up sound. Your child's cochlear implant should have a cover over part of the microphone to protect it, but you might also try to keep food, dirt, soap, hair oil, hair spray, creams and anything similar away from it.

Processor

The **processor** is a component of the external device that converts sounds into electronic information. The processor is extremely important because it takes in speech and environmental sounds, analyzes them and changes them into a digital format. The internal device then uses this information to activate the appropriate electrodes. Although the technical name for this is the sound and speech processor, it's often referred to as the **processor, speech processor** or **external processor.**

Coil, transmitter and magnet

Depending on what brand you are talking about and who you are talking to, cochlear implant lingo will differ slightly as far as the **coil, transmitter** and **magnet** are concerned. The gist of it is this: When your child wears the external device, part of it fits around her ear (similar to the way a hearing aid is worn). A short cord connects the part around her ear to a circle-shaped piece. That piece is most commonly referred to as the headpiece, but might also be called the coil, magnet or transmitter. A magnet is located inside the circle-shaped piece so the external device attracts and connects to the magnet in the internal device. After the processor converts the environmental sounds into digital information, the information is then sent from the processor to the coil. The information is sent across the skin and hair using radio frequency waves.

Cords

Although some newer devices are cordless, many have a cord that connects the headpiece to the processor. Some configurations also require a second cord to connect the processor to the battery pack. This second cord is for configurations in which the battery pack is not located at ear level, but the processor is. If your child's device has one or more cords, your pediatric audiologist can show you how they connect to ports located on the external device.

Controls

The controls on your child's external device vary depending on the specific device your child wears. Some external devices have an actual power switch. Others turn on when the battery is connected. Your pediatric audiologist can show you how to turn the external device on and off.

Because some children often like to "adjust" their own devices, many external devices have a lock feature that disables those controls until you or your pediatric audiologist disengages it. This prevents your child from being able to turn the device on or off or change the settings. It also gives you a little more peace of mind that she is not secretly adjusting the controls when you're not looking. For children who wear the battery pack on their shirts, the lock feature can help avoid setting changes as your child moves, plays, leans against something, etc. Your pediatric audiologist can describe all of these features when your child is fit with her device.

■ Maps and programs

Cochlear implant processors contain a small computer chip that holds maps. A **cochlear implant map** holds detailed information assigned to each electrode. The **cochlear implant program** is the slot where these maps are stored. Each processor has a defined number of program slots that can hold a map. The audiologist may put one map into all program slots so that the same map is being heard even if the program switch is bumped or switched. Or the audiologist may put a different map into each program slot for a specific listening situations (e.g., a noisy restaurant or listening on the telephone).

During testing sessions, your pediatric audiologist creates maps. A map is a specifically numbered group of settings based on information gathered about your child. Your pediatric audiologist determines levels for electrodes that allow sounds — from soft and loud levels — to be heard comfortably. These levels are often referred to as the Ts (thresholds or soft levels), Cs (comfortable levels) and Ms (most comfortable levels).

Appropriate maps contain levels set so your child can hear very quiet sounds at speech frequencies as well as louder sounds at those same frequencies. At the beginning, her maps will be set very conservatively as her auditory nerve acclimates to the new stimulation. Over time, her responses — her Ts, Cs and Ms — will become more refined; therefore, her maps will need to be updated and refined as well.

Over time, your child's auditory nerve will become more accustomed to handling the new sound. This is great! She's making progress toward becoming a talking child! Her auditory nerve will then need increased levels of stimulation so she can continue to access more complex sounds. The pediatric audiologist will check her Ts, Cs and Ms again with the expectation that these levels have changed. Then the pediatric audiologist will load new maps into your child's program slots to allow for even better access to sound and further development of listening skills.

As your child gets used to her implant, she will start "growing into" her maps, meaning she will become used to listening with the settings on her device. Next, your pediatric audiologist might introduce you to the concept of progressive maps. She will load maps into the program slots that vary slightly with increasing levels of stimulation that are all based on your child's Ts, Cs and Ms. Progressive maps allow your child to build proficiency gradually by listening to the many sounds that occur in our world. Between appointments, your job will be to observe your child's responses to sound and slowly begin to move your child from one program to another as she continues to develop listening skills.

Eventually, when your child is a proficient cochlear implant user, your pediatric audiologist might load some differing maps into your child's program slots that will allow better access to sound in various listening situations. For example, she might have different maps for the classroom, the playground, home, a movie theater, a restaurant or for using other audio accessories such as a phone or mp3 player.

■ **Hook**

Some, but not all device configurations include a hook, or ear hook. The **hook** is usually made of clear, hard plastic, but the appearance varies depending on the manufacturer. It is curved and is attached to the top of the processor on one end. For people who wear an earmold with their external device, the tubing for the earmold attaches to the hook. The curve of the hook should fit nicely to your child's ear to ensure that the external device hangs on the ear appropriately.

■ **Remote control**

Some cochlear implants come with a remote control with lots of great features for manipulating the function of the external device. The remote control helps you monitor your child's device from a distance without necessarily having to take it off her. It has a display that gives you lots of useful information about the way her device is working. Your pediatric audiologist can show you exactly how to use the remote control.

■ **Accessories and related equipment**

☐	battery caddy	This small container, used to hold spare disposable batteries used in the cochlear implant, is easily attached to a backpack, purse or key ring.
☐	battery charger	This electronic device is used to charge rechargeable batteries. Your child's cochlear implant may come with rechargeable batteries and a charger so that you can charge the batteries each night or whenever they lose their charge.
☐	battery tester	This small device is used to determine if disposable batteries are good. You will need this if you use non-rechargeable batteries rather than the rechargeable ones.
☐	dehumidifier	This electronic device is used to pull moisture away from the external device. Although it's very effective, it's not portable.
☐	easy wear, mic lock or snuggie/huggie	Cochlear implant manufacturers make small tubular rings of plastic that fit onto the external device and around the ear. They are very helpful for holding the device on soft little ears. Many sizes are available to fit specific devices as well as ears of all shapes and sizes. These should be attached in such a way as to ensure that the microphones are unobstructed.
☐	adhesive	This special tape can help hold the external device in place by gently sticking the device directly to the skin behind your child's ear. Although many audiologists have this available for purchase in the office, you can also use wig tape from a barber shop or beauty supply store.

☐ cochlear implant clips These clips with lanyards attach easily to the external device and then clip securely to the back of your child's shirt or collar. They can help you to avoid losing the device if it falls off or your child takes it off. Many hearing aid companies have these cute clips available for purchase. Your pediatric audiologist can help you find what might work best for your child.

☐ tubing This short plastic tube extends from the hook of the external device to the earmold. Tubing is used only by those who wear an earmold to anchor the external device and hold it in place.

☐ earmold An earmold is a small piece of soft yet sturdy material that fits snugly into your child's ear. Since the external device might be a little big for a tiny ear, your pediatric audiologist might recommend an earmold to anchor the external device and hold it in place. Unlike a hearing aid earmold, the earmold attached to a cochlear implant does nothing more than hold the device in place. The earmold is custom-made to fit your child's external ear. An earmold impression is molded out of a silicone material and sent to a lab, where it's used to make an earmold. (See pages 82–85 for a complete description of the earmold process.) Earmolds can be either a full earmold that fills your child's outer ear space down into the ear canal or a **skeleton earmold** that's not solid. It's just the frame of a full earmold, which allows for better ventilation and may be more comfortable and/or less noticeable.

How Does a Cochlear Implant Work?

Now that you know about all the parts of a cochlear implant — both internal and external — it may be helpful to look at how all those parts work together to help a person hear sounds. First, sound moves through the environment and is picked up by the microphone on the external device. The sound is sent to the processor and converted into digital information. The digital information is sent from the processor to the coil, which transmits the information across the skin to the internal device. The magnet allows the external device to affix to the head so the information can pass from the external device to the internal device. The digital information is transmitted from the coil on the external device to the internal receiver using radio waves. The internal receiver converts the digital information into electrical signals or impulses. Those electrical impulses are carried and/or transmitted to the electrode array. Depending on the intensity and frequency of the original sounds, certain electrodes along the array are activated. As electrodes activate, the auditory nerve adjacent to the electrode is systematically stimulated. The detailed sound information is then carried to the brain by way of the auditory nerve. The brain interprets the information as sound.

Cochlear Implant Surgery

During cochlear implant surgery, the internal component of the device is surgically placed in the head and ear. The process involves preparation beforehand, the surgery itself, recovering from surgery and procedures to follow once back home.

Preparing for Cochlear Implant Surgery

Each cochlear implant manufacturer provides information for parents preparing their children for cochlear implant surgery. It is recommended that you help your child understand what will be happening as best you can dependent upon her age and ability to understand. Cochlear implant manufacturer websites and many pediatric audiology teams provide information written specifically for parents, as well as other information written specifically for children, to help them understand what will happen during and after surgery. This information is offered in many forms including videos, books, coloring pages and lists. Choose the forms that are most appealing to you and your child.

Since this is a surgical procedure, your child will receive anesthesia. Most surgeons will not perform surgery on a child who shows symptoms of illness. For this reason, prior to the surgery, try especially hard to keep your child healthy. You will also be instructed to keep her from having anything to eat or drink for several hours before surgery. The hospital staff will give you lots of specific information about how to physically prepare her for surgery.

The Surgery

The day of the surgery, your child is admitted to the hospital and taken to a patient room. Although surgery centers vary, many allow you to stay with your child and help her change into a patient gown while the medical team prepares her for surgery. The medical team starts an IV, intravenous line, usually in your child's hand or forearm. This IV provides the anesthesia and pain medication to keep your child sedated and comfortable throughout the surgery.

Meningitis Vaccine

The Centers for Disease Control and Prevention (CDC) and the Food and Drug Administration (FDA) recommend that any child preparing to receive one or two cochlear implants first receives the age-appropriate meningitis vaccination. Your child's cochlear implant team can help you learn more about this vaccination.

Usually, parents are asked to give a big hug and a kiss to their child just before the nursing staff or anesthesiologist wheels her on the bed into the operating room. You can then proceed to the nearest waiting room, where you will likely receive updates on your child's status throughout the surgery.

In the operating room, the surgeon makes an incision behind your child's ear. He creates a small opening through the mastoid bone, providing an opening through which he inserts the electrode array. He also removes some of the bone to make a shallow divot in which the internal receiver will lie securely. The surgeon slides the electrode array through the bone, through the middle ear and into the inner ear where the cochlea is located. The electrode array lies in the cochlea.

Before the surgeon completes his work, an audiologist tests the function of the newly implanted device. The audiologist makes sure the electrodes are able to stimulate the auditory nerve appropriately and ensures the electrodes are not stimulating other nearby cranial nerves. This is certainly important because the surgeon and audiologist want to make sure the device is appropriately placed before your child leaves the operating room to avoid having to repeat the surgery. At this point, the audiologist or other medical staff member will meet you in the waiting room with an update on the success of the surgery.

Once the device is determined to be working properly, the surgeon stitches or glues the skin back in place behind your child's ear. The anesthesiologist begins waking your child as the anesthesia wears off. Your child is moved to the recovery room where the nursing staff monitors her vital signs as she awakens from the anesthesia. As soon as she is awake and alert, the staff will come get you and bring you to see her.

Recovering from Cochlear Implant Surgery

By the time the surgery is finished, parents are typically so happy to be reunited with their child, they often are not prepared for how the child will look, feel and act. Your child will have gauze or a neoprene bandage wrapped all the way around her little head, which looks big, bulky and unusual. She will most likely look sleepy and slightly disoriented. This is typical for children who have received anesthesia.

Your child will feel groggy, but should not feel pain. Occasionally, children feel dizzy and/or nauseated after anesthesia, which the nurses can treat with medication. Your child might also cry as a response to disorientation from anesthesia. Crying should not be a result of pain. If you are concerned that your child is in pain, you can alert the nursing staff so they can take steps to alleviate your child's discomfort.

Your child may not act like her usual self right after surgery. Some children act very sleepy. Other children seem very mellow or clingy, and some quickly regain their energy and return to their normal selves within a short period of time. If you're concerned about the way your child is acting, don't hesitate to consult the medical staff.

At-Home Procedures After Surgery

Each implant center varies in the protocol following implant surgeries. Some allow a child to go home the same day as surgery. Others require a stay for observation overnight and then allow the child to go home the next day. Before you leave the surgery center or hospital, the medical staff will give you a list of dos and don'ts as well as information about medications, washing, changing bandages and activity restrictions.

You will schedule a post-op visit about one week after surgery. At this time, the surgeon will check the incision site to be sure your child is healing properly. Some families feel comfortable sending their children back to school or daycare prior to the post-op visit, while others choose to keep their child home for a longer period of time. The surgeon will make a recommendation about this, too.

Once your child is home, keep her less active than usual as the incision heals. This can be very tricky for many children who are naturally active. If your child wore a hearing aid at the implanted ear before surgery, she will no longer benefit from wearing it at that ear. After the incision has some time to heal and the swelling goes down, your child will be ready to return to your pediatric audiologist for the initial stimulation of her cochlear implant.

Initial Stimulation

Before using the external device, your child will need some time to heal and allow for any swelling to dissipate. You must schedule an appointment with your pediatric audiologist for your child's initial stimulation. This is the appointment at which your pediatric audiologist first maps the external device and puts it on your child. (Usually, more than one pediatric audiologist helps with a child's initial stimulation.)

Children react to hearing their first sounds with a cochlear implant in a variety of ways. Some children's faces light up, their eyes widen and they demonstrate an obvious reaction to the sound. Other children barely seem to notice the new sound and might not even pause from their play. Some children seem to get scared and react by crying or reaching for the external device. The pediatric audiologist watches closely for any reactions your child may have, no matter how subtle or obvious. By being aware that your child may react in a number of ways, you might be able to better prepare yourself for the various possibilities.

This is an emotional and exciting moment for most children, parents and pediatric audiologists. It will be the first time your child hears sound with this new device. For some children, it's the first time they really hear at all. Try to go to the initial stimulation appointment with an understanding that you might be very emotional. It's not uncommon for parents to cry. It's not uncommon for parents to jump for joy. It's also not uncommon for parents to be worried and scared. These are all perfectly acceptable emotions for such a huge moment in your life. Try to embrace these emotions. It's okay to feel however you feel. Your pediatric audiologist will not only reassure you about the process for the initial stimulation, she will also help comfort you and join in your excitement and emotion.

Videotaping the Initial Stimulation

Some parents like to bring a video camera to record this moment. Other parents don't. Consider this in case you might want to have that recording some day down the road.

Explaining Your Child's Cochlear Implant to Others

Now that your child has received a cochlear implant, you may find yourself faced with questions from your friends, family and maybe even strangers. You might need to describe the cochlear implant to the people around you and answer questions about why it's necessary for your child.

Labels for a Cochlear Implant

First things first. It's not uncommon for people to label a cochlear implant incorrectly. As you teach the people around you about the cochlear implant, you want to be sure to use the correct terminology.

Correct labels

- Cochlear implant — My daughter Jane wears a cochlear implant.
- Implant — Billy's implant is at his right ear.
- CI — Sally, let's head to the audiologist so she can check your CI.
- Specific manufacturer brand name — Joey just got the N-5 to replace his Freedom.

Incorrect labels

- Ear — Some parents have the urge to refer to their child's cochlear implant as her "ear." *Definitely avoid this!* Although it may seem cute and child-friendly, the cochlear implant is not an ear. Your child needs to learn the difference between her ear and her cochlear implant, especially as she learns to name and label her body parts — and then later when she is old enough to describe the device on her own. It will be important for her to learn how to tell about her ear, if it hurts or needs attention, and it will also be important for her to talk about her implant.
- Cochlear — Because the implant is placed in the cochlea, we use the adjective "cochlear" to describe it. But simply calling the device a "cochlear" is, in fact, incorrect. It is a cochlear implant.
- Coke-You-Ler Implant — This word is cochlear (pronounced /*koe-klee-erl*/, particularly if you live in the U.S.).

Describing Your Child's Cochlear Implant

As you decide on a cochlear implant for your child, and then after she has it, people will naturally have lots of questions about it. You're likely to feel much more confident about the decision you've made and the device itself if you have a simplified, yet informative, way to describe the device to friends, family and people in your community. Here are a few questions you might be asked and some suggestions for answers:

Possible Questions	Possible Answers
"Oh, what's this?" "What's that on her head?" "Why does she have that?" "Why does she need that?"	"This is a great little device called a cochlear implant. Since Ramona is deaf, she has the implant to help her hear sounds. This implant will help her hear so she can learn how to talk."
"What is that thing?"	"This is Mary's super-cool implant. Even though she's profoundly deaf, it helps her hear sounds."
"Is that a hearing aid?"	"It's not a hearing aid. It's a cochlear implant. Hearing aids didn't help her, so Ruby got an implant to help her hear and learn to talk."
"What's inside her head?"	"Emma had surgery to put part of the cochlear implant in her ear. It will stay there for the rest of her life. The other part is what you see on/near her ear. She puts this part on each morning and takes it off each night."
"Is that stuck to her head?" "Does that hurt her?"	"There is a magnet under the skin and another magnet on this (external) part. The two magnets work together to hold it in place. It's very comfortable and doesn't hurt at all."

Audiology Appointments for Cochlear Implant Users

As described earlier, the very first audiology appointment with the cochlear implant is the initial stimulation. After that, you will have regular appointments with your pediatric audiologist. These audiology appointments will likely focus on mapping, adjusting the device's settings and troubleshooting. Your pediatric audiologist will give you a lot of information about the device. She will adjust the cochlear implant to suit your child's ear. In addition, you always have an opportunity to ask questions and learn more. You can continue to ask questions about all the equipment until you are comfortable with it.

Your pediatric audiologist will test your child's hearing, both without the devices (unaided) and while wearing devices (aided). For more information about a typical audiology appointment, see the section called Walking Through a Typical Audiology Appointment in Chapter 3.

Some children who wear cochlear implants might need earmolds to anchor the ear level devices on their small ears. If this is the case for your child, the pediatric audiologist may need to do an earmold impression at your audiology appointment. The process for a cochlear implant earmold is the same as it is for a hearing aid earmold. For more information on earmolds and earmold impressions, see pages 82–85.

When Should Your Child Wear the External Cochlear Implant Component?

The best answer to this is *always*. The only exception is when your child is sleeping. Another exception could be while bathing or during water play, but this depends on what device you have. Some devices are waterproof and submergible, so children can wear them during all waking hours. Others are water-resistant but not submergible and some can't get wet at all. Try to accomplish full-time use as quickly as possible so your child doesn't continue to miss the important talk around her. Full-time cochlear implant use is considered to be *all waking hours,* except during water play or bathing with devices that can't get wet.

Children vary in response to new cochlear implants. Some wear them happily from day one and some try to remove them constantly. Many fall somewhere in between these two extremes. Children who wear cochlear implants happily right away might do so because the sound is interesting to them, because they have taken on your positive attitude or because they typically do what is expected anyway. After being in quiet so long, children who start out resistant to cochlear implants might not understand what the sound is. It will just take some time.

Introducing the External Component to Your Child

Your child's first at-home introduction to the external component is important. Your point of view lays the foundation for hers. The most significant factor determining whether a young child wears the device or not is whether the parents have made up their minds the child will do so. First and foremost, start with a positive attitude. You might find it emotionally difficult that your child needs to wear something visible on her ear. Remember that your goal is to help her listen so she can talk. With consistent cochlear implant use, you are giving her that opportunity. This is something to feel good about because it's so important! Tell yourself you want her to have the best possible sound input and this is the way to begin. Your positive, determined attitude sets the stage for your child. Decide today that consistent cochlear implant use is a necessity as you remain focused on your goal to help your child develop into a talking child. Remember, for your child to learn how to listen and talk, she must be able to listen with her cochlear implant during all waking hours.

What You Need

Start out by collecting some materials. As you do this, remind yourself that this is the preparation for providing sound to your child on a regular basis. You need the following:

- **External device**
- **Storage location**
  Locate a place to store the cochlear implant and some related equipment to use each day. Choose a location above the reach of small children, such as a dresser top or kitchen cabinet. Decide today that when the cochlear implant is not on your child, you will return it to this location. This helps avoid wasted time looking for the cochlear implant or related equipment.
- **Sturdy storage container**
  This container holds all of your accessories and related equipment. This could be a decorative tin or a zip-up cloth pouch (perhaps a small purse). Ideally, you want the container to look nice, interesting or colorful because it helps make a positive statement about the importance of the cochlear implant. In some families, it's an advantage if small children are unable to open the container on their own.

Checking and Testing Cochlear Implants

Check your child's cochlear implant first thing every day, so you can put it on her as she gets up. Here's a list of the steps to take:

1. If you're using rechargeable batteries, exchange the battery for a fresh, fully charged one. If you're using disposable batteries, remove them and test them in the battery tester. If they're good, put them back into the cochlear implant. If not (even if they're borderline), get fresh batteries and insert those.
2. If you have a brand with a power switch, turn on the cochlear implant. If you're able to adjust the volume, turn it down and slowly move it up to the recommended setting.
3. Some brands indicate (with a flashing light, beeping or digital display) that the device is not on your child's head. Be sure to understand the codes for your child's device.

Putting on the Cochlear Implant

1. Turn on the cochlear implant.
2. Sit or kneel beside your child, so you're at ear level. Tell her that you are going to put on her cochlear implant and show her the device. Put the hook of the cochlear implant around your child's ear so the processor is hanging just behind her ear. Put the magnet on the external device up against the spot on her head over the magnet in the internal device. You will feel the two magnets connect. The external magnet will remain in place as you take your hand away.

3. Say something to your child. You might say:

   ☐ "Hello (her name)."

   ☐ "Here's your CI. I love you!"

   ☐ "babababba." The advantage of using this nonsense vocalization is that, after daily repetition, your child might learn to say it to you as soon as you have put the cochlear implant on and turned the power on. This is a clear indication she is hearing the sound of your voice!

   ☐ "ah," "oo," "ee," "s," "sh," "m" and silence (Ling test)

4. If your child's device has a volume control, gradually raise the volume to the recommended level. Over the next few minutes, continue to turn up the volume a little at a time until you are at the volume recommended by your pediatric audiologist. As you gradually raise the volume, you are doing what is called "walking it up." Once you have the volume on the setting recommended by your pediatric audiologist, your child will more likely be able to respond to your vocalizations and imitate you.

Hooray! You've done it! Even if it seems tricky at first, it will certainly get easier over time. The more times you do it, the better you'll be at doing it!

Ensuring a Good Fit

Sometimes keeping the cochlear implant on a child is a challenge. Often, it's a matter of identifying the problem and finding a solution. If you feel like you've tried everything and the device is still presenting a challenge, ask your pediatric audiologist about the many tools and some tricks you can try that might help make the device more comfortable.

Steps to Accomplishing Full-Time Use

Remember that use during all waking hours is a necessity for your child to become a talking child. Now that you know how to put the cochlear implant on and keep it on, here are some suggestions for accomplishing full-time use.

1. For the first week or so, expect your child to wear the cochlear implant for some short periods each day rather than for the entire day. Select several times when your child is well rested and when you can interact with her, closely supervise her and keep her busy. If you choose an activity in which your child's hands are busy (such as eating, swinging or playing with a favorite toy), she'll be less likely to touch or remove the cochlear implant. Some children enjoy clapping with you as you say "Hooray!" each time you put the cochlear implant on.

2. If your child doesn't bother with the cochlear implant at all, try leaving it on a while longer than planned; however, if at all possible, you should take care to anticipate and remove it before she thinks to do so. This teaches her that *you* take it off — not her.

The Ling Test

The Ling test is a quick and easy way to ensure that, while wearing her devices, your child has access to the range of speech sounds that we use when we talk.

To perform a standard Ling test, first put one device on your child. Make sure it is turned on. Place yourself next to or behind her so she can hear you but can't see your face. Say the following sounds one at a time and teach her to repeat each sound after you say it:

- "ah" (as in hot)
- "oo" (as in boo)
- "ee" (as in bee)
- "s"
- "sh"
- "m"
- silence

Say the sounds in a different order each time you perform this test.

If your child has two devices, take the first one off and put the second one on. Make sure the device is turned on. Repeat the Ling test with that device. Then put the first device back on so she is wearing both with both turned on.

Note any difficulty your child has repeating these sounds back to you with the device(s) and report any consistent problems to your pediatric audiologist.

For more information on the Ling test, including how to perform a modified version on infants and babies, see page 149.

Tell Your Child

It's good practice to tell your child what you are going to do before you put her device on and before you take her device off. For example, before you put the device on your child, show her the device and say "I'm going to put on your cochlear implant now." Make eye contact, nod your head and wait for her to acknowledge you. Then put the device on.

Similarly, when you go to take the device off, get in the habit of saying "I'm going to take your implant off now" or "Are you ready for me to take this off?"

Eventually you'll get to the point where you can ask your child to put her device on herself and take it off herself. Until that point, it's nice to tell her what you plan to do before you do it. Besides being respectful and mindful of her personal space, this will teach your child that her involvement is important!

3. If your child reaches up or tries to remove the cochlear implant, tell her "No" in a calm and firm voice. Try to hand her something else to keep her hands occupied or change activities to otherwise distract her. You can also say things like "Leave it on" and/or "No touching." If you overreact, she may develop the habit of reaching for the cochlear implant just to see you get excited, so avoid overreacting. At the end of the wearing time, take off the cochlear implant by gently removing the magnetic connection at the coil and taking the processor off her ear at the hook. If your child has an earmold, huggie or other retention device, you need to gently remove those too.

4. Repeat Steps 1–3 several more times during the day. Then increase the wearing time so she is wearing the cochlear implant a little bit longer today than on the previous days.

5. Next, try to get as close as possible to full-day use. This means keeping the cochlear implant on as long as possible between sleep times and bath or water play (if the device can't get wet). Take care to remove the cochlear implant before your child gets crabby with exhaustion and tries to do so herself. This will reinforce the notion that you are in charge of wearing times but are reasonable in your expectations, too. During these weeks, be sure to include some outings and outside play — and keep your eyes on that cochlear implant at all times! If your child is ill, exhausted or unusually irritable on a day without full-day use, try to anticipate the need for a "break" and remove the cochlear implant, as needed, before your child does.

6. Congratulate yourself because you and your child have accomplished quite a lot. Full-time cochlear implant use is approaching! If you are unable to accomplish these steps on your first attempt, try not to get discouraged. It's okay to start over and go through the steps again. If you have to start over, don't worry. You won't be the first parent who has had to try again. Remember that your goal is a talking child and use this idea to motivate you!

Increasing Cochlear Implant Wear Time

Some children are reluctant or stubborn about wearing a cochlear implant. If this is true for your child, remain calm but determined. You will no doubt feel frustrated, but if you look frustrated rather than calm, your child will have gained an edge on control. Your firm, gentle insistence will go further toward success than your appearing ruffled, annoyed or upset.

Set aside a period of about 15 minutes when your child is well-rested and when you can give undivided attention to her. Set a goal that she will wear the cochlear implant for those 15 minutes. Try to arrange things so you can avoid everything else during this time. Select a fun activity that requires your child to use both her hands and do the activity together. You might try making pudding, floating toys in water, swinging, dusting and sweeping or blowing bubbles she can pop.

Assemble the materials needed for the activity ahead of time. When you're ready to begin, hand your child two of the items, one for each hand. Put your child's cochlear implant on, say "Hooray!" and clap your hands. Be ready to begin the activity quickly. Each and every time she reaches for or removes the cochlear implant, say "No," "Leave it on" or "No touching" and replace it. Say nothing else and do nothing else about the removal or the attempt. Hand her something else and continue the activity. When things are going along well and she is fully absorbed in the activity, resist the temptation just to leave the cochlear implant on her. After your goal is met (about 15 minutes), remove the cochlear implant. Your removing it builds toward success because your interaction involved your not allowing her to take it out and your being willing to take it out after a reasonably short time. Try a similar activity and repeat these same techniques again later. The more times a day you can do this, the sooner your child will wear the cochlear implant all day.

Most children who are busy and happy are distracted from thinking about and touching the cochlear implant and learn to leave it alone during these periods. You should see some improvement in a week or less. Improvement can be measured by a decrease in your child's attempts at removal or actual removal of the cochlear implant.

When you have noticed improvement, choose another few times a day when you can supervise but not be totally involved with the activity. Giving your child a meal can work well, especially if it's a few minutes past regular meal time and she is truly hungry. Have everything ready ahead of time. If appropriate for your child's age, plan ahead to include some finger foods to keep those little hands busy.

Once your child is seated, put the external device on, clap and say "Hooray!" Then quickly supply the meal. Sit or stay nearby and follow the same routine of responding with "No," "Leave it on" or "No Touching" and replace the cochlear implant as needed. After some time, you should have many periods each day when your child is wearing a cochlear implant agreeably for about 15 to 30 minutes at a time.

There's no real time frame for this. Some children accomplish use during all waking hours in a couple days. Others take a couple weeks. In the end, it doesn't matter. You and your child can work up to the point of wearing the external device during all waking hours and reaping the benefits of this incredible device.

Accomplishing Full-Time Cochlear Implant Use as a Working Parent

You can see that getting your child used to wearing the cochlear implant all day might be more easily accomplished if you're with your child all day. While this is true, there are also ways to accomplish full-time cochlear implant use even if you're not with her all day. The most common approach for working parents is to use mornings, evenings and weekend hours (when you are with your child) as the initial wearing times.

Once your child is successfully wearing the cochlear implant when you're with her, arrange an hour to teach your child care provider how to manage it when you're away. You

Guess What? She Keeps Taking the Cochlear Implant Off!

If your child pulls her cochlear implant off over and over again, try this: One last time, put it on your child. Do whatever you need to do to distract her and keep her from taking it off.

- Hand her a toy to keep her hands busy.
- Gently hold her hands and sing her a song.
- Hold her close to you and rock her.

Leave the cochlear implant on for 30 more seconds. Then, *and this is the most important part,* YOU remove her cochlear implant so she learns it's okay only for YOU to take it off — not her.

A short while later, put the cochlear implant back on and try this process again.

It's also important to anticipate the times your child might be likely to take off the cochlear implant. When she feels crabby, ill, exhausted or unusually irritable, plan for a break and remove the cochlear implant, as needed, before your child does.

learned how and so will the child care provider. If your child care provider understands that the cochlear implant is necessary for your child to learn to listen and talk, she should be willing to work with you. Sometimes parents can arrange for their early interventionist to assist with a cochlear implant orientation.

Involving Your Child in Cochlear Implant Care

When your child seems ready and has been wearing the cochlear implant cooperatively for six months or more, it's important to increase your expectations just a bit in terms of cochlear implant care. Now your child is ready to begin helping with this. Yes, even toddlers can start learning!

When it's time to remove the cochlear implant, tell your child it's time and reach out your hand for the cochlear implant to be placed there. In the beginning, guide her hand up to the cochlear implant and help her remove the external component. Once this habit is established, and your child has the motor coordination, encourage her to remove the cochlear implant herself when asked. Help her as needed until she can successfully hand you the cochlear implant when you ask for it. Show her how it always goes into the special container when she's not wearing it. Your child will benefit by learning independence and this will develop her self-esteem. Remember to praise her for her accomplishment!

Cochlear Implant Use in the Car

If your child is in the habit of putting things in her mouth, you might be cautious of device use in the car. Many parents remove hearing devices for car trips until these behaviors have diminished. Also be aware that young children have been known to toss things out the windows of moving cars. For this reason, travel with the windows up until your child has developed consistent and appropriate cochlear implant use in the car. If you have window locks in your car, this is a great time to use them.

Problems with the Cochlear Implant

Some cochlear implant problems are simple and you can solve them yourself. Others have to be solved by your pediatric audiologist. Still others require that the equipment be returned to the manufacturer. Little children (and family life) can be hard on devices like this. Insurance will save you hundreds of dollars if the device gets lost or damaged. Most cochlear implants come with a three-year warranty. Because your child will use it for longer than that, you should arrange for insurance coverage to begin when the warranty expires.

Cochlear implants may be covered by homeowner's insurance. Contact your insurance agent for more information. In addition, your pediatric audiologist can tell you about companies that provide insurance specifically for hearing devices. This insurance is reasonable in price and provides adequate coverage for children's devices. No matter what insurance you get, be sure to look at the coverage for both repair and replacement so you understand the exact coverage you're getting.

Static Electricity and Cochlear Implants

One of the biggest and most common threats to your child's cochlear implant is static electricity. We are all susceptible to static — particularly in areas with very cold and dry weather. Depending on where you live and the season, you may or may not have much static in your environment. Static interferes with the function of the external device and is capable of scrambling or wiping out the maps your pediatric audiologist loaded into the processor. If this happens, your child will no longer have access to sound through the external device. Although this isn't the end of the world, it does require another lengthy audiology appointment you otherwise might not have needed. In addition, because the internal device is an electrical device, static could potentially affect it as well. If you prefer to be very conservative, it's certainly best to avoid any static electricity, whether or not your child is wearing her external device. Static build-up can be caused by (but is not limited to) the following:

- plastic slides, climbing structures and riding toys
- trampolines
- parachutes (often used in gym classes)
- tunnels
- bouncy houses
- ball pits
- wool hats in the dry winter
- walking/running in socks on carpet
- rubbing a balloon on a child's head
- wearing/using wool and fleece fabrics

Cochlear implant manufacturers continue to look for ways to prevent static from affecting these devices. As technology continues to improve, manufacturers will likely introduce even more advanced devices with static-resistant components.

Simple Ways to Reduce Static Electricity

Here are some inexpensive, yet effective methods to reduce the amount of static to which your child is exposed:

- **Liquid fabric softener + water solution**
  If you have carpet in your home, you may want to try this simple trick. Add one part liquid fabric softener to two or three parts water in a clean spray bottle. Shake it up so it mixes well. Spray the solution on your carpet to reduce static build-up.

- **Dryer sheets**
  Any brand of static reducing dryer sheets can be very useful. Rub the sheet on your child's hair and clothing to help eliminate static build-up.

- **Anti-static sprays**
  A few brands of static reducing sprays are available at most grocery and drugstores. One common brand is Static Guard.

- **Increase humidity**
  A humidifier can help in the cold, dry winter months.

- **Grounding static**
  Grounding static means that you take away the charge when you expect your child is carrying one. To do this, touch your child on her leg or arm — far from her head and the external device. You may feel a shock, but you will have discharged the static and prevented the charge from coming in contact with the cochlear implant.

Troubleshooting Cochlear Implants

Many problems with the cochlear implant must be handled by your pediatric audiologist. You should not hesitate to contact your pediatric audiologist with your questions or concerns. Frequent testing and mapping are necessary during the first few years of using the device. Thereafter, you will want your child to see the pediatric audiologist at least every six months. The following problems should alert you to contact your pediatric audiologist:

1. Your child stops responding to sound to which she previously consistently responded.
2. Your child's speech production or voice quality changes noticeably for the worse.
3. Your child's overall behavior or mood changes for reasons you cannot otherwise explain.
4. There is regression (and/or inconsistencies) in your child's speech perception ability.

Take the following steps to troubleshoot problems with the cochlear implant:

1. Make sure the cochlear implant is on.
2. Make sure the batteries are charged or fresh and keep spares available at your home, school and child care setting.
3. Check to see that the speech processor controls are set as your pediatric audiologist recommended.
4. Reattach the coil if it falls off and/or remind your child to do so.
5. Replace the processor on your child's ear if it falls off.
6. Replace cords that seem worn, intermittent or discolored.
7. Be sure cords are adequately plugged into the ports.
8. Check the surgical incision site on your child's head and the location of the magnet for swelling, redness or irritation. If these are present after the initial programming, ask your pediatric audiologist whether you should contact your ENT surgeon.

Now What?

Whew! Learning about the cochlear implant, having surgery and accomplishing full-time use is a lot of work. You and your child deserve a lot of praise. Take a bow! Now you can move forward in accomplishing your goal of helping her learn to listen and talk. Keep using the device during all waking hours every single day. You don't want to deprive your child of even a few minutes of listening time.

Observe her response to sound and to talking rather than trying to test her in some way. With your observations and some time, your pediatric audiologist should be able to give you more information about what your child might be hearing. Now you're ready to talk to her, have her listen to you and develop her ability to vocalize and talk. The following chapters will guide you.

References

Pollack, D., Goldberg, D. & Caleffe-Schenck, N. (1997). *Educational Audiology for the Limited-Hearing Infant and Preschooler: An Auditory-Verbal Program* (3rd ed.). Springfield, IL: Charles C Thomas Publisher, Ltd.

Sindrey, D. (2002). *Listening Games for Littles* (2nd ed.). Washington, DC: Alexander Graham Bell Association for the Deaf and Hard of Hearing.

Chapter 10

Listening and Auditory Development

Learning to Listen

As adults, we listen throughout the day without paying much attention to exactly what we are hearing. We hear the alarm go off in the morning and know it's time to get up. We hear the meteorologist explain the forecast for the day as we pick out our clothes. The phone rings and we know to pick it up to see who is calling. The microwave beeps, the smoke alarm blares, a horn honks from the car behind us. The list goes on and on. Without conscious thought, we hear those sounds and know the source; we may even launch into action. However, young children must be taught to associate sounds with meaning.

A baby with typical hearing quickly calms to her mother's voice because she has learned that a soothing voice is usually accompanied by her needs being met. For a child with hearing loss who has had more limited opportunity to experience sound, a properly fit hearing device opens a whole new world of sounds. The big task at hand is helping your child experience each of those new sounds and associate meaning with them. It's important to point out sounds as they occur, to show your child the source of the sound and to use a label or name for that sound. One example is when the phone rings. You say "I hear the phone ringing." Then you go answer it. In this simple interaction, your young child has heard a noise, observed your actions (walking to the phone, picking it up, talking into it) and heard you say "Hello."

Now think of all the sounds in your daily routine and all those opportunities to teach your child to listen! It can be overwhelming to do this all the time, but it will be so rewarding when your child begins to respond consistently to sounds.

Listening with the Brain

As young children we were taught some very basic things about our bodies and senses. Eyes are for seeing; ears are for hearing. Actually, it isn't quite that simple. In fact the "simple" act of hearing is a complicated process that involves the brain. Time and time again parents say "My child can definitely hear, but she doesn't always listen." Now, with the use of hearing devices, even children with profound hearing loss can hear sounds and voices. But the hard work has only just begun. Next, they must learn to listen. The hearing devices help your child gain access to sounds and voices, but those important sounds and voices can't be understood until the message is received by her brain.

"We hear with the brain . . . the ears are just the way in."

(Cole & Flexer, 2011)

The problem created by a hearing loss is that it blocks messages from getting to the brain. If we give children optimal hearing devices, we can bypass that blockage, giving them access to the sound, and then messages can get to the brain.

Are you confused by all this talk about hearing and listening? Hearing is about getting the sound in to reach the brain. We can help a child hear with hearing devices and by setting up good listening environments.

Listening is what your child does when she pays attention to the sound she is able to hear. This occurs when your child has had enough opportunities to hear and experience a sound, so then she can think and remember what that sound means to her.

So Many Terms…

Auditory — sound information
Audition — the process of hearing and listening
Hearing — sounds and voices going from the environment to the ear to the brain
Listening — the brain making sense of sound

Brain Development for Listening

Do you know the brain has specific areas dedicated to taking in and making sense of auditory information? These areas develop because auditory information makes its way to the brain. When sound doesn't get to the brain, there is no auditory information there to stimulate those auditory areas (Cole & Flexer, 2011). Auditory access, or the act of sound information getting to the brain, is necessary for a child to develop functional listening skills. Studies in brain development show that auditory input greatly affects auditory centers of the brain (Berlin & Weyand, 2003; Boothroyd, 1997; Chermak, Bellis & Musiek, 2007, as cited in Cole & Flexer, 2011). To develop appropriate listening skills, the auditory portion of the brain must have auditory input, or access to sound.

Wearing Hearing Devices

To become a proficient talker, your child must develop listening skills. To develop listening skills, your child needs sounds and voices constantly available to her through her hearing devices. This is necessary so she can learn to rely on using her hearing, just like people with typical hearing do.

Setting the Stage for Learning to Listen

Helping your child learn to attend to sound and associate meaning with that sound requires lots of action on your part. To ensure you're giving your child the best chance possible to learn to listen, check to be sure the following are in order:

- Your child has accurate audiologic testing.
- Your child's hearing devices are fit and working properly.
- You have a solid understanding of your child's hearing loss and devices.
- You are committed to helping your child wear her devices during all waking hours.
- You take immediate action when a medical or audiologic situation arises.

One of the most important things you'll do during this process is to ensure your child's devices are working at all times. For babies and young children who cannot tell you when a device isn't working, it's a good idea to check the devices periodically throughout the day. There isn't any point in wearing a device unless it's working! (For more information on troubleshooting hearing devices, see Chapters 7–9.)

Since you want your child to have access to sound during all waking hours, it's important to have a plan should your child's device break down. Wear and tear can be especially prevalent for devices worn by children. Discuss the options for backup or loaner devices with your pediatric audiologist before you experience a breakdown — so you're prepared if one actually occurs!

Teaching Your Child to Listen

While your child's listening skills are developing, she needs to tune in to sounds happening around her. You can help! First, model listening yourself. Do this by pointing to your ear or cupping your hand around your ear when you hear a sound you think your child might be able to hear. Then tell your child "Listen! I hear the _____."

Think of this as teaching her, not testing her. You may need to do this for several weeks or months before expecting a response. Because listening takes effort and concentration from your young child, provide exposure during all of her waking hours, but give concentrated attention to sound when she is at her best. Eventually, if she is able to access the sound using her hearing devices, your child should notice and attend to sound on her own.

Your child should listen both to sounds happening in her environment (environmental sounds) and to voices (talking). Think about the sounds around you. Here are some examples of environmental sounds to point out:

- sound-making toys
- vehicle sounds (motor sounds and sirens from cars, planes and so on)

Timing of Cochlear Implantation

Many parents who are considering a cochlear implant for their child wonder when the best time is to get the implant. Moreover, many parents wonder if they should hold off on getting the implant until later in the child's life. These are good things to wonder about.

Research suggests children who receive cochlear implants earlier may benefit more from the relatively greater plasticity of the auditory pathways compared to children implanted later (Geers & Nicholas, 2012; Harrison et al., 2005; Manrique et al., 1999; Sharma et al., 2002; Svirsky, Teoh & Neuburger, 2004). In other words, the brain is ready to take in auditory information before a child is born. As the child ages, the brain becomes less able to respond to and sort out auditory information within the brain. The easiest way to think about providing access to sound for a child with hearing loss is . . . the earlier, the better.

- knocking on the door, phones and doorbells ringing
- machines in the home and yard: dryer buzzing, microwave beeping, lawn mower roaring
- sounds produced by contact: hitting, hammering, dropping
- thunder/rain
- music from stereo, instruments, songs, finger plays and so on
- animal sounds (which provide a good transition from sound to speech)

At first, environmental sounds may be louder and more interesting than talk. Remember, your first job is to notice and comment on sound yourself. Next, look for signs your child may be noticing sounds on her own. She may stop her activity, look up, raise her eyebrows, become quiet and seem to listen or even look around when she has noticed a sound. How exciting! She's beginning to pay attention and listen to sounds around her!

You also can help your child learn that sounds are interesting and fun. Act interested and pleased when a sound occurs; seek or look at the source and point it out to your child. Provide repeated exposure to the same sounds day in and day out. Keep telling your child to listen, and associate that with a helpful gesture of pointing to your ear or cupping your hand around it. In the beginning, bathe your child in sound without worrying about receiving a response from her.

Above all, make it fun. If it's game-like, your child will want to play. Once you indicate you have heard a sound and you shrug your shoulders to show that you wonder what it is, you and your child can move around looking for the sound source. Once you find it, point to it and try to get the sound to occur again. Praise your child when she finds the sound source. Clap your hands and say "Hooray." This helps her begin to make the association between the sound and its source. By developing awareness of sound sources, you're working toward teaching your child that sound has meaning.

Stages of Auditory Development

Just like all kinds of development, children progress through auditory development in stages (Sindrey, 2002). The stages of auditory development are:

- **Detection — "Was there a sound?"**
  Detection means your child notices a sound when it occurs. She may or may not know what it is or where it is coming from. Examples of responses that let you know she detects sound are startling and looking up from play.

- **Discrimination — "Is this sound different from another sound?"**
  Discrimination means she can listen to sounds and determine whether they are the same or different. It's fairly difficult to test a child for discrimination until she has already progressed to the next level, which is identification.

- **Identification/recognition — "What is this sound?"**
  Identification, or recognition, means your child knows what the sound is and can indicate its source by looking at it or pointing to it. For example, the doorbell rings and she looks to the door. It can also mean that she can accurately label a speech stimulus by pointing. For example, multiple food items are on the table. You say "apple" and she points to the apple.

- **Comprehension — "What is the meaning of this sound?"**
  Comprehension means your child can understand some speech by listening. For example, a parent says, "Woof, woof" and the child says "Doggy." Or a parent asks "Where are your shoes?" and the child says "Outside."

The Most Important Sound — Talk!

Now is the time to think about listening to voices and talking. Since she will be learning to talk, spoken language is the most important sound for your child to hear. It is believed that when a child listens to speech, specific parts of the brain process that spoken language. But when a child listens to environmental sounds, other parts of the brain process the message. This makes it important for you to provide input of both talk and environmental sounds to develop your child's listening attention and ability. Remember, your child needs to hear spoken language that is just a bit louder than the background noise. This doesn't mean you should talk louder, because when we speak in a louder voice, we tend to distort how we speak. The talking should be rich in both pitch and duration. So be expressive to grab your child's interest. Instead of raising your voice in noisy situations, try to eliminate or reduce the background noise to set up a better listening environment.

Here are some tips to make listening easier and more interesting for your child:

- Be sure the hearing aid, bone conduction device or cochlear implant is optimally set (by your pediatric audiologist).
- Make sure background noise is minimal.
- Speak clearly at close range to your child (1–3 feet) and at ear level if possible.
- Use varying intonation.
- Make your talk interesting, meaningful and fun.
- Associate sound with meaning by using objects, actions, pictures and natural gestures, as needed.
- Provide daily, focused attention to sound and speech.
- Provide lots of input before expecting responses.
- Use the *Techniques to Encourage Talking* in Chapter 13.

Ways of "Giving" Information

During the process of teaching your child to listen and talk, you might hear a few different terms that relate to the way in which you "give" information to your child. Some of the terms used to describe the support or cues you give are:

- Auditory-only — cues your child hears (talking or other sounds)
- Visual — cues your child sees (facial expressions and gestures)
- Auditory-visual — cues your child can hear and see

Auditory-Only Information

One way to develop listening skills most effectively and efficiently is to give your child opportunities to listen without the aid of visual cues. To do this, give auditory-only information. In other words, talk to her without using visual cues. This gives her a chance to learn to understand what you're saying just by listening. You can easily make conversational talk an auditory-only experience by changing your position relative to your child. If you hold your child on your lap with her facing forward, you are giving auditory-only information. If you sit next to your child instead of across from your child, it's more likely that you will provide auditory-only information. It's not recommended to create an auditory-only interaction by blocking your face with your hand or other object because that may distort or interfere with your talk.

The Auditory Sandwich

Other times, your child might not understand an auditory-only cue. This is not uncommon. Even with her hearing devices, your child may not hear perfectly — especially depending on the background noise in the listening environment. Because of this, she might learn to fill in some missing information with visual information. This includes gestures you use, reading lips (or speech reading) and watching the speaker's face.

If you find your child doesn't understand an auditory-only cue, repeat what you said while adding a visual cue (pointing, showing, etc.). When you see that she understands, repeat what you said once more without the visual cue so your child can practice listening. Always begin and end with auditory-only information to really boost those listening skills. Some people refer to this as an "auditory sandwich."

Over time, you might see your child's listening skills develop more and more. You might notice she is gradually able to understand more without the visual cues, particularly when you're talking about something you talk about every day. This is exactly what you want to see! She is learning to understand through listening alone!

Calling Your Child's Name

To begin encouraging your child to detect speech, call her name to try to get her attention. Do this only in situations in which it's natural and logical to call your child, perhaps as she sees you, perhaps even with your hands around your mouth in a calling gesture. Also do this when you're nearby, but out of her range of vision. This is best done from behind or beside your child, but still from just two or three feet away. Alternate between providing your child a view of you calling her and not letting her see you. Sometimes call her so she sees you, then right afterward repeat the call out of her range of vision. This is particularly helpful for getting your child to focus on the sound of her name. You may do this for weeks or months before your child responds without being able to see you calling. It's critical that you call your child's name only when you actually need her attention. Children are smart, and if you're constantly calling your child's name with nothing to show or tell her, she will lose interest in your voice (sort of like the boy who cried "Wolf!").

Listening Opportunities Throughout the Day

The best times to practice listening are as sound occurs. You don't need a special environment or special activities to show your child the importance and value of listening. Instead, think about making listening a priority throughout the day. Draw attention to the relevant environmental sounds and provide lots of talk. You should even talk at times she can hear you, but not see you. Use the following daily routines as opportunities to provide lots of rich and interesting talk.

- **When she wants a drink of milk**

   An ideal time to give auditory-only information is when your child already gets the idea of your meaning — most specifically, when she wants something. Once you've established she wants milk, say it to her. Say: "Oh, you want milk? I want milk, Mommy." Then, perhaps while pouring it, say "milk" again from beside or behind her, giving her the opportunity to listen to the sound of the word. You can repeat the word again while pointing to the milk.

■ **While giving her a banana**

You might discuss the banana she'll eat and talk about it as you peel it. While she listens and looks, you might say "Banana. Here's your banana. Peel the banana. Pull it down. Mmm, banana!" You might then change your position so you're beside or behind her so she has an opportunity just to listen to what you say. You could repeat what you've already said or try something new. You might say "Okay, here's the banana. How about a bite of banana? Do you wanna take a bite? Mmm, banana is so good!"

■ **While pushing her in a stroller**

When you're pushing your child in a stroller, lean down and talk to her. This is a very authentic auditory-only situation because it's likely that you are next to your child or above your child, not directly facing her. In this scenario, you can point out an airplane that flies overhead or a lawn mower in the next yard over, all without directly showing your child your face. It's far more natural for you to share a gaze at the sound source than it is to make eye contact and then look back at the sound source.

■ **While sharing books**

Make the sounds for pictured items and animals. Get dramatic and use lots of sound effects for actions in the story — the car beeping, the baby crying, the airplane flying, etc. Reading books while holding your child on your lap is a great position to provide an authentic auditory-only interaction. Both of you can see the pictures and share a mutual gaze. Your voice is likely very close to the microphone on your child's hearing device.

■ **While playing with toys**

Use sound-making toys and other toys that don't make sounds so you can use your voice to create sound effects. Change your voice when talking to a baby doll, when crashing block towers down or when being dramatic.

■ **While cooking**

Cooking offers lots of potential for listening to sounds and words: The blender that goes on and off, the microwave that beeps, the spoon hitting the metal bowl, etc.

■ **During routine activities**

Talk as you feed and dress your child. Tell her about your own actions, and give her the words for the actions as she moves and works. Point out sounds like the toilet flushing, the snaps on her onesie as you dress her or even the doorbell if someone comes to your house.

■ **While singing and listening to music**

Act out songs, nursery rhymes and finger plays with or without props. Try to use songs or melodic talk while you transition from one activity to another. Make up songs to go with different times of the day (time to go sit down, time to clean up, etc.).

■ **During activities that require movement**

Sometimes you just need to get the housework done. At these times and others (such as outside play or yard work), try to take a few moments to notice, point out, highlight and enjoy the sounds that accompany the activity while in close proximity to your child. Consider getting within arm's length for optimal auditory input. Don't forget to squat down to get at your child's level. Remember: Even if you stand next to your child, your voice might be farther away from her ear than arm's length.

Listening Progress

Your child benefits from listening. Eventually, you will expect her to use these skills to demonstrate comprehension of what you say. Some very young children are able to listen without looking at you. They can point to items you name, point to an animal when you've said its sound, indicate different-colored items you describe, and so on. Despite their hearing loss, many children are strong auditory learners; therefore, most of their learning could occur by listening alone.

The Ling Test

Your child's pediatric audiologist or early interventionist may have mentioned something called the Ling Test (Pollack et al., 1997; Sindrey, 2002). Professionals who work with children with hearing loss use a series of six sounds (*ah, oo, ee, s, sh, m*) and later, a moment of silence (starting at about age 3) to determine if a child has access to all the sounds required to listen to spoken language. When you look at a familiar sounds audiogram (see page 58), you will see a shaded area called the speech banana. You may recall that this shaded area visually represents the broad spectrum of speech sounds. As you locate the six Ling sounds, notice that they cross the entire audiogram, indicating that they span several frequencies. These sounds encompass the entire range of frequencies and intensities critical to developing and listening to spoken language. This is handy because when you're on the go with your little one, you can use the Ling test to make sure she has access to both low- and high-frequency sounds as well as sounds that are less intense and more intense.

If you have a baby or young toddler, you're likely responsible for doing your own Ling test many times each day. In the morning before you put the devices on your child, use a stethoset (for hearing aids) or monitor earphones (for cochlear implant microphones) to listen to your child's devices. Say each of the Ling sounds aloud to yourself as you listen. Remember what the sound is like through your child's devices. If, on any day in the future,

Why Is It Called the Ling Test?

Daniel Ling was an audiologist, an educator of the deaf and a pillar in the field of listening and spoken language instruction for children with hearing loss. Dr. Ling described this test as "a simple and effective way of using speech to check whether, in real-life conditions, hearing aids and cochlear implants meet the minimal requirement of providing detectable levels of spoken language . . . over the speech frequency range" (Ling, 2002, page xxiii).

you don't hear one of the sounds, or if any of the sounds seems distorted, contact your child's pediatric audiologist. Keep in mind that when a device starts to act up, it isn't always all or nothing. Certain sounds can become distorted. If you had been checking the device only by saying "Hello. Hello. Test 123," you might not notice if one frequency is malfunctioning. By using the Ling test, you can isolate specific pitches.

Performing the Ling Test

Ultimately, you will want your child to respond to a standard Ling test in which you say the sounds and your child repeats them. Although a 2½-year-old can usually learn to do a standard Ling test, babies and infants can't. While your child is very young, you can perform two modified versions of the Ling test to ensure she is hearing optimally with her devices. These modified versions include looking for nonverbal as well as verbal responses. You can use these methods as long as necessary, but know that your ultimate goal is to perform the standard version of the Ling test.

Modified Ling Test: Observing Nonverbal Responses

For a baby, you can say the Ling sounds and determine whether or not she detects them. You can learn to recognize certain nonverbal responses, or behaviors, that indicate detection of sound. The steps for performing a Ling test with a baby are as follows:

1. Find a quiet spot where you can do the test without background noise.
2. With the baby facing away from you or at your side (so she can't see your face), say a Ling sound such as *oo.*
3. Look for any noticeable change in behavior in response to the sound. She may widen her eyes, look around or stop moving or sucking on a pacifier.
4. Respond to her by saying "Yes, that's right! You heard 'oo!'"
5. Touch her little ear and repeat the sound.
6. Repeat this procedure with each of the six Ling sounds: *ah, oo, ee, s, sh* and *m.*
7. If your child wears two devices, repeat all six Ling sounds with each device individually.

Modified Ling Test: Using Toys

Once your child demonstrates consistent eye contact and tracking in response to sound, you can teach her to use toys to indicate detection of the Ling sounds. This usually starts around age 2. Young children can learn to throw a block in a bucket, add a piece to a puzzle or put a ring on a peg after hearing each sound. When you initially teach this task, you need to help your child place the toy after the sound is presented. Here are the steps for using toys to perform a Ling test, including the steps for teaching her the task:

1. Find a quiet spot where you can do the test without background noise.
2. Put a toy in your child's hand and hold it up to her ear with your hand over hers.
3. Cue her to listen to you say one Ling sound aloud, such as "oo." After you say it, help her place the toy by moving her hand toward the target and dropping or placing the toy along with her.
4. Fairly quickly, after she catches on to this task, you'll notice that she can manipulate the toys herself without your help. At this point, you can sit next to or stand behind her so your face is not visible as you say a Ling sound. She should respond by placing the toy, but only after you say a sound.
5. Once she has truly learned the task using toys, you can begin each Ling test by placing the toys in front of her and instructing her to "listen." Then sit or stand in a spot where your face is not visible and say each Ling sound, waiting for her to place each toy after each sound. If she places a toy without a sound, remind her to "listen" and start again.
6. If your child wears two devices, repeat all six Ling sounds with each device individually.
7. At this point, you need not expect your child to repeat each sound. The act of placing a toy indicates she heard it.
8. Many children can accurately respond to Ling sounds using toys by age 2½. At this point, you'll also want to teach your child to give verbal responses to simple questions. Ask common questions a child with devices will likely hear often, such as "Can you hear me?" or "Are your hearing aids working?" Help your child respond to these questions so she learns that you're counting on her to respond verbally.
9. Note any difficulty your child has responding to the Ling sounds or the questions you ask. Report consistent problems to your pediatric audiologist.

Standard Ling Test

After the child is proficient at responding verbally to simple questions, you can teach her to respond to the standard Ling test. Again, this is the fastest and most efficient way to determine if her devices are working optimally. It's especially important to do a Ling test first thing in the morning when you put the devices on, whenever you put the devices back on after removing them or after they fall off, or whenever you suspect a change in the child's responsiveness. The standard Ling test includes all six sounds plus a silence stimulus. Below are the steps for performing a standard Ling test:

1. Find a quiet spot where you can do the test without background noise.
2. If the child wears two devices, put only one on your child, perform the Ling test and then switch. Be sure to perform the test separately with each device.
3. Place yourself next to or behind the child so she can hear you, but can't see your face.
4. Say the following Ling sounds one at a time and teach the child to repeat each sound after you say it. The sounds are *ah, oo, ee, s, sh* and *m.* Include a moment when you say nothing and expect the child to respond by saying "Nothing" or "No sound."
5. Each time you perform this test, give the sounds and silence in a different order. If you always say them in the same order, your child might memorize them one way and just repeat them back, without actually listening for a prompt.
6. Use unpredictable intervals between each sound so your child has to respond only after you provide the stimulus (sound or silence).
7. Note any difficulty your child has repeating these sounds back to you with each device. Report any consistent problems to your pediatric audiologist.

Why Does the Standard Ling Test Include Silence?

You may wonder why silence is used in addition to the individual speech sounds. A silence prompt gives your child an opportunity to say she didn't hear a sound so she learns not only to differentiate between different sounds, but also to note accurately when no sound is presented. For example, the *s* sound is one of the softest, and so it's easier to miss. Make sure your child actually is hearing that *s* sound so you know she's hearing really soft speech. Remember, a child needs to be able to hear soft speech to learn to listen and talk. If you say the *s* sound and she doesn't hear it, you're likely to say something like, "Did you hear that? I said '*sssss*.'" If this happens a few times, your child will learn that when she doesn't hear your prompt, she should say "*s*" in response. This would make you think she's hearing that sound when really she is not. The silence prompt allows your child to distinguish between no sound and really soft sounds.

The Six Ling Sounds Plus Silence

a h h h

o o o

e e e e

s h h h

s s s s

m m m

silence

The Auditory Hoop

At some point, you may see a professional using something called an auditory hoop to perform the Ling test. This is typically an embroidery hoop with a piece of speaker fabric stretchd across it. Professionals cover their faces with the hoop when performing listening tests or when helping a child build listening skills. A hoop allows one to face the child while talking, but eliminates facial cues the child otherwise might see. The speaker fabric allows the professional's voice to remain undistorted. A hoop is a handy device for teachers, therapists and pediatric audiologists to use for performing the Ling test or any other listening activities, but it's certainly not necessary.

References

Cole, E.B. & Flexer, C. (2011). *Children with Hearing Loss: Developing Listening and Talking — Birth to Six* (2nd ed.). San Diego, CA: Plural Publishing.

Geers, A.E. & Nicholas, J.G. (2012). Enduring advantages of early cochlear implantation for spoken language development. *Journal of Speech, Language, and Hearing Research, 56*(2), 643–655. doi:10.1044/1092-4388(2012/11-0347).

Harrison, R.V., Gordon, K.A. & Mount, R.J. (2005). Is there a critical period for cochlear implantation in congenitally deaf children? Analysis of hearing and speech perception performance after implantation. Wiley Periodicals, Inc. *Developmental Psychobiology, 46*(3), 252–261.

Ling, D. (2002). *Speech and the Hearing-Impaired Child: Theory and Practice.* (2nd ed., p. xxiii). Washington, DC: Alexander Graham Bell Association for the Deaf and Hard of Hearing.

Manrique, M., Cervera-Paz, F.J., Huarte, A., Perez, N., Molina, M. & Garcia-Tapia, R. (1999). Cerebral auditory plasticity and cochlear implants. *Journal of Pediatric Otorhinolaryngology, 49*(Suppl. 1), S193–S197.

Pollack, D., Goldberg, D. & Caleffe-Schenck, N. (1997). *Educational Audiology for the Limited-Hearing Infant and Preschooler: An Auditory-Verbal Program* (3rd ed.). Springfield, IL: Charles C Thomas Publisher, Ltd.

Sharma, A., Dorman, M.F. & Spahr, A.J. (2002). A sensitive period for the development of the central auditory system in children with cochlear implants: Implications for age at implantation. *Ear & Hearing, 23*(6), 532–539.

Sindrey, D. (2002). *Listening Games for Littles* (2nd ed.). Washington, DC: Alexander Graham Bell Association for the Deaf and Hard of Hearing.

Svirsky, M.A., Teoh, S.-W. & Neuburger, H. (2004). Development of language and speech perception in congenitally, profoundly deaf children as a function of age at cochlear implantation. *Audiology and Neuro-Otology, 9*(4), 224–233. doi:10.1159/000078392.

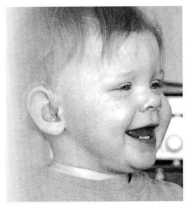

Chapter 11

Language, Speech and Learning to Talk

When educators and therapists refer to children learning to talk, they often use a lot of technical terms. Experts sometimes forget that, in the real world, many people don't know the technical differences among words like *talking, speaking, speech* and *language.* When they add words like *comprehension, expression, vocabulary, syntax, grammar, utterances, spontaneous, elicited* and *prompted* into the mix, they lose many people entirely. This chapter is meant to give you some basic explanations of these terms to help you understand them better.

You may be wondering how children actually learn to talk. More to the point, how do children with hearing loss learn to talk? This chapter also describes the way all children, whether they have typical hearing or not, learn to talk and the stages of language development they go through while learning to talk.

Language and speech: Are they the same?

Although some people use these words interchangeably, the correct answer for the above question is "No." One of the most important distinctions for families to understand is the difference between language and speech.

Language

Language refers to words and how they're connected together to make complete thoughts. The term language is used to refer to the understanding and use of words, phrases and sentences. Language is, simply, ideas put into words. Language is connected to thinking. Words are units of language that enable us to talk about what we are thinking.

In describing a young child's language, we might say:

- She understands a few words.
- She understands many words and uses a few.
- She understands and uses a large vocabulary of single words.
- She combines words into two-word phrases.
- She understands some sentences and uses two-word and three-word phrases.
- She understands and uses a variety of simple sentences.

Receptive and Expressive Language

Early interventionists and hearing professionals may describe your child's language in technical terms. You likely will hear them refer to both receptive language and expressive language. These two terms describe two aspects of language development. You need to know about these terms so you can understand the distinctions being made about your child's language development. You may wish to use these terms to describe her language development to others as well.

What is receptive language?

Receptive language is the language a person understands. One way to remember this is to notice that the base word, or root word, of receptive is *receive*. Receptive language is the language your child receives from someone and understands. Receptive language could include words, phrases, sentences and longer passages such as stories. Initially, children with hearing loss who are learning to speak rely on cues such as those provided by the situation to understand the words, phrases and sentences said to them. These cues enhance receptive language and can be a bridge to the understanding of words, phrases and sentences. Another word for receptive language is comprehension. It's important to be aware that your child actually might not understand some of the language directed toward her. Also, some young children are so adept at reading situational cues, they give the impression they understand words they really don't understand yet. However, a child's ability to use situational cues will help her eventually understand words, phrases and sentences.

Receptive language = what your child understands

What is expressive language?

Expressive language is the language a person uses. You can remember this by noticing that the base word, or root word, of expressive is *express*. Expressive language consists of the words, phrases and sentences your child is able to *express* or say. We often refer to the words or vocalizations that come out of your child's mouth as "utterances." Many children with hearing loss use cries, vocalizations, body language and natural gestures before they're able to use actual words. These nonverbal and vocal expressions can be a bridge for your child to use words to express herself. Other words for expressive language are *talking, speaking* and *verbalizing*.

Expressive language = what your child says

Children who use American Sign Language have receptive and expressive language. Even if they don't communicate by speaking aloud, children can understand the signs their parents use. That's their receptive language. The signs they use are their expressive language.

Which comes first: Receptive or expressive language?

In general, receptive ability (comprehension or understanding) comes before expressive ability (talking); however, these skills develop in tandem, and both progress gradually over time. Receptive language comes first in that your child usually will understand a word before she uses it. Her understanding of words (receptive language) will lead to her using them (expressive language). So your child may understand a few words (receptive language) for a few months before she uses them (expressive language). Once she begins saying words, both receptive and expressive language will continue to develop. Typically, receptive ability comes a little bit faster than expressive ability. For example, a child might understand short phrases (receptive language), but use only single words (expressive language) during the same time period.

Vocabulary

Many educational programs put an emphasis on how many words a child understands or says. These words are all part of a child's vocabulary, which is one element of the broader category of language. A child has words that are part of her receptive vocabulary. That is, she understands what those words mean and can demonstrate this understanding by retrieving an object, pointing to a picture or performing an action. A child also has a separate, but related, expressive vocabulary. These are the words she can say or use in her talk. Understanding and using vocabulary are very important because vocabulary allows children to start communicating with words rather than relying on gestures. Using vocabulary, children begin to understand and make comments and requests and give answers or acknowledgement. It's important for young children to learn lots of new words so their talk can become more descriptive, diverse and interesting.

A lot of vocabulary is learned incidentally, meaning young children learn new words by overhearing other people use them. Usually, we don't have to directly teach every word a child has in her vocabulary; but remember: Children with hearing loss have more difficulty overhearing things and so may not learn as many new words incidentally. For this reason, specific vocabulary often must be taught to children with hearing loss.

Though extremely important, vocabulary isn't the only component of language. We want to make sure that educational services continue to focus on both receptive and expressive language, not just single-word vocabulary learning. It's also important for children to learn different names for the same basic objects or actions. We don't want to limit them in their talking — and, eventually, in their writing — with only basic vocabulary. For example, at age 2, it's appropriate for a child to learn to say "potty" when she needs to go to the bathroom. However, older children and adults know that many other words have similar meanings, including: *bathroom, toilet, facilities, restroom* — and even regional words like *loo* and *john*. Another example is the use of the word *owie* — as in "I've got an owie on my knee." Children need a more extensive vocabulary to describe their hurt with words like *scrape, cut, blister, wound, scratch, bruise* and so on. In addition, to be a proficient talker, a child must understand higher-level vocabulary words. For example, the word *big* is one of the first words children learn, but eventually, we all learn the meaning of *huge, gigantic, humongous* and so on.

Our vocabularies are never really complete. As adults we learn the terminology related to our chosen professions. We learn new words as they come into popular culture. And some people learn new words when faced with new life situations, such as raising a child with hearing loss.

For more information on vocabulary, see Chapter 15.

Speech

Speech refers to a speaker's ability to pronounce words and sentences clearly when talking. Speech is the ability to use vowels (like *ah* and *ee*) and consonants (like *b* and *sh*) and to combine them understandably into words. The three main components of speech are **voice (or breath), articulation** and **suprasegmental aspects of speech**.

Breath is a key component of speech. Without breath, there would be no speech. To produce spoken language, a person must control the air moving in and out of the lungs in a way that differs from breathing. Spoken language requires breath control that allows for producing certain kinds of sounds. Breath and breath control are closely related to voice or voice quality. Good voice quality is the lack of breathiness, hoarseness, raspiness and/or atypical nasality (too much or not enough breath for speech through the nose).

Articulation is the way we move our articulators — tongue, teeth, jaw, lips and other parts of the mouth — to pronounce certain sounds and combine them to form words. Articulation can also be thought of as the way we produce certain individual sounds and the way we put those sounds together to make words. For example, we can produce the individual sounds /b/, /aw/ and /l/. If we put those individual sounds together, we articulate the word, *ball*.

Suprasegmental aspects of speech refer to all of the intricacies of speech that alter the meaning of our message. Successful use of suprasegmental aspects requires the ability to vary all of those different aspects appropriately. Suprasegmental aspects of speech include:

- pitch (high and low)
- volume (loud and soft)
- duration/timing (long and short)
- stress (on syllables in words and words in phrases/sentences)

As an example, think about the way your pitch goes down at the end of a statement. Then think about how your pitch goes up at the end of a question. Say the following out loud:

Statement: The dog is outside.
Question: The dog is outside?

Even though the words are exactly the same, the way we say them is different. The difference is in pitch. This slight change in pitch makes a big difference in meaning. Just as children have to learn how to articulate each sound of speech, they also have to learn how to apply suprasegmental aspects to their speech correctly. This makes what we say meaningful and understandable.

Describing Speech Ability

Speech can be described in many ways, including:

- Her voice quality sounds very natural.
- She has good breath control.
- She imitates a number of vowels correctly in modeled syllables and words.
- She correctly produces the sounds /-o-/ as in hot, /-u-/ as in cut, /b/, /d/ and /m/ at the beginning of words.
- She correctly produces /f/ and /sh/ at the end of words.
- She omits, distorts and substitutes some consonants in long sentences.

Recap: Examples of the Difference Between Language and Speech

You can have good language and poor speech.

Examples of this include:

- Trying to talk after you visit the dentist and half of your face is still numb.
- Your grandma trying to speak without her dentures.

You can have good speech and poor language.

Examples of this include:

- A person with a certain kind of brain injury who still might be able to pronounce the words clearly, but the message comes out mixed up.
- A child who says, "Me go no night-night." You can understand the speech and intent of her message (she doesn't want to go to bed), but she's using some of the wrong words, the word order is mixed up and some words are missing.

In the case of poor speech and poor language, a specialized teacher or therapist is needed to help develop skills in both areas.

The Relationship Between Language and Speech

Speech and language develop at the same time in young children. Sometimes parents observe growth spurts in one area and not the other. Children who are typically developing can be expected to have fully refined speech by the time they are around 7 or 8 years old.

As your child's communication ability develops, you will focus on different aspects of that communication. A progression is important, although it's not as simple as this list might suggest:

- nonverbal communication or body language and gestures
- receptive language or comprehension (understanding what's said)
- expressive language or talking (producing language)
- speech production or clearly pronouncing the vowels and consonants of words

This sequence will occur in the beginning, as your child first learns words; then the last three aspects re-occur again and again with each new language skill and stage. Children do not leave one aspect behind as they focus on the next. Instead, they add areas of focus as their communication progresses. Based on your child's strengths and needs, particular aspects of language may continue to need special attention.

In other words, in the beginning, focus more attention on the language than on the speech. Before you can focus on improving the clarity of words your child needs some amount of language skill with the ability to convey ideas. Too much attention to the clarity of speech can discourage a young child from trying to communicate her ideas using spoken language. As her language improves, you can focus on both language and speech with activities directed at improving each. Before that, the vocal play of just making sounds and imitating will help prepare your child for eventual formal speech and language instruction.

When a child has hearing loss, both speech and language development must be monitored. For a child to monitor her own speech and practice saying the sounds without errors, she must hear words pronounced clearly, which requires good access to sound. It's also important to make sure a child can hear all the talk happening around her so she can make sense of what's talked about and continue to learn new language.

In most cases, children with hearing loss benefit from the support of a speech-language pathologist, teacher of the deaf or auditory-verbal practitioner to help refine their speech skills. Speech teaching or therapy is quite complex and requires specialized training. Expectations, training and progress vary based on a child's ability to access sound in addition to other factors like a child's intelligence, life experience, motivation, attitudes and personality. When you have the opportunity to work with an expert in spoken language, she will help you understand the process of speech and language development, give you some suggestions about what to expect, teach you how to surround your child with rich and interesting talk and demonstrate how to help improve your child's speech.

How Do Children Learn to Talk?

The short answer to that question is: They listen, listen, listen and practice, practice, practice. Children learn to talk by listening to other people talk, by practicing talking and by listening to their own talking. Like many people, you've probably never considered how you learned to talk. If you have other children, or have been around other children, you may have chuckled at funny little phrases young children pick up or mistakes they make with language. But you may not have noticed that those incidents are evidence of a very important language learning process taking place. Learning to talk doesn't just happen by chance. Parents and caregivers teach their children how to communicate by communicating with them!

Try to recall a time when you interacted with a baby or young child or when you observed someone else's interaction. You may have noticed the baby getting lots of exposure to adult talk. People behave as if baby talk is interesting, important and meaningful. People speak to babies as well as to one another while around babies. While all of this talk surrounds the babies, they practice expressing themselves through crying, cooing and babbling.

By 6 to 10 months of age, a baby typically develops comprehension, or understanding, of a few words. Around the baby's first birthday, she starts using a few actual words. By age 2, she uses short phrases, which is enough to make her point understood, and she even understands entire sentences. By age 3, now a growing toddler, she typically uses true sentences. Eventually, the sentences begin to include more and more words that make the talk sound like proper English. By the time a child grows to be approximately 5 years old, she is able to understand and use all the complexities of the English language (Easterbrooks & Baker, 2002). New vocabulary, or new single words, will continue to develop throughout her entire life. However, the structure of language — that is, how to understand spoken language and how to join words together meaningfully — will have firmly developed by approximately age 6.

The human brain is an incredibly amazing organ. In the early years, it's pre-programmed and ready to learn any kind of language being spoken nearby. A baby's lips, teeth, tongue and vocal tract are programmed to practice making sounds that are at first meaningless to a baby. As the ear picks up more and more talk, the brain understands more. As a baby practices vocalizing, true words emerge. Before long, language bursts forth, and its development progresses rather rapidly. In most cases, this means no lessons, no effort, no muss, no fuss. It just naturally happens. We expect babies to learn to talk, and they do. We participate in the process, observe it and take pleasure in it. Yet when the ears don't allow a clear and accurate signal to get to the brain, this whole process is interrupted. This leads us to how children with hearing loss learn to talk.

How Do Children with Hearing Loss Learn to Talk?

The short answer to that question is similar: They listen, listen, listen and practice, practice, practice; but remember, children with hearing loss learn to talk only if they can hear the talk around them. Therefore, they need to use their well-fit hearing devices consistently to receive good access to sounds and voices. They need lots of exposure to talking — and this exposure must be focused. Focused talk can be directed to a baby when she is attentive. As she learns that this talk is interesting, useful and worthwhile, she also learns to be attentive. A baby with hearing loss takes in focused talk more easily than the other talk around her. A special kind of ear-to-ear and eye-to-eye attention is needed. Parents and caregivers can alter their talk to make it more meaningful and more intense to help keep their little one focused and interested in listening. This kind of focused talk is one of the key ways to help your child become a talking child.

Helping Your Baby Learn to Talk

It's important to behave as if a baby's vocalizations are important and meaningful. Think about how to position yourself and the baby to maximize the baby's opportunity to learn from talk that is directed to her and occurs around her. Reinforce vocalizations by first imitating the baby's sounds. This will help teach her that those vocalizations are important. She then will start to imitate her own sounds. Talk, talk and talk. Talk simply, meaningfully and interestingly. Pause to allow time for your baby to respond. She might respond, but she also might not. Either way, you're exposing her to some great language and teaching her that talking involves taking turns.

More on the Brain . . .

Developmental synchrony is the idea that a child develops certain skills and abilities at the precise moment her brain is "developmentally" ready to do so (Cole & Flexer, 2011). It's the most efficient and effective way to learn new skills, including language.

It's important to acknowledge that, regardless of a child's chronological age, skills must be acquired and mastered in developmental order. For example, in any domain of development (language/speech, motor, self help, feeding, social, emotional, etc.) children acquire skills in a typical order. Certain skills are prerequisites for others. For example, babbling comes before talking in phrases and sentences. Crawling comes before walking and riding a bike. In general, we know the brain is ready to babble by 8 to 10 months, to start producing single words by 1 year and to combine words closer to 2 years old. This is not to say a child who is delayed won't acquire these skills, and in the established developmental order, but we do know that it would be most efficient to acquire these skills at the time nature intended. This concept of developmental synchrony is closely related to what many experts consider the "critical periods" of development. The critical language learning window is from birth to approximately 3 years of age when brain neuroplasticity is the greatest (Sharma, Dorman & Spahr, 2002).

A child's brain is not the same as an adult's brain. Much of the primary brain development occurs by age 2 or 3, but full development doesn't happen until later in adolescence. The portions of the brain (e.g., the frontal lobe) in charge of "executive function" (organization, planning, inhibition of impulses, etc.) continue to develop even into the mid-20s!

Keep in mind a few key features of a developing infant brain:

- **The brain is "plastic."** — The neural pathways and synapses are quickly changing and evolving, so lots of good stimulation is key. The period of greatest neuroplasticity is the first three years of life.
- **The brain is efficient.** — Without stimulation of certain areas, the brain will rewire or map itself to perform different functions. So children who don't receive enriched early auditory and language input may have brains that reconfigure to spend the energy on other skills like visual input. Since we know that complete maturation of the central auditory pathways is required for typical development of spoken language in children, it's important to provide early access to sound and enriched language environments (Sharma, Dorman & Kral, 2005; Sharma, Dorman & Spahr, 2002).

It's hard work to listen! Keep encouraging and teaching your baby to pay attention to talkers. Your baby needs encouragement to listen. Use simple words, phrases and sentences over and over again, so she can learn from repetition. Vary the words and sentences you say to keep interest high and to provide exposure to our rich language. Remember: Comprehension of a word usually comes before the use of that word (receptive before expressive). Parents often are excited at the first evidence their baby is understanding words, even if cues are available to help the baby or toddler understand.

A child with hearing loss progresses through the same sequence of developing language that a child with typical hearing does. Your child will produce her first word, then a few words and then many words. Next, she'll use some short phrases, then sentences that will eventually become longer and more complex. It's important to note that your child will benefit from increased practice and focused attention on your part. This process of learning to talk may go more slowly than for a child who hears clearly, but with good hearing devices and hard work, using spoken language usually is possible. You will benefit from an early interventionist who specializes in working with babies with hearing loss. Your early interventionist will guide and support you at the beginning of this journey.

You can do a lot to help develop your child's brain and prime her for listening and spoken language. This will require significant effort. With high expectations and the right help, most children with hearing loss can learn to talk. By participating in the process, you'll get to observe the milestones and take pleasure in your child's accomplishments! When she talks to you, you will know it was well worth your family's efforts.

For more information on techniques to use while talking to your baby, see Chapter 13.

Incidental Learning

Children with typically developing listening skills learn a lot about the world incidentally. This means that even very young children overhear talk — from adults and other children — and learn to understand and use this talk in their own conversations. Sometimes we hear young children experimenting with incidentally acquired language and wonder, "Where did she hear that?" Over the years, this kind of experimentation has embarrassed many parents. It can happen at the grocery store, at school or anywhere. A child uses a bad word, slang or even a harmless phrase she may have heard her parents say. Children with hearing loss often miss opportunities for incidental learning.

Remember, a child with hearing loss who uses hearing devices must *learn* to listen — and this involves focusing on the speaker, ignoring the background noise and homing in on the important message. However, the kind of talk children pick up incidentally often occurs in a less direct way — like overhearing a mother who lowers her voice when talking on the telephone or hearing children on the playground using bad words only when out of their parents' earshot. Children with hearing loss often miss this kind of talk because it isn't directed at them, but we still want them to learn these things!

You may be thinking, "No, thanks. I don't need my little one learning naughty talk." However, for your child to learn the multitude of things children with typical hearing learn in a day, she must develop the ability to learn incidentally. In addition, to fit in with her peers, learn jokes, use slang and produce casual talk not formally taught, she must be able to learn incidentally. This is just another reason why it's so critical for your child to have appropriately fit hearing devices that ensure good access to sound.

Some Important Stages in Language Development

It's not uncommon for children with hearing loss to progress through the stages of receptive and expressive language development more slowly than children with typical hearing. Yet the order of progress is very similar no matter the hearing ability. The order of these important general stages is as follows:

Receptive language
- understands nonverbal communication using situational cues
- understands single words
- understands short phrases
- understands simple directions without situational cues
- understands entire sentences
- understands connected sentences

Expressive language
- uses nonverbal communication
- uses single words
- uses short phrases
- uses sentences
- uses connected sentences about a topic

Try to be a careful observer of your child to determine, in general, her levels of receptive and expressive language. Remember that receptive ability usually precedes expressive ability. Even before your child speaks, she gazes at people or objects you name as she learns to understand the words. Try to determine if it's the words or other cues and gestures to which she responds. That is, if you eliminate the other cues and gestures while you are naming things for her, will she still gaze at the person or object you named? If so, her receptive language is at the single-word level. If not, you'll know she is responding to cues and gestures, meaning her receptive language still is primarily nonverbal in nature.

Young children whose receptive comprehension is in the early stages can appear to understand words or phrases, especially if they're good at reading the cues of the situation. If you hold out a wadded-up piece of paper and say "Throw it away," a child with nonverbal receptive language can make a good guess and throw away the paper due to her knowledge of the situation. However, if you give her the same wad of paper and say "Throw it to Mommy," and she does it, you can be sure the child understands words and maybe even phrases. If she goes to the wastebasket to throw it away, she still may be reliant on cues and gestures, which is considered the nonverbal receptive language stage. Possibly, she understood the word "throw" and put it together with her knowledge of situations. This is a great skill, but it also indicates there's room to grow. Keep working to build comprehension. Before you know it, your child will have enough mastery of language to understand jokes, engage in silly girl talk with her friends and follow complex classroom directions. Remember that, in the beginning, your baby or young child might have very little receptive language. Don't worry! Even if she doesn't understand words or phrases yet, keeping a realistic view will enable you to help her progress.

You can expect your child's expressive language (her use of words and word combinations) to be unclear, especially in the beginning. Her word approximations, or close attempts to say the intended word, will likely sound less clear than those of other kids her age with typical hearing, who are usually understood only by their parents at first. You'll learn to recognize your child's words because they contain a vowel and/or a consonant of the intended word and because she uses them with consistency in appropriate situations. Thus, "oo" may mean "shoe" if your child says "oo" each time someone's shoes are the focus of her communication.

Now you might be interested in learning some specific techniques for early development of listening and spoken language. See Chapter 12 for more information on Early Communication and Chapter 13 for Techniques to Encourage Talking.

References

Cole, E.B. & Flexer, C. (2011). *Children with Hearing Loss: Developing Listening and Talking — Birth to Six* (2nd ed.). San Diego, CA: Plural Publishing.

Easterbrooks, S. & Baker, S. (2002). *Language Learning in Children Who Are Deaf and Hard of Hearing: Multiple Pathways*. Boston: Allyn and Bacon, *43*.

Sharma, A., Dorman, M.F. & Kral, A. (2005). "The influence of a sensitive period on central auditory development in children with unilateral and bilateral cochlear implants." *Hearing Research*, *203*, 134–143.

Sharma, A., Dorman, M.F. & Spahr, A.J. (2002). "A sensitive period for the development of the central auditory system in children with cochlear implants: Implications for age of implantation." *Ear & Hearing*, *23*(6), 532–539.

Chapter 12

Early Communication

Now that you've ensured good access to sound with well-fit hearing devices, you may be wondering what comes next in the process of teaching your child to talk. First, know that it's an absolute myth that simply putting hearing aids or cochlear implants on your child will be enough for her to learn how to talk. That is false. A lot of time and effort will go into helping your child become a talking child. The devices and good audiologic management are really important first steps. Now comes the fun part! You will see your child make wonderful progress as you actively teach her how to communicate using spoken language. This is a huge, important, wonderful and sometimes overwhelming task; however, you *can* do it. And the reward will be immeasurable.

Communication Before True Words

Even though your child may be unable to use words, she communicates with you, right? Before she uses words, a child communicates her needs, wants and ideas. This is so important! This nonverbal communication is the foundation for language. Your child began communicating with you as soon as she was born. She tells you things by the ways in which she behaves, and you reinforce those communications by responding to her. This is a key ingredient to helping your child learn to talk.

Communicative intent is the term used to describe the various ways your child expresses meaning without using words or formal language. Before your child can learn to talk, she must have the intent to communicate. You can notice your child's communicative intent when she tries to tell you something with any of the following behaviors:

- crying
- moving
- cooing
- smiling
- pointing
- pushing
- pulling
- vocalizing
- gesturing
- making facial expressions
- using body language

Responding to Communicative Intent

You may wonder why communicative intent is important. Think of it as the foundation for your child's communication with you. Initially, she may use only communicative intent, but then you can teach her how to use words to describe what she intends to communicate. When your child shows communicative intent, you have a perfect opportunity to use spoken language to respond to that intent. This process helps your child understand what communication is all about. It helps her realize that communication is a powerful tool. It helps her develop the desire or need to communicate. It also helps her learn to respond to you by using words.

At this point, the most important thing you can do is lovingly acknowledge and appropriately respond to your child's communicative intent. Try to acknowledge every attempt she makes to communicate. This is very important. Your child needs to know that when she tries to communicate, you will respond. When your child cries, you probably already know whether the cry indicates hunger, discomfort or anger — and therefore you respond appropriately. Likewise, when your child pulls on your leg, you know it means, "Get up," "Come with me," "I need you," "Pick me up" or "Let's go."

Each of your child's attempts at communication indicates something important to her. When you respond to your child's communication, it shows her she is important to you and it encourages more communication.

We all gain power and control over our environment by communicating. Children who learn they can obtain responses from others by communicating acquire a sense of importance that leads to feelings of confidence and positive self-esteem. Communication then leads to more communication. Encourage and reinforce your child's communicative interaction whenever you can.

The best responses you can give your child are responses that ooze attention, love and affection. Interaction between you and your child helps develop your loving relationship as well as your child's communication skills. When she communicates, you respond. Try to respond with simple, complete language. This doesn't mean you should do each and every thing your child indicates; nor does it mean you should give her everything she wants. Rather, be attentive to her communication and let her know when you have understood it.

Five Categories of Communicative Intent

The intent of a child's communication, even before she uses words, can be thought of as different types of communication to convey different meanings. The five categories of communicative intent are:

- request for action
- comment
- acknowledgment or imitation

- answer
- request for information

Hearing status aside, children communicate with intent. Communicative intent can be expressed in three ways: nonverbally (with gestures or body language), vocally (with sounds that aren't words) or verbally (with words). The following are examples of the nonverbal use of each category of communicative intent.

What Your Child Does (Category)	What She Means (Intent)
Request for Action	
Child reaches out her hands.	Pick me up.
Child hands you an empty cup.	I want more.
Child pulls a cabinet door and looks at you.	Open it.
Comment	
Child points to a picture on the wall.	Look at the horse.
Child points to a spill on the floor.	I spilled right there.
Acknowledgment or Imitation	
You clap in praise and the child claps.	Hooray for me!
You wave and the child waves.	Bye-bye.
You say "No" and shake your head and the child shakes her head, too.	No.
Answer	
You ask "Where's your nose?" Child points to her nose.	Here it is.
You say "Where's Daddy?" She looks at daddy.	There's my dad.
You say "Do you want to eat?" The child walks into the kitchen.	Yes, I do.
Request for Information	
Child points at her foot missing a shoe.	Where's my other shoe?
Child points at a box, shrugs and looks at you.	What's that?
Child pulls you to the door with a questioning look.	Can we go?

Variations of Communicative Attempts

These communicative intents are all examples of *nonverbal* attempts. It's important to note that your child might also vocalize during these attempts by adding an accompanying sound or sounds to her action. These are *vocal* communicative intents. Further, your child's communicative intent might include a related word or words. Any communication using spoken words is considered *verbal*. The following example includes nonverbal, vocal and verbal variations of the same communicative intent:

Nonverbal   Child reaches out her hands.
Vocal   Child reaches out her hands and vocalizes, "Ah."
Verbal   Child reaches out her hands and says, "Up."

When your child conveys communicative intent nonverbally, you might first determine what she means and then provide her with the words to describe her intent. This helps because she cannot yet say the words by herself, yet she knows the meaning associated with her intent or idea. The more you can provide her with the language throughout her day, the sooner she will use words to communicate.

If your child already uses words or short phrases, you can easily expand on this technique. Listen carefully to what your child does say. Determine her meaning. Then say a more complete, correct phrase or sentence that expresses her idea. Your child can extend her language by imitating your expanded version. You can read more about techniques such as modeling and imitation and how to prompt language in Chapter 13.

Responses to Your Child's Communicative Intent

For a while, your child will use nonverbal actions to communicate with you. Make an attempt to figure out her meaning and respond accordingly. Always try to respond with simple, complete language. The following page includes some actions you may notice. Try to interpret — and then respond to your child's actions with spoken language. Your response can be anything from a comment to a question or even a nonverbal gesture. Every time you react to your child's communicative attempt, you're teaching her how to respond appropriately.

Pointing to, reaching for or handing you an object

- When your child points to an object, label it for her.
  - ☐ Child points to her milk.
  - ☐ "That's your milk." "Do you want some milk?" "Milk."
- When your child reaches for a toy, label the toy as you give it to her.
  - ☐ Child reaches for a ball.
  - ☐ "There's your ball." "Do you want the ball?" "Ball." "Go ahead, get the ball."
- When your child points to a person, name that person for her.
  - ☐ Child points to a person.
  - ☐ "That's Daddy." "There's Grandma." "Hi, Mommy!"
- When she hands you something, label it and comment.
  - ☐ Child hands you her sock.
  - ☐ "It's your sock." "You don't want your sock."

Tugging on you

When your child tugs or pulls on your leg or your arm, acknowledge her action by getting up and following her. Then use language to label whatever she wants or means.

- When your child tugs on you and then leads you to the door, you can say:
  - ☐ "Out." "Do you want to go out?" "Yes, we'll go outside."
- When your child pulls on you and points to an object she wants, you can say:
  - ☐ "Cookie." "The cookie." "Do you want a cookie?" "Did Mia take your cookie?"
- When your child tugs on your arm and eventually leads you to the refrigerator, you can say:
  - ☐ "Open." "Open the door." "Do you want me to open the door? ""Do you want to eat?" "Do you want a drink?" "Drink?"

Pushing something away

When your child pushes something away, it's probably because she doesn't want it. Respond to her actions by using language to confirm her protests.

- When your child pushes away her plate and appears to be finished, you can say:
  - ☐ "Are you finished?" "All done?" "You don't want any more?" "No more!"

Using Common and Natural Gestures

When your child uses a common gesture, respond by using the appropriate language and sometimes by also using the gesture yourself. This will help your child get the idea of imitation, which is an important concept for learning to talk. Here are some common gestures:

- waving hello and goodbye
- clapping for praise or joy

It's extremely beneficial for your child to learn the phrase, "I don't understand." Think of how often in your life you've said this, or something similar that makes someone clarify what was said. This is a skill she will need to know and use. You can start teaching it to her from the beginning!

- nodding head yes
- shaking head no
- moving, pointing arm/hand for "go"
- reaching out arms for "come"
- shrugging shoulders for a question
- covering face/head for peek-a-boo
- meaningful looks
- When your child scowls or makes a face at a food item, you can say:
  - "Yucky!" "Is that yucky?" "You don't want that?" "Oooo, is that awful?" "No more?"
- When your child raises her eyebrows and shrugs her shoulders, you can say:
  - "Where's your ball?" "It's all gone." "Let's look for the ball."
  - "What's in that box?" "I don't know." "Let's open it."

Misinterpreting Intent

Despite your best efforts, there may be times when you may feel like you said the wrong thing, and you're unable to figure out what your child means. You might attempt to respond to her communication, but she might get frustrated and indicate you haven't figured out her intent. Keep trying — at least for a few moments. This indicates you want to understand her and will give it your best effort. You can say "This one?" "Is this what you want?" "Do you want the (object)?" "No?" "No, not the (object)?"

If you can't figure out your child's intention, it's important to tell her. When this happens, *avoid* nodding and smiling as if you understood. Your child will know by your facial expression, your body language and your response whether or not she has been understood. After a reasonable effort, you might need to give up. Use a look and manner that goes along with your words, saying something like, "I'm sorry. I don't understand." This helps build an honest relationship and encourages your child to try again the next time. Once you've done this, you can try using distraction to change the scene.

In general, communicating and interacting are more important than complying with every wish or demand. Your job is to reassure your child that you want to communicate with her and that you will put effort into trying to understand her. At times, you need to indicate that you have understood her, but you can't always do or give her what she wants.

Sometimes this communicative effort just requires being in tune with your child. Other times, it may feel like you have to be a mind reader! Communicating with your child with hearing loss may leave you feeling frustrated at times. However, when you're able to succeed in communication, and your child becomes a talking child, the rewards are infinite!

Auditory Feedback Loop

Auditory feedback is the information a person gets from listening to herself produce sounds. It occurs any time a child listens to the sounds she makes. If a baby likes what she hears when she babbles, she'll continue to make more noises. A child makes noises, hears her own voice, likes the sounds she hears, then makes more and different noises. Initially, a child with hearing loss may babble; but without auditory feedback (the ability to hear herself) she may not be motivated to continue experimenting. When a child with hearing loss has quality access to sound, she can hear herself. Moreover, quality access to sound allows her to eventually correct her own vocalizations to make them sound right. This is a cycle. She vocalizes and listens to herself, then makes changes in her next vocalization. This is called the **auditory feedback loop.**

Parents can encourage the auditory feedback process by playing games that excite their children into discovering their own voices. This is a very important step in the long road to becoming a talking child.

To encourage development of the auditory feedback loop, consider the following:

- Help your child notice, then produce, sounds with toys or rattles.
  - Young children can receive auditory information from toys in addition to their own vocalizations. If you shake a rattle then hand it to your baby, you're allowing her to discover this noise-making capability by getting that auditory information from the toy. As she discovers the power of her actions, she will realize that shaking the rattle makes sound happen. You may want to play a short turn-taking game in which you shake the rattle, give it to her for a turn, then take it back and show her

Did you know that, regardless of their hearing status, all children babble? Babbling is an important stage of speech and spoken language development because it leads to more intricate speech and spoken language skills. Babies as young as 4 to 6 months old begin changing their coos and gurgles into babble sounds like "bababa," "mamama" and "dadada." However, if a child can't hear herself make those sounds, the excitement will likely fade — and so will the babbling. Children with typical hearing continue to babble because they receive auditory feedback how it works again. Be sure to leave short periods of not-shaking in between so your child can start to recognize the presence and absence of sound.

- Imitate your child's vocalizations when they occur naturally.
  - □ For example, if your baby is having tummy time and starts cooing, get down on her level, make eye contact and say "I hear you. Ah, oo, ah, oo." Then provide a bit of wait time by remaining quiet but maintaining eye contact. See if she fills the silence with more cooing. If so, then she's getting it. If not, try making the cooing noises again to entice her into this game of give and take.
- Take turns with the same imitation game, but change up your vocalization to keep it interesting.
  - □ For example, your child may say "Ma, ma, ma, ma." Then, on your turn, try to say something slightly different, such as "Da, da, da, da." See if she notices the change in your vocalizations. You may observe just by her facial expression that she recognizes the difference, or she may even change her own vocalization on her turn. Remember, it's less important that she produces the exact same "da, da, da, da" sound you did, but more important that she begins to tune into the fact that you have the power to change your voice — and so does she!
- Keep your voice interesting!
  - □ Sing songs, read books with a dramatic voice and change the volume of your voice (louder and softer talking) to continue to engage your child. Read stories to her with excitement and varying voices for each character. Respond to your child when she changes her voice, too. You could say "My, my. I hear your big loud squealing voice!" or "Are you telling me a story? You have so much to say!"

Helping Your Child Localize Sound

A child is able to **localize** sound if she can hear the sound, know where it came from and have an idea about how far away it occurred. This is an important skill. It takes practice to learn where sounds come from. First, a child looks around, searching for the sound. Children sometimes look toward their parents when they can't find the source. Parents can help by pointing out important sounds as they occur.

When they have access to sound at both ears, children have an easier time localizing sounds. Children with unilateral hearing loss may have more difficulty learning to localize. People with typical hearing at both ears can localize because sound arrives at one ear a microsecond before it gets to the other ear. The sophisticated brain uses that split-second difference to recognize which direction the sound is coming from. When a child doesn't have the benefit of two ears, it's more difficult to localize.

- To help your child begin to localize sounds, think about the sounds that occur in everyday life and point out environmental sounds as they occur.
    - If the phone rings, before you answer it, draw your child's attention to the sound (so she can look in the appropriate direction to find the source) and point out the ringing phone. Say something like, "I hear the phone. Here it is!"— all before answering the call. Think about using this trick when the dog barks ("I hear the dog. Where are you, doggy?") or the microwave beeps ("Listen. Beep, beep. I'm going to open the door.").
- Stage opportunities to listen to sounds and voices that come from varying directions.
    - Activate noisemaking toys just out of your child's view. This could be a rattle under a blanket. Or it could be something as simple as two family members with two different noise-producing toys positioned in different parts of the room. If your child is sitting on the floor engaged with a toy, try activating one noise-maker and see if she alerts to the sound. Don't forget to acknowledge her recognition of the sound and then show her the source. Have the other family member activate her toy next and see if your child searches for this different sound. If your child decides to play along with your "hide and seek" sound game, give plenty of positive feedback.
    - Have a family member call you from the next room. Help your child notice the voice. Then scoop her up and take her with you as you hunt down the person calling your name. "I hear Daddy. Where is Daddy?" (Walk to Dad.) "Oh, there you are!" If your child has had enough listening experience to recognize her own name, play this game and have different family members call her by name. Be sure to see if she searches for the voice, then help her locate the person calling her. Reward her for her search with a big hug!

Creating Joint Attention

When a child and a caregiver share an experience, it's known as **joint attention**. Shared experiences occur when both the child and caregiver are looking at, listening to and/or paying attention to the same thing. This is really an important skill for learning to listen and talk, but before children are able to pay attention to a sound through joint attention, they develop joint attention through eye contact. Mothers and babies begin developing joint attention during nursing or bottle feeding — times when they have an excellent opportunity for face-to-face contact. Playing with toys or sharing books are other great opportunities for joint attention. A caregiver can encourage joint attention by demonstrating for the child where to look or by saying things like "Look!" and gently pointing or positioning her in the right direction. Exciting animated toys, bubbles and entertaining family members can all be great motivators to encourage joint attention in a practical way that is interesting to young children.

Promoting Turn-Taking Skills

When a caregiver and a child "talk" to one another, either with true words or even nonsense syllables, they're engaging in conversational **turn-taking**. If a child vocalizes, and the parent imitates the vocalization or smiles back, the parent has encouraged the child to use her voice. Then the child vocalizes again and the parent takes another turn. This back and forth is a precursor to adult conversation in which each partner shares information, asks questions and makes comments.

How is this exchange different if the child has a hearing loss? Sometimes when parents find out their child can't hear (before the child has access to sound with hearing devices), they may stop engaging in this back and forth interaction with their child. At this point, a common question from parents is, "If my child can't hear me, why should I keep talking?" The truth is that the child needs to be engaged in your talking interactions! This will have both of you primed and ready for promoting turn-taking when your child gains access to sound with her new hearing devices.

Before your child is able to take turns with her voice, you might observe her turn-taking skills in a nonverbal manner. This nonverbal turn-taking is often in the form of motor activity such as rolling a ball back and forth. Children who are unable to demonstrate this back and forth interaction with nonverbal motor activities (and who are without physical developmental delays) are unlikely to engage in vocal turn-taking. Just as caregivers can encourage turn-taking through vocalization, they can encourage turn-taking through play with common toys or household objects.

What does nonverbal turn-taking look like? If you can say to yourself, "My turn, your turn, my turn, your turn," then it's likely a fine opportunity to practice taking turns. Here are just a few example activities:

- rolling a ball back and forth
- beating a drum
- hitting a spoon on the highchair tray
- stacking blocks on a tower

You can also teach your child about turn-taking by developing an expectant look. You can make up your own look and do it however you'd like, as long as it's what you consistently use to let your child know you're expecting something of her. You can just look her in the eye and wait, raise your eyebrows, lean toward her, then lean in a little more. Give this expectant look when it's her turn to vocalize.

It's good to pay attention to and encourage both nonverbal responses and vocal responses that aren't yet words. These are your child's first efforts to communicate and they can be shaped into talk! For nonverbal responses, give your child the words for what she meant to convey. If she holds up her untied shoe, you might say "Tie the shoe" as you tie it. If she vocalizes "oo" after you've said "Do you want juice?" nod and smile and say "Juice!" or "I want juice." The process might go like this:

- Child says "oo."
- You say "Juice. Do you want juice?"
- You use your expectant look waiting for your child to respond to your question.
- Child says "oo" or "oos" or simply nods her head.
- (Hooray! She took a turn!)
- You encourage your child's response and the fact that she took her turn. You say "Yes! Good for you. You want juice. Here's your juice. Let's pour it in the cup. . . ."

Encouraging Vocalizations

If your child is paying attention to you but not vocalizing during these types of interactions, you can try to encourage vocalizations in some other ways. At any time, you can imitate random vocalizations she makes and try to get her to repeat after you. Try to do this as much as possible, even if she doesn't vocalize or imitate again right then. You can also hold your child on your lap and just babble, talk baby talk or talk about anything at all. Leave pauses for her turn and look at her expectantly. After a moment if she's silent, talk again. If she vocalizes, praise her with your smile, touch, clapping hands and another vocalization. Many young children will vocalize into a toy telephone (or a real one) or a toy microphone because they've seen adults use these items. Try holding the phone or microphone as you talk. Then pass it to your child. Pause and let her try. Praise her when she does. These activities will help your child learn that talking involves using our voices, pausing and taking turns.

Improving Vocalizations

Once your child begins to vocalize on her own and to imitate your vocalizations, you'll notice that she might sound different. Her attempts to use correct speech will be "off" at first. This is very normal! In fact all children, whether they have typical or atypical hearing, produce vocalizations that don't sound quite right. That is an important part of the process of learning to talk.

If you notice your child's vocalizations aren't quite right, try to help her match them to yours. First, you'll have to figure out what she means, then model that word. Look at her expectantly to encourage her to say what you said. This is imitation. It's an important step to learning in general, but also to learning how to talk.

In the beginning, praise your child even if her vocalization isn't close to your modeled word. As you continue doing this, you might notice she changes her vocalizations to more closely resemble yours. Remember not to push too hard. You want your child to be eager and willing to do this, not unsure and unwilling.

Many young children with hearing loss first produce just the vowel in a word (such as "oo" for shoe or "uh" for up) or perhaps just the beginning consonant (such as "buh" for ball or "mmm" for more). Accept these efforts. They are approximations, which means they are close to or approximate the intended word. Temporarily withholding a desired object can entice some children to try to imitate your model. Feel free to try this and see how your child responds. Your encouragement will help her know you're on her side!

Early Communicators Become Talking Children

When your child has access to sound with well-fit hearing devices, she needs you to recognize and respond to her early communication attempts. Remember, sometimes these occur without words, via eye gaze or gesture. Sometimes these early communication attempts are made to request, protest, comment or imitate — or merely for the purpose of entertainment.

Do your best to acknowledge your child's intentions, but the reality is that adults often misinterpret children's earliest communication attempts. That's just fine. Stay focused on the greater goal of raising a talking child. Know that every time you engage your child and respond to her attempts at engaging you, you are laying groundwork for more complex communication. Keep reading for more suggestions of ways to support your early communicator as she grows into a talking child.

Chapter 13

Techniques to Encourage Talking

One of the most important ingredients for your child learning to listen and talk is the talk you provide to your child. Listening to you talk enables her to learn a lot about verbal communication. Your child will learn that talk is interesting and informative and that it involves at least two people.

As parents or caregivers, you will want to learn all you can about how to get and keep your child's attention and how to build listening and understanding. This will help your child learn to talk. You will want to respond to and reinforce your child's communication, even when it is baby talk. The more you listen to and talk with your child and the more your child listens to you, the sooner and better she will talk.

This chapter contains 15 techniques you can use to encourage your child to talk. These techniques may seem overwhelming at first. Feel free to try them at your own pace. If the most you can focus on right now is one technique, then do that. (Start with Technique #1.) Gradually, you can add more techniques. The more you try them, the more comfortable you'll feel using them.

Technique #1: Continue full-time use of hearing devices (during all waking hours).

Technique #2: Create a good listening environment.

Technique #3: Create a language-rich environment.

Technique #4: Recognize and respond to communication attempts.

Technique #5: Acknowledge and understand the purpose of gestures.

Technique #6: Acknowledge and understand the importance of situational cues.

Technique #7: Talk about things important to your child.

Technique #8: Vary the types of talk; use naming and labeling, self-talk and parallel talk.

Technique #9: Avoid common traps.

Technique #10: Use modeling and imitation.

Technique #11: Prompt your child to use language.

Technique #12: Listen for and promote spontaneous language.

Technique #13: Use acoustic highlighting.

Technique #14: Understand typical communication.

Technique #15: Set expectations for communication.

Technique #1: Continue Full-Time Use of Hearing Devices (During All Waking Hours)

Whew! Accomplishing full-time use of hearing devices probably took a lot of work. You and your child deserve praise. Take a bow! Whether you already had accomplished this or just recently did so following this guide, now you can move forward toward your goal of helping your child learn to listen and talk. (For more information on achieving full-time use of hearing devices, turn to Chapter 7, 8 or 9.)

Keep up the device use during all waking hours, every single day. The more your child hears the sounds of everyday life, the more you will be preparing her to eventually talk. You wouldn't want to deprive your child of even a few minutes of listening time. All the time she spends listening will help her learn to understand what those sounds mean. She needs this to become a talking child.

Technique #2: Create a Good Listening Environment

A good listening environment is essential for children with hearing loss who have just begun the full-time use of hearing devices. Take the following steps to create a good listening environment:

■ **Control background noise.**

As a child first begins to perceive the sounds around her, she benefits from a whole lot of rich language from you and a limited amount of background noise. You may be wondering why. Some parents wonder, "If my child now has access to sound, why can't she listen in noise just like any other child?" The simple answer is that when your child first has good access to sound, she has not yet developed the ability to filter useful information (like talk) from noise in the environment. As her skills increase, she will begin to distinguish between important talk and background noise.

Many people with typical hearing don't usually notice some sources of noise that can be problematic for new listeners. For example, you might not notice the sound of the dishwasher running, but your child will notice this when she is a new hearing device user. Other sources of background noise include television, radio, computers, fans, heating/cooling systems and many more. Although these are all common and necessary at some point during the day, you might choose specific times to use them so you can improve the listening environment for your child. You might run the dishwasher, watch TV or play computer games after your child has gone to bed for the night. It's especially helpful to avoid these noise-producing items if possible during language, reading and listening activities with your child.

■ **Get down and get close.**

When your child first begins listening with her hearing devices, place yourself strategically so she can most easily hear your voice. It's best to be at the same level as your child — sitting or lying next to each other on the floor, sitting at a table together or having her sit on your lap. That way, you're talking at the level of her hearing devices.

■ **Focus on the everyday sounds in your life.**

At this point, many parents are tempted to "test" their child by making loud noises and seeing if she turns to look. Instead of testing her, try to observe her responses to typical sounds such as the phone ringing, the water running, the doorbell ringing, the dog barking, the microwave beeping, the toilet flushing and, most importantly, talking. You may notice she turns to look at you when she hears a sound. Or she may turn to find where that sound is coming from. She even may go to the source of the sound. With your observations and some time, your pediatric audiologist should be able to give you some more information about what your child might be hearing.

Technique #3: Create a Language-Rich Environment

One of the most effective techniques for helping your child learn to listen and talk is to create an environment in which your child is bathed in language. Living and growing in a language-rich environment is of utmost importance. You're probably wondering exactly how to create such an environment for your child. The most effective way is to talk to her often.

Why You Should Talk to Your Child

Many parents think, "Why should I talk to my child if she can't hear me very well? What good will talking to her do?" It's not a surprising question. Many people don't realize the importance of talking to children with hearing loss. However, all children learn to talk by being talked to, and your child needs to be talked to as well. In fact, to learn to talk, children with hearing loss need to be talked to more than children with typical hearing do. Even most children with profound hearing loss who use hearing devices can at least hear voices and variations in volume, rhythm and intonation of speech. No matter what her level of hearing loss, your child must be exposed to lots of talking in order to learn to talk herself.

No matter what, children with hearing loss miss out on important listening time. Even children who are diagnosed and achieve full-time hearing device use really early in life miss some amount of listening. Most importantly, they miss thousands of language-based interactions. Think about all the talking that goes on in your home or during outings just in one day. That's a lot of language! Talking a lot to your child now will help make up for some of that missed time.

When to Talk to Your Child

Talk to your child whenever you have an opportunity. Many times throughout the day lend themselves to stimulating your child with language. At other times, you may want to say only a few words or sentences. Use "love talk" often to express your feelings for her. Take advantage of your daily routine. Use the activities in your day to feed language into your child. Talk to your child as you play with her. Talk to your child as you do your chores or carry out your daily routine nearby. Talk to your child as you dress or undress her. Take advantage of every opportunity you have to talk to your child. Talk when you have your child's attention. It's a good idea to label people, objects and actions in your child's environment. Do so in meaningful situations as often as you can.

Each of the daily activities below provides opportunities to help your child by talking to her in simple words, phrases and sentences with an expressive voice.

- wake-up time/getting out of bed
- putting hearing devices on
- getting dressed and undressed
- preparing meals
- eating meals
- setting or clearing the table
- taking care of pets
- washing dishes
- playing together
- bathing and brushing teeth
- doing the laundry
- cleaning the house
- exploring the outdoors
- going to the grocery store and other places visited regularly
- running errands
- visiting friends and family
- going to bed/night-time routine
- taking hearing devices off

Try to make each of these activities interesting for your child. This will make it easier for you to keep her attention. Entice her so she is eager to listen, watch you and participate. You can do this by including her in the action of the activity and by creating some fun.

How to Talk to Your Child

Natural, rich, expressive language is interesting, grammatically accurate and varied in its structure and intonation. Try to make your talk . . .

■ **Rich but redundant**

Use natural, rich language that says a lot, but with just a few words. You can use this language during the various routines and play activities during your day. It's important that the language you use with your child both fits the situation and is very expressive. In addition, use repetition as much as possible. Redundancy gives your child the chance to hear all of that great language multiple times within context. Your daily use of language that is rich, yet redundant helps your child learn to listen and talk.

■ **Simple and easily understood**

Sometimes, really complicated talk will make your child think that since she doesn't understand, she might as well not even listen. The simpler the talk you use, the more likely she will understand and gain some meaning from it. Talking to her simply will help her realize that talk really is worth listening to. In the beginning, talk in short, simple phrases and sentences. Remember that the intonation of your voice is important. Words and sentences spoken with expression and varying intonation may be more easily heard and are more interesting for your child than the same words and sentences said in a monotone. Be sure to include simple, single words such as the names of people, objects and actions. Also include words that describe things. Talk about the objects you're touching or holding. Talk about the toys and other things in which your child shows an interest. Talk about what you're doing, while you're doing it. You don't need to say a lot. Just acknowledge your child's interest in what's happening by stopping for a minute to say a few relevant words, a short phrase or a simple sentence.

■ **Detailed (for some part of the day)**

This may seem contradictory, but at least for some part of the day, take some time to use detailed language that is truly directed toward your child. Although some children with hearing loss need language to be simple and easy to understand for much of the day, they also need some exposure to more complex and detailed language. Many parents get caught in the trap of constantly simplifying language, so their children never have a chance to listen to the complicated and varied language to which babies with typical hearing are exposed. Think about talking to an infant with typical hearing. In a very soothing voice, we might say something like: "Oh my goodness! I hear you crying! Are you hungry? I bet you are because it's been a while since you last ate. My, my! We better give you some milk so you feel better. There you go. Oh, is that better? I bet your tummy feels so much better now."

Now, think about this: We freely and easily go on and on saying things like this to a teensy person whom we would never expect to say anything in response. We even ask questions and then answer them ourselves. It seems silly! Yet we, as humans, are programmed to do just that. We provide incredibly rich, detailed language to infants, babies and children even though we know they might not understand. This is our natural way of teaching our language. By using language above the child's ability to understand, we essentially teach the language. Babies learn what this all means by hearing the language over and over and by making sense of the meaning within the context of various situations. Babies with hearing loss need this exposure so they, too, can be challenged to make sense of the rather complicated language used in the world around them.

▪ Animated, expressive and dramatic talk

Think of how much more fun it is to listen to someone who is animated and expressive compared to someone who is monotone and boring. Your child picks up on this, too. Spice up your talk as if you were a performer. Be dramatic! The more expressive you can be while maintaining a natural style of talk, the more your child will pay attention to what you say.

▪ Repetitive use of vocabulary

Along with richness and repetition of all the language you use, repetition of vocabulary is particularly important. The word *vocabulary* refers to the single words used to label people, objects, actions and qualities, as well as words used as exclamations. Within the rich language you use, try to repeat simple vocabulary again and again from activity to activity. This kind of repetition helps your child discover the meaning of the repeated words as you use them in various routines and play activities throughout the day, week and month. This leads to your child using the words — first with your encouragement and later on her own.

Especially for young children who are not yet talking much, think about how you can use the same labels for similar items from one activity to another. Using "baby" as a label for a doll, rather than "doll" or "Susie," gives you a word that can be used more and in more situations. You can call your own baby "baby" and call the doll "baby," and you can use the word *baby* to refer to any baby you see around you or in books. This adds redundancy to the rich language used in varied activities.

▪ Varied language patterns

Think about how interesting and diverse language can be. We would be bored with language if it always had the same patterns. Can you imagine? The dog walks. The car goes. Daddy waves. Mommy talks. Cows moo. Cats meow. Birds fly. Telephones ring. Babies tune out.

Even with short phrases and sentences, you can use many different patterns. Sometimes the main or key word is at the beginning of the phrase; sometimes it's at the end. Occasionally it's in the middle. Sometimes there is an exclamation word! Sometimes a word is repeated over and over several times. Sometimes you might vary the pitch of your voice from low to high or high to low. You might also vary the volume of your language. These variations help ensure that your child will stay interested in your talk.

Although you don't have to be too elaborate, try to avoid constant repetition of just one or two patterns as in the examples in the paragraph above.

Here are some examples of varying patterns:

Use short phrases and repeated labels.
"That's your truck . . . truck. Push the truck. Push, push, push."

Use enthusiasm in your tone as you say things.
"Wow! It's a very big balloon!"

Narrate your child's day by describing her actions.
"You're taking your sock off. Pull your sock off. There's your sock! Pee-Yew! That's a stinky sock!"

Natural and accurate

One of the easiest traps for talking to a child with hearing loss is to talk like a robot. People do this in an attempt to provide a clearer message, but really, doing this does your child a disservice. It's important to teach your child how to listen to natural language and talk. If you talk like a robot, you're teaching her to understand robot talk, but most people don't talk like robots. People usually talk in a natural, flowing, quick and sometimes messy way. It's normal for us to say something like this:

"You wanna goda Gramma's?"

It's not natural at all to say it in a robotic tone like this:

"Do . . . you . . . want . . . to . . . go . . . to . . . Grand . . . ma's?"

Try to make a conscious effort to talk in a natural way. Sometimes people automatically make their talk unnatural by slowing it down. It's a good idea to slow down your talk for some parts of the day. But even when your talk is slow, it should be natural. It certainly is possible to have slow talk that is still natural-sounding. Practice saying "You wanna goda Gramma's?" really slowly. If you sound robotic in any way, then try again with a more natural flow. It may take some practice, but it will be well worth it!

In addition to using a natural flow in your talk, also be sure to use words correctly. Be sure to use articles such as *a, an* and *the*. Also avoid using a word when it just doesn't fit your meaning. It's fine to call a doll a baby and a sandal a shoe, but it's not sensible to call a balloon a ball. Remember to use accurate descriptions and labels when you talk.

Remember . . .

Even though it may be tempting to do otherwise, try to call hearing devices by their real names. Hearing devices are not ears. It's important to refer to your child's ears as "ears" and to her devices by their real names. If you've called them "ears" in the past, that's okay! You can soon begin to refer to your child's devices by their real names and help her to do that too.

What to Expect from Your Child

Attention! Your first task is to get your child to pay attention to you when you're talking. In the beginning, you may get only a quick glance or some small clue that she is listening. When you're animated and use lively facial expressions, your child may be motivated to pay attention to you. Showing her what you're talking about, using varying intonation and simple, natural gestures are other ways of enticing her to pay attention to you.

Once your child is interested in paying attention to you as you speak, you can expect her to do so for short periods as you are talking. Your child may only briefly pay attention and may not vocalize or imitate you for a long time, but remember to leave pauses for her turn. She can't take a turn if you don't pause. Once your child is consistently vocalizing, expect some vocalization as you are interacting with her. As your child begins to imitate and use words, expect her to imitate your words or attempt to produce words on her own. Your attention, your spoken response — or your smile, a nod or a pat on the shoulder — reinforces your child. You also can clap your hands and shout "Hooray" or "Yaaah!" After all, talking is really something to be excited about!

Leave Time for Taking Turns

Remember that even though you're doing a lot of talking, another important talker is your child! Talking is a two-way street. Some of the communication between you should represent your ideas. Some of the communication should represent your child's ideas. Avoid monologues. Too much talk at too high a level with too little attention from your child discourages the kind of attention and interaction you want to build. A few expressive words, phrases and sentences, spoken in such a way that your child attends to them, would be much better than dozens of phrases and sentences that are mostly ignored.

Even if your child is just learning to attend and not yet really taking a turn, be sure to pause after you speak, to leave space in time for her turn. This helps get across the idea that talking together is a two-way street. You also can use an expectant look during your pauses to help her get the idea you're expecting a response from her. This process — talking, pausing, giving an expectant look — helps your child understand all about how communication works. One of these days, she'll be ready to take a turn, too.

Value the Talk of Other Caregivers

Some children will spend most of their waking hours with mom or dad. Others will spend time with other caregivers during the day. You may be able to talk to your child during the day, but perhaps not all hours of the day. Remember, the talk of other adults helping you care for your child is very important, too. You might consider selecting caregivers willing and able to provide a language-rich environment. As you learn to communicate with your child, help others learn to do so, too. This will allow your child to benefit from mommy

This really can feel like hard work! Lean back, take a deep breath and pat yourself on the back. Your child might not be able to reinforce you yet with good attention, vocalizations or turn-taking. Time, along with your continued effort, will change this. Hang in there! You will know it was worth it when your child starts to talk.

talk and daddy talk and from talk with a variety of caring communication partners. Brothers, sisters and grandparents will want to share in the fun! If you have friends and neighbors who will join in, by all means teach them how they can help. Remind them of your goal to have a talking child and encourage their efforts. Having a supportive team helping you work toward your goal can make all the difference in the world.

Technique #4: Recognize and Respond to Communication Attempts

Your child will learn the usefulness and importance of communication if you demonstrate that it works! The first successful point of any communication attempt is recognition. If you consistently recognize your child when she is telling you something by her behavior or attempts at talking, she will learn that communication really does work.

After recognizing your child's attempts to communicate, the next step is to respond. That doesn't necessarily mean your child gets everything she wants. It just means you give a response and reinforce the effectiveness of her communication attempt.

Responding to Your Child's Communication Attempts

Here are two possible scenarios.

Scenario 1: Ignoring a communication attempt

A parent is talking with another adult about plans for the weekend. The child runs over and calls, "Mommy, Mommy!" The mother continues her conversation. The child, not having received a response when requesting one, increases her attempts to get her mother's attention by pulling on her shirt-tail and tapping her leg. Still she receives no response from the mother. Now the little girl is crawling between her mother's legs, still not receiving a response. Soon the child stands up and hits the mother! The mother stops her conversation and says "Please don't hit Mommy. What do you need?"

What has the child learned from this interaction? That using her words doesn't elicit the desired response from her mother. Instead, hitting gets a communicative response. Had the mother responded to her child when she initially called out, she may have averted this escalated situation.

Scenario 2: Recognizing and responding to a communication attempt

A parent is talking with another adult about plans for the weekend. The child runs over and calls "Mommy, Mommy!" The mother turns to the child and says "One minute. Mommy's talking."

In this scenario, the child makes a communication attempt, the mother recognizes the attempt and responds. What has the child learned from this experience? That using her words elicits a response from her mother. The child might not necessarily like that particular response, but the response appropriately acknowledges her communication attempt.

The difference between these scenarios is obvious. You should know that any positive response to your child's communicative attempts is fantastic! Reinforce her for paying attention to you as you talk. Reinforce her for vocalizing, even when no intelligible words are spoken. Reinforce her when she attempts to imitate what you've said. Reinforce her when she attempts to produce a word on her own.

Taking Turns

It's important for your child to learn that talking involves taking turns. Turn-taking during talking might look like this for you:

Mommy:	talks and pauses for the child's turn
Child:	may or may not take a turn
Mommy:	talks again

Your conversation might continue in this same way until it's ended. Remember that it's important to pause and use an expectant look even if your child has not responded to this in the past. Pausing indicates you're expecting something from your child and that you're creating a space in time for her response. If your child does not respond, rest assured that, one of these times, as you pause for her turn, she will vocalize or say something that will generate absolute joy in your heart.

In addition to pausing while turn-taking, it's also important for you to respond to your child's vocalizations, especially when you know what she means. If you do know, say what comes naturally, for example, "Oh, you want me to open the box. I'll open it." If you don't know your child's meaning, try to determine it by asking and showing her various things you think she means.

If she is just vocalizing and has nothing in particular to convey, you can still smile and praise her by responding, "I hear you talking. That's good talking." Even if she doesn't understand the words, she'll respond to the positive tone of your voice and your smiling facial expression. Remember, any effort your child makes at communicating with you or with others deserves a lot of attention and praise!

Technique #5: Acknowledge and Understand the Purpose of Gestures

Gesture communication is a term used to describe a talker's use of natural movements of the body, face and hands to communicate. Many people use gesture communication to accompany their talk. They do this to add expression, interest, emphasis or clarification to what they're saying. Early on, your child may be especially attentive to gestures because they help her understand spoken language.

Remember that for your child the emphasis should be on listening and talking. Even so, children with typical hearing (as well as children with hearing loss) may tune in to common gestures. Here are some very common and natural gestures:

- waving "hi" or "bye-bye"
- moving your hand toward you to indicate "Come here" or "Come on"
- shrugging your shoulders to indicate "I don't know"
- widening your eyes, giving a serious look and leaning forward to indicate "I mean it"
- nodding as you say "Yes" or shaking your head back and forth as you say "No"
- giving a thumbs up to indicate "Great job," "All is well" or "That's okay"

Communicating Using Gestures

For some children, gestures provide beginning attention to communication. If this is true for your child, you will want to determine that she also is attentive to talk, not just to gestures. Also, your young child may imitate gestures, such as waving "hi" or "bye-bye," then get the idea of imitating the spoken words. Praise imitation!

Usually, some gestures develop before the use of spoken language, regardless of a child's hearing ability. It's a good idea to tune in to your child's gestures so you understand her ideas. Then you can provide the words to convey your child's intended meaning.

Some early developing gestures are:

- nodding the head "yes" or shaking the head "no"
- pointing to people or objects
- reaching the arms out to be picked up
- pushing away something that is not wanted

Think about the words you would use to give meaning to the examples above. Be sure to emphasize the talk.

Technique #6: Acknowledge and Understand the Importance of Situational Cues

Situational cues help an observer understand what's happening. It's common for all of us, regardless of hearing ability, to use situational cues to determine meaning. Usually, situational cues are accompanied by spoken language, and the two together help communicators understand one another. Your child may attend to these situational cues to help her understand spoken communication. This is a great start! Here are some examples of common situational cues:

Situational Cue
You hand her a wadded-up piece of paper.
You walk to the front door expectantly.
You set the table for dinner.

Observe your child to see if she attends to situational cues. You will know she does if she seems to understand what will happen or what to do based on the cues. Here are some examples of situational cues and possible behaviors that indicate your child understands:

Situational Cue	Your Child's Behavior
You hand her a wadded-up piece of paper.	She goes to the trash can and throws it away.
You walk to the front door expectantly.	She says "Dada!"
You set the table for dinner.	She climbs up in her chair.

Combining Talk and Situational Cues

Once you see that your child is using situational cues to help her understand, observe whether she attends to your talk. It's certainly okay for her to use cues to assist in understanding. However, the cues should occur simultaneously with the appropriate talk that goes with the situation. Learning to understand the talk related to the situation is key to your child's learning how to listen and talk. Using the situational cues listed previously, here are some examples of the talk you can use:

Situational Cue	Talk	Your Child's Behavior
You hand her a wadded-up piece of paper.	"Throw it away." or "Put it in the trash can."	She goes to the trash can and throws it away.
You walk to the front door expectantly.	"Daddy's home!" or "I think I hear Daddy's car."	She says "Dada!"
You set the table for dinner.	"Time for dinner." or "Are you ready to eat?"	She climbs up in her chair.

Could Your Child Be Overly Reliant on Gestures or Situational Cues?

Since you want your child to listen and talk, you must emphasize the listening and the talking! If gestures or situational cues seem to be your child's focus, try providing simple talk without either. Then, if she doesn't understand, give the spoken message again with the situational cue or the natural gesture. Follow this up with only the spoken message again. Thus, your child hears the same message repeated all three times and only once with a gesture or cue. This concept is called the **auditory sandwich**. The auditory-only cue with no visual support (the bread) surrounds the combined auditory cue and visual cue (the meat, cheese and veggies). When put together, you end up with an auditory-only cue, then auditory plus visual cues and, finally, an auditory-only cue. This allows your child to hear the spoken message three times, with a little extra visual support the second time.

Technique #7: Talk About Things Important to Your Child

Caregiving

There's no better time to talk to your child than when you're taking care of her. Your loving care is of great importance. You have her undivided attention and she has yours. When you're doing things for your child, like feeding, dressing or bathing her, you're close to her, making your voice easier to hear. Talk to your child about what you're doing as you care for her. Although she may not understand you at first, if you frequently repeat the same words, phrases and sentences, eventually these words will have meaning to her.

The Here and Now

Talk to your child about the here and now. Talk to her about things she can see. Talk about what's happening at that moment. Talk to her about what you're doing with her. This helps her begin to make sense of your talk. In the beginning, avoid talking about things that are in another room or things she cannot see. For example, talk about the cereal, milk, bowl and spoon while eating breakfast together, but not about how you will be going to Grandma's after you take a bath and eat lunch. Eventually, you'll work up to talking about more abstract things, but at the beginning, try to stick to what's happening at that moment.

Follow Your Child's Lead

Let your child's interests guide your talk. Naming clothing as you dress her is a great idea, but she may be more interested in the hole in the sock or the picture of the dog on the shirt. Talk to your child about her ideas. Give her the language for what she wants to say. Your pauses will give her a chance to let you know what interests her.

Find the Right Balance

Bathe your child in language, but don't drown her. Some talkers make the mistake of barely talking to a child with hearing loss at all. Others make the mistake of rattling on and on without the child's attention. Minimal talk on your part won't lead to a talking child. Constant talk quickly can become meaningless and boring, and your child may tune you out. Sometimes, it's easier to ask your child's other parent (or another caring observer) if you're talking too little or too much, rather than trying to assess this yourself. Your early interventionist can help coach you, too.

Technique #8: Vary the Types of Talk — Use Naming and Labeling, Self-Talk and Parallel Talk

To keep your talk interesting and robust, consider varying the types of talk you use. Here are some possibilities:

- name or label objects and actions in a variety of situations
- use self-talk to describe your actions as they occur
- use parallel talk by describing your child's actions as they occur

For these different types of talk, it's important first to notice that you and your child are both focused on what you're talking about. Language exposure using naming, labeling, self-talk or parallel talk is effective only if your child is paying attention to what you're talking about. This joint attention ensures that your talk is related to what the child is seeing or thinking about.

Naming and Labeling

Naming and **labeling** are done by stating the word for an object, action or descriptor. Naming and labeling can be used to expose your child to new words or to teach a different word for an object, action or descriptor she already knows. Think of how many words we use each day that can be replaced with other, more descriptive vocabulary. Young children with hearing loss begin by learning only one basic word they may use for lots of things, but don't forget to teach them all the other words with related meanings. For example, your child might understand the word "big." So now it's time for her to learn lots of other related words like "large," "huge," "gigantic," "giant," "humongous" and even "ginormous." It's important to use these words in your talk after you know your child understands the meaning of the word "big." She will use situational and context clues to learn these new words based on her understanding of the word "big."

Vocabulary Words Young Children Might Know	Other Labels
Kleenex	tissue
puppy	dog, doggie, canine, beagle
kiss	smooch, peck, sugar
run	jog, trot, hustle, sprint, race
candy	Skittle, M&M, chocolate, taffy, gum, lollipop, Jolly Rancher
owie	boo-boo, scrape, cut, blister, scratch, bruise, wound
mama	girl, lady, teacher, woman

Self-Talk

You might try to use self-talk to encourage your child to talk. **Self-talk** is the act of describing your own actions. As you prepare a meal, you can say "I'm looking at the recipe. What do I need next? The milk. I can pour the milk in the bowl. Now I have to stir and stir." This sort of self-talk is valuable only if the child is interested in what you're doing. The talk must match the thought so the correct meaning is established in the child's mind. Use self-talk when you're engaged in an activity with your child so you can be sure her interests match your talk.

Parallel Talk

You can also use parallel talk to expose your child to the language that goes with your everyday lives. **Parallel talk** is play-by-play narration that describes things your child is doing, noticing or observing. This includes:

- **Actions or activities of your child**

  Parallel talk can be used to describe what your child is doing as she's doing it. Here are some examples:

  "I see you're trying to fit all the toys in the box. It is overflowing! Whoa, it's too full!"

  or

  "My, my, what a big girl. You pulled up your pants all by yourself. And now you are buttoning them. Oh, that button is tricky, but you are really trying! Good for you!"

- **Actions or activities in which neither the child nor the caregiver are involved**

  Parallel talk also can be used to describe actions and activities that you and your child are not doing yourselves. You and your child may be taking a walk around the neighborhood. You both notice a neighbor mowing the lawn. You can stop pushing the stroller, squat down to be in a good position to talk with your child and say:

  "I hear the lawn mower. That man is cutting the grass. Wow, it's loud!"

  Mowing the lawn is probably not something your young child will experience herself, but she will likely witness such an event. Use of parallel talk allows your child to hear the language associated with the activity she's observing.

  Just when you think you've run out of things to say, try to enrich your talk by incorporating naming and labeling, self-talk or parallel talk into your day. Your talking child will thank you for it!

Technique #9: Avoid Common Traps

Some parents find that a list of things to avoid while talking is helpful as they get started in this process. Here are some things you might want to avoid while talking to your child:

- talking too little
- talking too much
- using only messages that are too long or too complicated for your child to attend to or understand
- pausing too infrequently so your child may not know when it's her turn
- speaking too fast or unclearly
- using monotone and uninteresting talk
- mumbling

- talking like a robot
- talking with inaccurate grammatical structure, such as leaving out articles like *a, an* and *the*
- talking with inaccurate meaning, such as calling a balloon a ball

Children usually will give some sort of warning sign if talk is not appropriate in some way. The warning signs include the child:

- does not appear to be listening to or looking at the talker
- averts her glance from the talker intentionally, or even refuses to attend to certain talkers or all talkers
- immediately crawls or walks away from the interaction

In the very beginning, don't be alarmed if your child gives these warning signs. She may not yet have learned talk is interesting, helpful and fun. As you continue to talk to her, she gradually will improve her attention and length of attention to familiar talkers.

Technique #10: Use Modeling and Imitation

Children with typical hearing learn to talk by listening to talk around them and then imitating it. They hear themselves talk and alter the sound of that talk until it matches the talk of the people around them. That's why babies from Texas talk like people from Texas and babies from Wisconsin say "How 'bout a bottle, ay?" Just talking to and around children with typical hearing eventually results in their understanding, and that understanding or comprehension results in their learning to talk.

Similarly, a child with hearing loss needs to imitate in order to learn to talk. The difference here is that a child with hearing loss doesn't necessarily imitate automatically like children with typical hearing. This is because the quantity of talk she hears is less than the quantity of talk spoken around her. The quality of the talk she hears also may be less than what those with typical hearing hear. Because a child may miss out on the talk going on around her, it is important to find ways to supplement her language development. One such way is through an ongoing process of give and take known as modeling and imitation.

Modeling language for your child to imitate is one of the most fundamental ways to help her listen to your good and correct model, then try to use it herself. It is used widely because it works! **Modeling** (what you say) allows your child to hear the language of the world around her, especially language that corresponds to your lives. **Imitation** (what your child repeats from your model) allows your child to practice saying what you said. Think of all the great things your child might learn to imitate from hearing your model. You can model the language that describes everything you do, see, think, hear and want to do. Your child can imitate that language and learn to understand its meaning.

Modeling

Parents can enrich their talk and teach their children new language by modeling language. They do this by saying exactly the kind of words they eventually want to hear coming from their child. For example, when a baby cries and mother knows it's time to feed her, she could model, "I'm so hungry. Feed me." The mother doesn't actually mean that she herself is hungry. Instead, she is modeling the kind of words she would like to hear her baby say instead of crying. We know the youngest babies won't actually say those words, but by the mother modeling them, the baby can experience the rich, complete language. Over time, the baby learns to associate the modeled words with her feelings, making a connection between language and meaning. When a young child hands her mother a toy that needs to be activated, the mother could model, "Help me please! Turn it on." Once again, the language the mother models might be beyond the child's current abilities, but the child will learn that those words go with that action.

Imitation

A secondary element associated with modeling language is the expectation that the child will imitate the parent's model. The first step to this process involves nonverbal or motor imitation. We do this right away with babies, usually without being aware of our actions, when we smile and a baby smiles back. Or a baby makes a sad face and a mommy imitates that face while asking what's wrong. Other forms of nonverbal imitating are waving, kissing and clapping. Children like to imitate adults, so this type of modeling and imitation can happen quite naturally. This is also a great start to turn-taking, a necessary skill for conversation.

Since young babies may be able to imitate only nonverbal movements or nonsense syllables or sounds, another important behavior for caregivers to practice is imitating their child's vocalizations. You've probably witnessed an exchange between caregiver and child similar to this one: The baby coos and the mother coos back. This exchange continues for several turns. The baby and the mother both vocalize. At times, the mother imitates her baby's vocalizations. But if the mother changes her vocalization to say "Mamama" and the child follows suit, then the child imitates her mother.

Modeling and Imitation

Once your child begins to listen, talk and understand what some words mean, she is ready to begin to imitate modeled words and phrases. The key to modeling is the use of an expectant look. This lets your child know you expect her to say something. It's best to start by modeling words that are important to your child, or those she'll likely hear many times during her typical day. The steps to helping your child learn to imitate are best described within the context of an example:

Step 1 — Modeling before imitation is firmly established:

Your child climbs up to the kitchen table and points to the refrigerator. You know this means she wants some milk.

You remove the carton, but you stand right by the refrigerator, not moving to her yet. You make eye contact with her and say "Milk." You pause and look at her lovingly and expectantly.

Your child looks at you, pauses as if to think, then says "Uh."

You smile, move right to her with the carton, take her cup and pour some, saying "milk" again, just letting her listen as you give it to her. With your positive facial expression, your action and your praise, you let her know she communicated effectively.

Step 2 — Once your child is vocalizing most of the time when you model words for her to imitate, lengthen your response, as follows:

After your child says "Uh," pour the milk and move closer to her. Say "Here's your milk. Milk." Pause again and look at her lovingly and expectantly. Your child responds with "Mu!" Now it's time to praise her improved imitation! You might say "Good girl, you want some milk!" as you hand her the cup of milk.

Modeling and imitation are very important because they eventually will lead to your child learning new words, phrases and sentences. When you first model words for your child to imitate, you might find she seems to be thinking, but not imitating. That's fine. Just keep at it. One time she'll respond with a vocalization and you can praise her enthusiastically. As children hear modeled language and practice saying the words on their own, they begin to refine their spoken language even more through modeling and imitation.

Parroting

Mommy asks:	"Where are you going?"
Child responds:	"Where go?"

Attempts to teach your child to imitate may have one negative effect. When you say or ask something, she repeats the exact same thing . . . just like a little parrot! Occasionally, there comes a point at which it's obvious you're simply asking too many questions. When children don't understand a question, or don't have an answer, they often repeat what's asked of them. Children also may parrot non-questions, but it just doesn't seem so awkward because we think they're practicing their language.

Parroting is a common pitfall for children who have learned just enough words to impress their parents with their new talking, but don't yet have a wide vocabulary or understanding of their parents' talk. When children learn that their excited parents expect a response, they may become so consumed with saying something back they don't really think about the message. The give and take of vocal imitation is an important milestone in the process of learning to talk; however, when children are parroting or over-imitating, it also can be a red flag indicating a lack of understanding. If caregivers overemphasize expressive language (what the child says), they might miss opportunities to expand their child's receptive language (what the child understands).

If this happens with your child, it's best to take a step back and refocus your efforts on modeling language strictly for exposure to language. For now, try to refrain from using pauses with an expectant look. This may invite your child to parrot. Instead, take the pressure off your child to say something and refine your talk to emphasize new words or phrases. Soon enough, the parroting will decrease and you can go back to pausing for her to respond.

More Specific Modeling and Imitation

Because of its effectiveness, modeling and imitation is a technique used by many listening and spoken language professionals to help promote spoken language development in children with hearing loss. These professionals are very proficient at using certain types of modeling and imitation techniques in which the model is intended specifically to give only as much support as the child needs. The main types are reduction modeling, complete modeling and partial modeling. You don't necessarily need to differentiate among the different types of modeling for your child to imitate. Your job is to model the language of your everyday life and expect your child to imitate it as best she can. Feel free to ask the listening and spoken language professional (your child's early interventionist, teacher of the deaf, auditory-verbal therapist or speech-language pathologist) which specific types of modeling and imitation are most appropriate for your child. Below are the three types of modeling and imitation with an example of each.

Types of Modeling

Reduction model: This provides the most amount of support and the lowest level of expectation on the child.

Example:

Child:	"I eat."
Parent:	"I want to . . . " (holding a banana with an expectant look)
Child:	"I want to"
Parent:	"eat the banana." (still holding the banana with an expectant look)
Child:	"eat the banana."
Parent:	"I want to eat the banana." (still holding and looking)
Child:	"I want to eat the banana."

Reduction modeling should include two chunks — no more, and no less.

Complete model: This is the most straightforward type of modeling and imitation.
Example:

Child:	"I eat."
Parent:	"I want to eat the banana." (holding the banana with an expectant look)
Child:	"I want to eat the banana."

Partial model: This provides the least amount of support and the highest level of expectation on the child.
Example:

Child:	"I eat."
Parent:	"I want to . . . " (holding the banana and with an expectant look)
Child:	"I want to eat the banana."

Technique #11: Prompt Your Child to Use Language

The next step in helping your child learn to talk is to prompt her to do so. To prompt means to give your child a cue so she says something. Prompting is most appropriate when you have the idea that your child may be able to say a certain word or sentence. You give a prompt to help her say the word or sentence without giving a model first. Prompting is often done by asking a question and/or using a natural gesture such as pointing, as in the following examples:

■ While reading a book about farm animals, you might ask "What do you see?" while pointing to the animal you think your child knows. Your child might then label that animal by saying the word or an approximation of the word. If you're pointing to a cow, she might say "Cow" or she might say "Moo." Time for lots of praise! Your child labeled the correct word after you prompted her to do so!

■ As you're putting your child in her car seat, you pull her sippy cup out of her bag, intending to give it to her. To prompt her, you might show her the cup in your hand, point to it with the other hand and raise your eyebrows with an expectant look. This may prompt her to say "Juice" or "oo." You can then praise and reinforce her. Say "You're right! That's your juice. Here's your juice." and hand her the cup. Time for lots of praise! Your child labeled the correct word after you prompted her to do so!

■ As you're preparing to go outside and play, you both put on your coats and go to the door. Before opening the door yourself, you might squat to your child's level as she stands at the door, point to the doorknob and say "Hmm, what should we do here?" with an expectant look on your face. Pause for a moment while your child thinks about what to say. She might say "Open" or "Open door." Time for lots of praise! Your child labeled the action correctly after you prompted her to do so!

If your child is able to do something like these examples, she is able to take a prompt. This ability is a great step on her journey to becoming a talking child!

More Specific Prompting

As is true with modeling and imitation, there are many different types of prompts to give. Listening and spoken language professionals use many, many different kinds of prompting to help promote spoken language development in children with hearing loss. If you're interested in the more specific types of modeling and imitation listening and spoken language professionals use with your child, talk to your early interventionist, teacher of the deaf, auditory-verbal therapist or speech-language pathologist. That professional will help you know which specific types of prompting are most appropriate for your child. Some are complicated and might be more than you want to do. Yet you might feel comfortable with others. It's your decision.

Below is a list of many types of prompting and some examples of how to give the prompt.

Nonverbal Prompts to Stimulate Talk	
Point.	Point to an object for your child to label.
Look expectantly. (shrug, raise eyebrows, lean in toward child)	Make your child know you're expecting her to say something.
Wait.	Do nothing until your child makes some sort of communicative attempt.
Withhold materials.	Put materials in a bag and look in it excitedly. Don't let your child see what's in the bag until she makes a communicative attempt.
Use sabotage.	Pour milk into a cup so your child can see. Keep pouring until your child makes a communicative attempt, even if the milk spills all over the table and floor. (*Warning! This can get messy!)

Gesture.	To elicit "Put the pudding in the bowl."
	Point to bag of pudding. Your child says "Pudding."
	Point your finger down into the bowl. Your child says "In."
	Point to or tap on the side of the bowl. Your child says "Bowl."
Use fingers as markers.	Hold up three fingers. Point to the first finger when saying the first word, the second finger when saying the second word and the third finger for the third word.
Give a natural look indicating that your child made an error.	Your child says something incorrectly that you think she might be able to correct on her own. Look at her with a confused or puzzled look. She will reconsider the way she said it and try again, hopefully the correct way.

Verbal Prompts to Stimulate Talk

Request information.	You see that your child notices a dog walking down your street. Say "Tell me about that." Your child says "Dog run."
Ask a question.	You notice your child is looking for her shoes. You look around for them and see they are in her closet. Say "Oh, here they are! Where were your shoes?" Your child says "in closet."
Make a comment to stimulate conversation.	Say "My favorite movie is *Cinderella*." Look at your child as if you expect her to say something. Your child says "I like *Toy Story*." Then continue with the conversation.

Verbal Prompts to Stimulate Talk *(continued)*	
Use a common utterance for asking to repeat or clarify.	Your child says something incorrectly you think she might be able to fix on her own. Say "Pardon?" Say "What did you say?" Say "Hmm?" Say "I'm not sure what you mean." Say "I don't understand."
Make a comment that provides the correct information.	Your child tells her friend about what she got while at the store. Your child says to her friend "I have more backpack." You say "You have a *new* backpack." Your child says to her friend "I have a *new* backpack."
Make a comment that provides more information.	Your child says "I have coat." You say "You have a *new raincoat.*" Your child says "I have a new raincoat."

Remember: Learning to prompt your child to use language takes lots of time, patience and practice. You won't learn the various ways to prompt overnight or from reading this just once. You will learn to do it over time. For now, choose one way to prompt that you think is doable at the moment. Practice using that one prompt until you feel comfortable with it. Over time, you can look back at this list and add to your prompting repertoire. Before you know it, you'll be prompting in all sorts of different ways.

Technique #12: Listen for and Promote Spontaneous Language

Once children have lots of opportunities to imitate language that is modeled and to produce language that is prompted, they go on to use the words or phrases on their own, when they need to and decide to do so. This is so exciting, such a huge accomplishment and exactly what you want your child to do. This is referred to as spontaneous language because your child produces it on her own without any help or cues from you. This spontaneous use of language is what you are after in the end, isn't it?

Many parents write down the spontaneous language their children use in a cute little journal or note pad. This is a great opportunity to see on paper the advancements your child makes over time, especially if you mark the date of each utterance. At the beginning, when

By now, you will see that the sequence of progress goes something like this:
- nonverbal and vocal imitation to . . .
- comprehension of some words to . . .
- imitation of some words to . . .
- producing the words with prompting to . . .
- spontaneous use of the words

your journal is empty, you can think about the fact that someday it will be full of cute, exciting and darling little things your child has said. Later, as you add to the list of words and phrases she's said, it will do your heart good to see the progress she's made with all of your efforts.

The best way to promote spontaneous language is to keep surrounding your child with lots and lots of rich and robust language. The more she can hear you talk about your life and interests, the more she will learn to do the same. Keep talking! And know that your child will reap the benefits of that talk.

Technique #13: Use Acoustic Highlighting

Acoustic highlighting is the term used to describe the act of emphasizing certain sounds, words or phrases while you talk. It's intended to focus your child's attention on the sounds or words you really want her to hear most. Think about highlighting in a textbook. You choose the most important concepts or ideas and highlight them with your yellow highlighter so you can easily identify the most important information.

You can do this with your talk, too! Because we are talking about highlighting the sound of our talk, we use the word *acoustic*, which relates to sounds. You can acoustically highlight in many ways. Try reading the following sentences aloud while acoustically highlighting the words in italics.

Pitch

Practice changing your pitch.

Make your voice a little higher on the acoustically highlighted word:
- *"Uh-oh!* You fell down!"

Make your voice a little lower on the acoustically highlighted word:
- "The cow went *'Moo!'*"

Volume

Practice changing your volume.

Make your voice a little louder on the acoustically highlighted word:
- "Look at the *balloon*!"

Make your voice a little quieter on the acoustically highlighted word:
- "Shhh! The baby's *sleeping*."

Stress

Practice changing the stress or emphasis on particular words in the same sentence.

Acoustically highlight the word *apples*.
- "Put the *apples* in the basket."

This implies there are more than just apples available to go in the basket, but only one place to put them.

Now say the same sentence aloud, but acoustically highlight the word *basket*.
- "Put the apples in the *basket*."

This implies you have only apples, but there are multiple places to put them.

Duration/Timing

Practice changing the duration or timing of your talk.

Slow your duration by drawing out the words in italics as you say them:
- "*Slow* down. You're going too fast."
- "*Pee-Yew!* That diaper is stinky!"
- "Go get your *shoes*. You need your *shoes*."

Now, quicken your duration by speeding up the words in italics as you say them:
- "*Quick, quick!* We have to hurry to the door."

For most people to feel comfortable, acoustic highlighting takes a little practice. You will see that it truly does help your child focus on the most important words you use.

Technique #14: Understand Typical Communication

Listening and Language

To truly understand the communication expectations for your child, it's important to understand which communication skills are typical for children with typical hearing her same age. The following table is a compilation of listening and language skills and the ages at which these skills typically develop.

Typical Listening and Language Behaviors

At birth . . .	■ exhibits startle reflex in response to sudden loud noises by stiffening, quivering, blinking, moving eyes (often fans out fingers and toes or cries in response) ■ recognizes and prefers mother's voice and quiets to mother's voice if crying ■ exhibits calm in response to low frequency sounds and rhythmic sounds ■ increases and decreases sucking in response to sound
3–6 months . . .	■ uses controlled movements rather than just reflexes ■ shows awareness of human speech; attends to voices ■ is excited by certain sounds (ex: approaching footsteps, running bath water) ■ awakens and quiets to sound of a caregiver's voice ■ uses nonverbal communication ■ localizes sound by turning eyes to the sound source ■ enjoys sound making toys ■ distinguishes between friendly and angry voices and reacts accordingly ■ reacts to music by cooing or stopping crying ■ shows great interest in human voice ■ discriminates between sounds of familiar people and strangers ■ coos ■ vocally responds to a caregiver's voice ■ produces a range of vocalizations ■ uses reflexive babbling with a variety of vowel-like sounds ■ uses sounds and cries to indicate contentment or discomfort ■ produces a variety of facial expressions
7–12 months . . .	■ begins to understand words in context ■ responds to sounds around the house (ex: phone ringing) ■ responds to her own name, "no-no" and "bye-bye" ■ enjoys games like Pat-a-Cake and Peek-a-Boo ■ raises arms when a caregiver reaches out and says "Up?"

Typical Listening and Language Behaviors

7–12 months . . . *(continued)*	▪ understands a few gestures and words for common items ▪ responds when called or gestured to (ex: "Come here." and "More?") ▪ responds to simple commands (ex: gives a requested toy) ▪ understands common verbs (ex: drink, go, come and give) ▪ responds to simple directions (ex: "Wave bye-bye.") ▪ likes songs and rhymes ▪ recognizes 12 or more objects when she hears the labels for them ▪ frowns when scolded ▪ cries at loud noises (ex: thunder) ▪ imitates sounds
12–18 months . . .	▪ by 12 months, understands about 50 words ▪ uses holophrases or one word to convey a sentence (ex: "Up" for "Pick me up.") ▪ produces a variety of sounds that may sound like words or short sentences ▪ uses a variety of gestures and vocalizations to request objects and direct attention
18–24 months . . .	▪ understands 150–200 words ▪ understands simple sentences ▪ knows her name ▪ begins to understand prepositional phrases ▪ begins to follow short, simple directions (ex: Wipe the doll's nose.) ▪ looks at objects in pictures when named ▪ points to common objects in a picture when asked (ex: point to the baby) ▪ points to common actions in a picture when asked (ex: point to the boy eating) ▪ points to basic body parts when asked (ex: eyes, nose, mouth and ears) ▪ points to family member in a picture when given name

	■ follows a direction with two critical elements (ex: "Give me the blue car.")
	■ enjoys listening to simple stories read from picture books
	■ responds to yes/no questions by shaking or nodding her head
	■ uses telegraphic language or combines a few words as simple sentences (ex: "Daddy work.")
	■ begins using adjectives (ex: dirty)
	■ begins combining two words
	■ repeats two numbers, letters or words
2–3 years . . .	■ by age 2, understands approximately 300 words
	■ learns two to four new words each day
	■ by age 3, understands 900–1,000 words
	■ enjoys listening to songs
	■ identifies objects by their use (ex: a brush is for hair; a spoon is for eating)
	■ follows related two-step directions (ex: "Pick up the ball and give it to me.")
	■ understands syntactic differences (ex: "Show me the car pushing the truck." vs. "The truck is pushing the car.")
	■ understands nearly all sentence structures
	■ produces sentences of three to five words
	■ talks about present, past and future events
	■ uses recognizable sentence forms
	■ asks questions using What? Who? and Where?
	■ overgeneralizes (ex: calls all four-legged animals "dog")
3–4 years . . .	■ by age 4, knows 4,000–6,000 words
	■ by age 4, can converse, ask questions and gain new information using spoken language
	■ listens eagerly to elaborate stories and repeatedly requests her favorites
	■ understands the use of objects (ex: "Show me the one you wear.")
	■ follows directions with three critical elements
	■ understands turn-taking
	■ understands most common adjectives
	■ shows an interest in explanations of why and how

Typical Listening and Language Behaviors	
3–4 years . . . *(continued)*	■ recognizes several melodies
	■ remembers four items of a story
	■ recalls three numbers, letters or words
	■ answers simple Who? What? Where? questions
	■ matches simple sound tones
	■ imitates 5- to 7-syllable sentences
4–5 years . . .	■ by age 5, knows 5,000–8,000 words
	■ follows three-step directions
	■ follows directions with four critical elements
	■ understands time phrases (ex: all the time, all day, a long time and for two weeks)
	■ understands irregular plurals (ex: child/children)
	■ understands possessives (ex: dog's)
	■ understands all pronouns
	■ understands contractions
	■ remembers five items of a story
	■ recalls four numbers, letters or words
	■ repeats two numbers backwards
	■ uses long, detailed sentences using adult-like grammar
	■ attends to stories and answers simple questions about them
	■ imitates 12- to 14-syllable sentences based on short-term recollection
	■ tells elaborate stories
	■ uses language as a means of socialization
	■ is very interested in communicating with peers
	■ responds correctly to complicated sentences
By 6 years . . .	■ understands 20,000+ words
	■ knows right from left
	■ imitates a 16-syllable sentence based on short-term recollection
	■ remembers six items of a story
	■ repeats three numbers backwards

(Easterbrooks & Baker, 2001; Gleason, 2001; Rhoades, 2003; Rossetti, 2001; Seefeldt & Wasik, 2006).

Speech Skills

In addition to listening and language behaviors, it's important to understand which speech skills are typical for children who have typical hearing. The following table is a compilation of speech skills and the ages at which children typically accurately produce sounds in isolation and in all positions of syllables and words (including words within phrases and sentences.)

Typical Speech Behaviors	
By 10 months . . .	All vowels: ■ /a-e/ as in *cake* ■ /ee/ as in *feet* ■ /i-e/ as in *pile* ■ /oa/ as in *boat* ■ /oo/ as in *pool* ■ /u-e/ as in *cute* ■ /-a-/ as in *hat* ■ /-o-/ as in *hot* ■ /-e-/ as in *bed* ■ /-i-/ as in *kick* ■ /-u-/ as in *cup* ■ /-oo-/ as in *cookie* ■ /aw/ as in *paw* ■ /oi/ as in *soil* ■ /ou/ as in *house*
By or at age 3 . . .	■ /m/ as in *more* ■ /n/ as in *nail* ■ /ng/ as in *king* ■ /p/ as in *pan* ■ /f/ as in *fire* ■ /h/ as in *hot* ■ /w/ as in *water* ■ /y/ as in *yellow*
By or at age 4 . . .	■ /b/ as in *ball* ■ /t/ as in *top* ■ /d/ as in *dog* ■ /k/ as in *kick* ■ /g/ as in *go* ■ /s/ as in *sun* ■ /sh/ as in *shut* ■ /zh/ as in *beige* ■ /r/ as in *run* ■ /ch/ as in *child*

Typical Speech Behaviors (continued)	
By or at age 6 . . .	■ /v/ as in *van* ■ /th[1]/ as in *thank* ■ /l/ as in *land*
By or at age 7 . . .	■ r-controlled vowels as in *girl* ■ /th[2]/ as in *the* ■ /z/ as in *zoo* ■ /j/ as in *jump*
Age 7–8 years . . .	■ accurately uses all blends and clusters in all positions of words

Sounds are indicated in General American Symbols.   *(Dieckmann & White, 2013; Smit, 1993)*

Technique #15: Set Expectations for Communication

Now that you have a clear understanding of what children with typical communication skills are able to do, it's important to set some expectations for your child. You can set expectations for communication to help guide her, depending on her age and language ability. These expectations need not be harsh or demanding; rather, they should give her the idea that you expect her to communicate with you and others.

Increase Expectations Over Time

As your child grows from an infant to a preschooler, you can increase your communication expectations. One of the most effective methods for deciding what communication expectations to have is to get to know some other children your child's same age who have typical hearing. When you have opportunities to observe typical communication behaviors, it's easier to know what to expect from your child. Some parents fall into the trap of learning some early communication strategies for promoting communication skills with their infants and toddlers but neglect to increase their expectations as the child grows and develops. In order to help your child gain the communication skills she needs to get and stay on track with her peers with typical hearing, you will need to up the ante as she gets older. For more information on typical communication skills for infants and young children, see Technique #14 in this chapter.

You may notice that having high communication expectations for your child also may lead to more acceptable behavior. It's kind of like a two for one. By helping your child communicate and expecting her to do so, you can promote more acceptable behaviors. If your child knows you expect her to listen and respond appropriately to you, then you potentially could avoid some undesirable behaviors. It's worth a try for so many reasons!

Be Aware of the Ignoring Trick

It's certainly not uncommon for very young children with hearing loss to miss opportunities to communicate. Sometimes your child might miss what was said or not understand it. This is something to look out for so you can be supportive and helpful when she really has missed what was said or doesn't understand.

Other times, your child may purposefully avoid communication. Sometimes it's just easier for her to avoid rather than work hard to communicate. You might have a difficult time distinguishing between your child's behavior and communication ability. In other words, sometimes your child will "act up" by ignoring what you said or purposefully avoiding communication with you. Aside from communication breakdowns, every child does her fair share of ignoring her parents. This is truly a behavior issue. Other times, you'll see that your child truly didn't hear you or doesn't understand. It's often easy to confuse the two, but as the parent, you know your child better than anyone else in the world. Over time, you'll learn to distinguish between behavior issues and communication breakdowns. At this point, be aware that your child eventually will be savvy enough simply to ignore you, and you will have a choice about how to respond.

Make Language and Speech Corrections When Appropriate

As your child begins to talk, you will, no doubt, be absolutely thrilled. Many parents report one of the happiest moments of their lives being when their children uttered those first words. This is so exciting and such a huge milestone. It doesn't matter how well she pronounces words. She's talking! While this is truly exciting, continue to help her make progress by promoting listening skills and by adding in some language and speech corrections.

During lessons or therapy sessions, listening and spoken language professionals use many strategies for teaching listening skills and for correcting and expanding children's language to be more proficient. They also have lots of strategies for correcting children's speech so it's easier to understand (or so it's more intelligible). Professionals use specific strategies for individualizing listening, language and speech lessons to suit each child's needs and maximize progress. Although you should never feel you need to replicate an exact lesson of a trained professional, you can do a lot to build communication skills by occasionally correcting her language and speech at home.

Ask your child's early interventionist, teacher of the deaf, auditory-verbal therapist or speech-language pathologist to give you some tips. She will give you specific strategies you can use at home based on your child's ability, interests and personality. These professionals are not only trained to work in a classroom or therapy setting, they are also trained to coach parents to help their children make progress in listening, language and speech at home. This includes demonstrating how to correct your child's language and speech in appropriate ways.

At this point, it may seem harsh to criticize your child's attempts at talking. Of course, you would never want to degrade a child who is attempting to talk. On the contrary, you certainly want to promote more talking with your reinforcing words and actions. There are many ways to encourage and positively reinforce your child for talking, including smiling, clapping, nodding, looking lovingly at your child, telling her how great she is and responding appropriately to her talk. You have the power to use whatever strategies you find work well for you and your child.

References

Easterbrooks, S. & Baker, S. (2002). *Language Learning in Children Who Are Deaf and Hard of Hearing: Multiple Pathways.* Boston: Allyn & Bacon.

Dieckmann, L. & White, E. (2013). *CID Speech Skills Rating Form.* St. Louis: Central Institute for the Deaf.

Gleason, J. (2001). *The Development of Language* (5th ed.). Boston: Allyn and Bacon.

Rhoades, E.A. (2003). Auditory Development Scale: 0–6 Years. Retrieved from http://www.auditory verbaltraining.com/scale.htm.

Rossetti, L. (2001). *Communication Intervention: Birth to Three* (2nd ed.). Australia: Singular Thomson Learning.

Seefeldt, C. & Wasik, B. (2006). *Early Education: Three-, Four- and Five-Year-Olds Go to School* (2nd ed.). Upper Saddle River, NJ: Pearson/Merrill/Prentice Hall.

Smit, A. (1993). Phonologic error distributions in the Iowa-Nebraska articulation project: Consonant singletons. *Journal of Speech and Hearing Research, 36,* 533–547.

■ ■

Chapter 14

Language for Daily Routines

All young children need routine in daily life, but children with hearing loss especially benefit from a structured routine to organize their days and nights. Imagine getting up in the morning with no control over your day and no idea what might happen from minute to minute. Although this might be interesting once in a while, it would be totally disconcerting if it happened day after day. If you establish a daily routine for your child, she will become more confident about her world and learn more readily about it.

Because her comprehension of language is likely to be delayed, your child needs some other way to understand the world around her. In the beginning, a routine will provide her a way to anticipate the future. The order of the routine doesn't matter as much as the consistency of having a routine.

Your routine will be unique and will vary depending on family size, parents' work schedules, child care arrangements, setup of your home, your values and so on. Take time to think through a typical day and see whether a routine or some parts of a routine are already established for your child.

Over time, your child will begin to anticipate certain events in the day. She might realize that it's almost nap time because lunch is ending or that it's time to go outside because she has finished her nap. A pattern provides reassurance and gives her an idea about what to expect next.

The Biggest Bonus of Having a Routine

The benefits of having a routine are numerous. Your child will be able to anticipate the parts of her day, she will feel comfortable in her daily activities and she will be confident in your daily lives together. But perhaps the very best reason for a routine is this:

> When your child feels comfortable and familiar with a regular and predictable routine on which she can rely, she will be able to dedicate more energy, thought and "brainpower" to learning the language that goes with her life.

If she feels comfortable with the activities, she will be able to concentrate more on listening to the language of those activities. She will spend far less time wondering what's going to happen next. Instead, she will be able to pay close attention to all the language and talk you provide for her. For many children, not knowing what's coming next causes stress and anxiety. Those negative feelings can hinder a child's ability to pay attention to language. You can attempt to eliminate potential stress and anxiety by establishing a consistent routine to follow each day. It will take some time, but rest assured it will be worth it for both of you in the end.

Establishing a Routine

- Establish a routine you can use every day that begins first thing in the morning.
- Include a number of daily activities you can be sure to accomplish each day. (See *Suggested Daily Activities* below.)
- Consider the talk you'll provide during each of the daily activities. You need not use the exact same language every day. In fact, that would bore both of you. Yet, if you commit to using lots of talk during all of your child's activities, you will train yourself to use lots of talk automatically.
- Make time for lots of playing and talking activities.
- Consider devoting some time to specific language activities. Your early interventionist, teacher of the deaf, speech-language pathologist or auditory-verbal therapist can help you know what language activities are appropriate for your child and how to carry them out.

Suggested Daily Activities

Wake-up routine

Many young children have a consistent wake-up time every morning. If yours doesn't, determine a reasonable time to wake your child each day. After a while, she will adjust to this time and might even start waking on her own.

Every morning when your child awakes, one of your first tasks is to put her hearing devices on her. Although it's tempting to wait until dressing time, it's even better if you can put them on at wake-up time. This builds the habit of wearing the devices during all waking hours and gives your child the best chance of hearing you talk. She needs to learn that her hearing devices go on first thing.

As you greet your child's smiling face each morning (no matter how early that is), be animated and pleasant. As you put on her hearing devices, help her out of bed and go about your morning, talk with her. Your established routine can allow you to take advantage of moments when your child is "listening for language" by waiting just an instant before carrying out some activity she expects. For example, if you're pulling up a shade in her room, pause once you're holding the shade. Your child will probably look up at you to see why you haven't pulled it up. At that instant, you have a chance to say a word or two or a short sentence. Take advantage of every chance you have to provide her with words.

Talk, pause, listen and talk again. Below is a list of some things you can say to your child during your morning wake-up routine. Be sure you add or substitute things that come up but are not mentioned here.

- "Hi, (child's name)."
- "Let's put on your hearing aids/ cochlear implants."
- "Good morning!"
- "Good morning, (child's name)!"
- "I love you!"
- "Mommy/Daddy loves you!"
- "Do you wanna get up/down?"
- "It's time to get up/wake up."
- "Oh, hug, hug, hug."
- "May I have a hug?"

- "I want a hug/kiss."
- "Oh, that's a big hug!"
- "Where's Daddy/Mommy?"
- "Do you want to see Daddy/Mommy?"
- "Where's the light?"
- "Turn on the light."
- "The light is on."
- "There's the light!"
- "Pull up the blinds. Pull, pull, pull."
- "Open the curtain."
- "Open the window."

Dressing routine

Establish a routine for getting dressed in the morning. Determine what your child can be responsible for in this process each day. It's a good idea to look out the window or door with your child and talk about what the weather is like. Then decide together what an appropriate outfit would be. Talk through each step of choosing what to wear, taking her pajamas off and putting her clothes on. This is a great time to talk about body parts and types of clothing.

Here are some tricks to help you get your child to pay attention while getting dressed or undressed:

- Play peek-a-boo with an article of clothing.
- Hide the clothes and look for them together.
- Tickle her gently with the article you just took off or are trying to put on.
- Creep the article of clothing across the floor toward her as if to "get her" with it.

Here is a list of things you can say to your child as you help her get dressed and undressed throughout the day. Remember to include words and phrases for the variations that occur in your setting. Don't forget to talk, pause, listen and respond to your child.

- "Let's get dressed."
- "Do you want to get dressed?"
- "Here's your shirt."
- "Put on your shirt."
- "Where's (child's name)?"
- "Peek-a-boo!"

- "Here's your arm."
- "There's your hand."
- "Cover up that tummy."
- "Let's change your diaper."
- "I need to change your diaper."
- "Go get a diaper."

- "The diaper's wet."
- "The diaper's yucky!"
- "Throw it away."
- "Throw away the diaper."
- "Open the drawer."
- "Close it."
- "Get your coat."
- "Button your shirt."
- "Let me zip your coat."
- "Pull up your pants."
- "Hang up your coat."
- "There's your leg."
- "Take off your shoes."

- "Here's a foot."
- "Put on your shoe."
- "I see your toes."
- "I want your shoes."
- "I can't find your shoe."
- "I'll zip your pants."
- "Zip! Zip! Zip!"
- "Take off your pajamas."
- "Roll up your pants."
- "Roll them up."
- "I see your belly button."
- "Two socks."
- "Blue socks."

Breakfast routine

Mealtime is one of the best times to talk to your child. For many children (and many adults for that matter), food is a great motivator. Lots of language goes with the act of eating and the food we eat. Label the food items and utensils as well as the actions that go along with them.

It may be helpful to commit to a certain order of events during meals as you provide lots of language.

Example 1: Baby

1. Seat your child in her high chair.
2. Give her a few toys to play with.
3. Gather the rice cereal and pureed fruit.
4. Bring the food to her high chair.
5. Show her and talk to her about how you scoop the rice cereal into her bowl.
6. Show her and talk to her about how you scoop the fruit into the bowl.
7. Show her and talk to her about how you stir the cereal and fruit together.
8. If she reaches for the spoon, let her help you stir while you model, "Stir, stir, stir. Stir the cereal. The spoon goes around and around. Do you want to stir fast?"
9. Help her eat her breakfast and describe how it tastes.

Example 2: Toddler/Preschooler

1. Help your child sit at the table in her usual spot.
2. Tell her you're going to the pantry to get the box of cereal.
3. Put the cereal on the table but out of her reach. Tell her it's her cereal.
4. Tell her you're going to get the milk out of the refrigerator.
5. Put the milk on the table out of her reach. Tell her it's the milk.

6. Ask her what you need next. If she knows, *great!* If not, tell her you need a bowl and a spoon.
7. Tell her you're going to get her a bowl and spoon.
8. Sit down next to her and help her with the cereal. Talk about the picture on the box, talk about opening the box and talk about opening the bag inside the box. Ask her if she wants to pour the cereal. See if she will imitate that language.
9. Help her pour the cereal. Say "Stop!" when there's enough in the bowl.
10. Do the same with the milk.
11. Help her eat her cereal and describe how it tastes.

Here are some examples of things you can say to your child while you're feeding her and while she is eating. Remember to talk, pause, listen and talk again by responding to your child. Remember to include words, phrases and sentences meaningful to the situation.

- "Sit down, please."
- "Sit in your high chair."
- "Do you want a boost?"
- "I like when you sit in your high chair like a big girl!"
- "Sit here."
- "Do you want a bite?"
- "Another bite?"
- "Open your mouth."
- "Take a big bite."
- "How about another bite of this yummy oatmeal?"
- "Here's your bottle."
- "I have an apple."
- "Do you want the pink cup or the green cup?"
- "Today I picked the pink cup with the doggy on it."
- "Here's a drink."
- "Take a drink."
- "Drink from the cup."

- "That's a big fork."
- "Your mouth is dirty."
- "Open the jar."
- "Take a sip."
- "Wipe your mouth."
- "Wow! Your mouth is really messy. Let's wipe it with a towel."
- "Use a spoon."
- "Here's a napkin."
- "Do you want more?"
- "More milk."
- "The pear is green."
- "That's sour."
- "It's hot."
- "All gone!"
- "Is it good?"
- "Yes, it's so good."
- "Yum, yum, yum."
- "How about you take another bite of this healthy food?"
- "What a delicious breakfast!"

Lots of language is also associated with the act of cleaning up. Show your child how to help you clean up and provide the language of that process.

Time for outings

It's important to allow time for outings. First of all, as a parent, you will need to go places — run errands, visit friends and family, have play dates, drop off your other child's lunch at school, go to doctor appointments — and lots more. Outings create great experiences for your child to learn about her world. Equally important, they allow an opportunity for you to describe these experiences with lots of rich and interesting language. Describe in advance what you are going to do, talk about where you are going and talk about what you are doing while there. Your child will love having these new experiences and learning the language that goes with them — even if it's just your regular trip to the grocery store.

Lunch routine

Establish a consistent lunch time. Try to have lunch in the same place (e.g., at home) each day, for the most part. For more information, use the procedures and language for mealtimes on pages 216 and 220.

Nap routine

Just like all babies and young children, your child needs lots of sleep. Establish a consistent nap time and length of nap. Ensure she is well-rested each day so she can be energetic and ready to listen and talk!

Outdoor activities

All of us need fresh air, sunshine and outside time. Being outside, even if it's just a few steps outside your front door, can open up your child's world to lots of new experiences. Even without toys or a planned activity, you and your child have lots to talk about when you step outside. Talk about what you see — birds, trees, cars going by. Talk about what you hear — birds tweeting, cars honking, a distant train whistle. Talk about what you feel — a chill in the air, a warm breeze, the hot sun shining on you.

In addition, you can always play games and play with toys outside. As you play, remember to include the language of that play, including things like:

- "Hey, do you want to play ball?"
- "I'll go get it and you stand right here."
- "Okay, I'm going to throw the ball to you. Put your hands out. Get ready!"
- "Oh! Yay! You caught it. What a big girl!"
- "Okay, I'll put my hands out. You throw the ball and I'll catch it! I'm ready!"
- "Yay! Good throw! I caught the ball! Hooray!"
- "I wonder what will happen if I throw the ball like this?"
- "Holy cow! You really threw it far that time!"
- "Wow! I had lots of fun playing catch with you."

Play time

Make time for playing together. Play is one of the single most important daily activities for a child. A child learns new concepts, vocabulary, language, motor skills, cognitive skills and literacy skills through play. Play expands a child's creativity and imagination. Play helps a child develop the ability to problem-solve, negotiate and reason. Gone are the days of considering play something for a child to do to keep her busy while the adults accomplish other things. Play isn't something for the child to do to free up adults. Play for young children should equate in all of our minds to learning.

It's important to make time each day to actively play with your child. In fact, this should include all of your children. Pretend play is especially fun and is a great way to help a child understand her world. For more information on play, see Chapter 16.

Most of the time, let your child be in charge and choose the toy you will play with and talk about. Whatever she's playing with at the time will be your guide to stimulate her language. Just a few words or phrases about what she is doing will show her you are interested. Your tone of voice can indicate your interest, too. What your child wants most is your attention.

Here are some examples of things you can say to your child while you're playing with her. Remember to tailor the talk to her toys, interests and ideas — and to pause frequently for her to respond.

- "Roll the ball."
- "Catch the ball."
- "A red ball."
- "Whoa! There goes the ball."
- "Can you kick the ball to me?"
- "Two blocks."
- "A brown block."
- "Wow, I built a big tower!"
- "Uh, oh! The blocks fell down."
- "Hey, let's build another tower with all these blocks."
- "More blocks."
- "The cow says *Moo!*"
- "Walk, walk, walk."
- "A tall giraffe."
- "The bunny hops."
- "Bear. This is a bear."
- "*Shhh,* the teddy is sleeping."

- "Here are some eggs."
- "I want a hotdog."
- "The coffee is hot!"
- "More juice. Pour, pour, pour."
- "Mmmm, this tofurkey sandwich is really good."
- "Clean up the dishes."
- "Pour some water."
- "The cup is green."
- "Push the car."
- "A fast car. *Zoom!*"
- "The truck is big."
- "Hug the baby."
- "Hold the baby."
- "The baby is crying."
- "I think this baby needs a clean diaper."
- "Put the baby's shoes on."

Time for music

As is true for many people, music may be an important part of your life. Many parents of children with hearing loss worry their children will miss out on the robust and various effects of music in life. Because of today's advancements in hearing device technology, children with hearing loss, even profound hearing loss, are able to access sound in such a way that they, too, can benefit from music. The benefits are the same for children with hearing loss as they are for children with typical hearing — enjoyment, relaxation, stimulation, motivation and so on. Consider making time in your day for music. This can include listening to mainstream music, singing songs to your child, doing finger plays with your child or dancing. For more information on the benefits of music and some ways to engage your child with music, see Chapter 17.

Getting ready for dinner

Food preparation and getting the table set are two great activities for stimulating your child's language. Think about how she can be an active participant in the kitchen, even if for just a few minutes. Label the food items and utensils as well as the actions that go along with them. Give your child small, simple jobs she will be able to complete successfully.

Here are some examples of things you can say to your child while you're preparing a meal together:

- "I think we need to use the can opener."
- "Open the can."
- "Do you want to open the can?"
- "Open it. Open."
- "The can is open."
- "Give everyone a napkin."
- "Where's the cup?"
- "I need the fork."
- "Clean the table."
- "What should we do?"
- "Wipe the table."
- "Should we pour the water?"
- "Uh-oh, the water spilled."
- "Give Daddy a spoon."
- "Two forks."
- "What do you want?"
- "A green cup."
- "Do you want to stir?"

- "Stir it. Stir, stir, stir."
- "A tall glass."
- "Drop the ice."
- "The ice is cold!"
- "Fill the glass."
- "Stir the soup."
- "When we put the soup on the stove, it got really hot."
- "Hot!"
- "The soup is hot!"
- "The eggs are ready."
- "It's ready!"
- "Be careful!"
- "A big spoon."
- "*Mmmm!* It smells good!"
- "Hold the spoon."
- "All done."
- "Cut the bread."
- "That's all."

- "That's a knife."
- "Push the button."
- "Put the butter on the bread."
- "The popcorn is cooking."
- "Spread the butter."
- "Get a bowl."
- "Lick the spoon."
- "In the bowl."
- "I put the applesauce in the bowl. Wanna see?"
- "Turn on the water."

- "That's Mommy's bowl."
- "A red apple."
- "Here's your corn."
- "Two cups."
- "Here's (child's name)'s bowl."
- "Put the plate on the table."
- "The cup is empty."
- "A little plate."
- "The glass is full."
- "The plate is heavy."
- "A big cup."

Including your child may increase your food preparation time by a few minutes, but when it's time to eat, you not only will have fixed a meal, you also will have stimulated your child by providing lots of rich and robust language!

Books and story time

Include a story time or some simple activities with books each day or evening. Help your child develop a love of books and reading from birth. It may seem silly to read to an infant who can barely focus on a page — or who falls asleep in the middle of the book — but reading aloud to your child from an early age will help her develop an interest in books that will prove invaluable in her life.

It's particularly important to read to children with hearing loss. Because language delays often occur as a result of hearing loss, and because literacy skills are so dependent on language skills, it's not uncommon for children with hearing loss to struggle learning early literacy and literacy skills. Because we know the ability to read is an important indicator of success as an adult, it's important to start early developing the skills that will help aid the process of learning to read. For more information on early literacy development, see Chapter 18.

You can choose how you want to read to your child. Sometimes you can point out the pictures, label each object and talk about what's happening on each page. Other times, you might read a simplified version of the story so your child has a better chance of understanding it. Still other times you might choose to read the exact text. Once you tune in to your child's interest level, you can decide which way you want to read.

It's helpful to really ham it up when reading. Children are inherently interested in listening to interesting stories. What often makes the stories interesting is the way in which they are read. If you have a dull, monotone voice, it probably won't be very interesting to your child. But if you read with great enthusiasm and gusto, your child will be much more likely to take interest. And so will everyone else in your house!

Bath time routine

Make bath time a fun routine. Many children love to play in the water. Equally important, many children get really filthy over the course of a day. Bath time can be not only a time to clean up, but also a great language activity. Since many hearing devices are water resistant or waterproof, your child may be able to wear her devices at bath time. Talk about her body parts as you wash her. Label her toys and describe what you're doing as you play.

If your child's hearing devices are not waterproof, you may wonder why you'd have a language activity when she does not have them on and is not hearing optimally. Yet, even at this time, it's important to demonstrate that you want to communicate with her at all times. Continue to talk to her. Perhaps you want to be sure that she can see your face. Bath time is usually conducive to face-to-face positioning. Talk about the process and play with toys.

Bed time routine

Have a routine with the same steps for getting ready for and going to bed each night: put on pajamas, brush teeth, gather dolls or other snuggly items, arrange the lights, say prayers or share other special rituals, remove hearing devices and give lots of hugs and kisses.

Helpful Practices for Establishing a Routine

Picture schedule

One way to help your child establish and keep a routine is with a picture schedule. A **picture schedule** is a one-page set of images corresponding to the activities that make up a child's day. It can be on a piece of paper or a poster board. Besides use in the home, picture schedules are popular in daycare and preschool classrooms because they allow children to:

- know what activity is coming next
- anticipate favorite parts of the day
- spend less time and thought wondering when certain things will happen
- focus more attention on the language of each activity instead of wondering what might happen next
- feel less anxiety or lack of control about the day

The picture schedule should look like a list. At the top, write your child's name. Next, draw a picture or glue a photo of your child doing the first thing she does each day. You could start with waking up or getting dressed. It can be as simple as drawing (or gluing pictures of) basic articles of clothing. It's also important to represent the hearing devices she puts on first thing in the morning. To the left of this set of pictures, you can write "Get dressed!" On the next line, draw pictures or glue photos of your child doing the second thing she does each day — for example, eating breakfast. Continue with this process to cover the course of a full day.

It's a good idea to create the picture schedule with your child. Making it can be a language-rich experience in itself. Talk about each part of your child's day as you draw it. Or, if you prefer to use photos, act out each part of the day while talking pictures.

Once the picture schedule is ready, start using it the next morning. Tell your child it's time to get dressed and point to that picture on the schedule. Then point to the picture of her devices and help her put them on. Continue with your day and be sure to point out each specific activity on the schedule.

Display the picture schedule in your house where your child can see it frequently — or at least where she can easily find it. The refrigerator is a great spot for this. After a few days, she will know to look at the schedule herself if she is wondering what will come next. You need do little more than ensure it's available to her.

Calendar of events

Buy an inexpensive 12-month calendar for your child to use. Allow this calendar to be her very own so that the events of her day aren't confused with the things you have on your own calendar. Draw simple pictures on each day to represent upcoming activities or events. Your child probably will not understand the first time you draw something specific, but if you talk about it when you draw it, then show her the picture again when you're about to do that activity, she might better understand the process next time. For example, the first time you draw a stick figure at a swimming pool on the calendar, she might not know what that means. Simply point it out just before going to the pool and again when you get home. The next time, or maybe after a few times, she will begin to understand the process and the pictures you draw. Don't worry if you aren't good at drawing. She won't know the difference.

Routines Away from Home

If your child is in daycare regularly while you work, or if your child goes to preschool, you can continue to follow a routine during the parts of the day you're with your child. In addition, it's important to choose a daycare provider or preschool with a good, consistent routine. When interviewing daycare providers and preschools, ask questions to help you determine if they have a consistent routine for a typical day.

Variations to the Routine: When Real Life Happens

It really is true that if you establish a routine, you and your child will both benefit greatly. Yet, as parents, we all know that there are just some days when even the best laid plans go straight south. It's bound to happen. At some point, your routine will totally fall apart. When this happens, remind yourself that this exact same thing has happened to every parent that has ever existed. The best thing to do is take a deep breath and attempt to get back on track with your routine. If that doesn't work, then make your way through the rest of the day as best you can and start fresh the next day. Sometimes a good night's sleep makes everything better — or at least it makes it seem a little better.

Chapter 15

Words! Words! Words!

The Importance of Vocabulary Development

Vocabulary is one of the most important areas of language development. A person's **vocabulary** is the collection of words she understands and uses. When it comes to vocabulary, the more the better. The more vocabulary your child understands and uses, the better she will be able to understand what you say to her, the better she will be able to talk *and* the better she will be able to learn new words. In many cases, children need to understand the meaning of lots of words to learn new ones. For example, if you explained to your child the meaning of the word *hungry*, it would be helpful for her to know other words like *tummy*, *hurt*, *eat*, *food*, etc. When you notice your child is hungry, you could say something like:

> "Oh, I think you're hungry. I bet your little tummy hurts because you're hungry. Do you want to eat so you aren't hungry anymore? Do you want some food? Oh, I don't want you to be hungry. Let's eat!"

In learning the new word, *hungry*, it's helpful to understand lots of other words. This way, the meaning of the new word becomes more obvious.

Increasing Your Child's Vocabulary

Because vocabulary development is so important, it's extra important for you to use lots of vocabulary around your child in meaningful ways. At first, you might want to keep your vocabulary relatively simple so your child understands the basic words used to label things, people, places, feelings, actions and descriptors.

Here are the language elements that correspond to the vocabulary you should be using:

Nouns — people, places, objects (ex: *Mommy, girl, home, park, shoe, milk*)
Verbs — action words (ex: *sleep, run, jump, eat, shout, walk, pull, go, push, listen, talk*)
Adjectives — words that describe (ex: *hot/cold, big/little,* colors)
Prepositions — words that describe relationships between other words
       (ex: *on, under, with, until*)

To help your child build vocabulary, start by labeling people, objects and actions. Do so as much as possible. In the beginning, talk in short phrases and sentences two to five words long. Use exclamation words (such as "Wow!" or "Uh-oh!") when you can. Young children often develop exclamations, nouns (labels for people and objects) and verbs (labels for actions) as their first words. In your short phrases, emphasize the noun, verb or exclamation that carries the key part of your message. Use **acoustic highlighting.** Say the words more slowly or loudly, or pause for a bit before and after the key word. Provide redundancy. This means you should pull the key word out of your phrase or sentence, repeat the key word, then say the phrase or sentence again. Remember to repeat the important words.

For example, if you're playing with a ball, the word *ball* and the related actions could be key words. If your child knows the word *ball,* you might say "Throw the ball. Throw!" emphasizing the action word *throw.* You might emphasize the label *ball* more if he doesn't yet know this word. You could say "It's a ball. Ball. Throw the ball." In the first example, the action word is said more often; in the second example, the object label is said more often.

Where to Begin: A Word List

You might want to develop a word list to use with your child. Certainly, many parents teach their children to listen and talk without a word list and the corresponding activities, but it is an option if you'd like to try it. A **word list** is a list of words you use frequently to communicate with your child. The list is intended to help you use the words often so your child has repeated exposure and practice with this set of words. Using a word list will lead to your child's eventual understanding and use of some of the words.

You want to choose words that are interesting and meaningful to your child and words that eventually will be useful to her for communicating with you and others. You want to choose words that come up frequently as you live and play with your child, because this will encourage understanding and use of the words. You can use the words in phrases and short sentences, as well as by themselves sometimes. Speak with expression and use the words when they're appropriate and meaningful to a particular situation.

Possible Words for Your List

The following are words most children learn to understand early and words most children have an interest in using when they begin to talk.

Hi	stop	mine	no
bye-bye	go	ball	Uh-oh!
Mommy	light	baby	Ow!
Daddy	on	outside	Wow!
(other names)	off	shoe	Yuck!
up	eyes	Hooray!	sock
down	nose	hot	All gone!
open	ears	cold	Peek-a-boo!
push	Mmm!	eat	mouth
pull	night-night	drink	sleep
(animal labels)	(animal sounds)	close	move
run	jump	fall down	walk

These words are important because they come up over and over again naturally in your play and daily routine, so there are many opportunities to say the words to your child. Young children love animals and animal sounds. Add to your list several of these you can say over and over again. Also, if you find that other words come up repeatedly at home, add them!

These words are suggestions; however, you may want to make your own personalized list. Choose 20 or more from the above list and add some based on knowing your child. Post the list in an obvious place so you and other family members see it frequently. Review it regularly until you have committed the list to memory. This will help you become natural about using the words whenever possible. As your child progresses in learning words, you can add more to the list. Remember, one day soon your child will know too many words to list!

Use the Words on Your Child's Word List

The following is a list of words and various ways in which to use each word. Notice that most of the phrases and sentences have the word at either the end or the beginning. Children with hearing loss may be more attentive to the first or last word in phrases or sentences during their early language development. Once your child attends to words, understands some words and uses some words, you can try to use phrases and sentences in which the highlighted word is embedded somewhere in the middle.

Hi and *bye-bye*
- Say these words every time someone enters or leaves the area or room.
- You can say things such as:
  - "Mommy is going bye-bye."
  - "Tell Daddy Hi."
  - "Say Hi to Grandma."

Mommy, Daddy and other names
- Say these words to label yourself and your child's other parent and family members.
- Say these words to label people in pictures.
- You can say things such as:
  - "Mommy."
  - "Daddy."
  - "Here's Mommy."
  - "Where's Daddy?"
  - "Give it to Mommy."
  - "That's Daddy."
  - "Daddy loves you."
  - "I see (other name)."
  - "Hi, (other name)."

Up and *down*

- Say "up" any time you pick up your child or when she is climbing or getting up on something.
- Say "up" when picking up an object.
- Say "up" when you're zipping up her coat.
- Say "up" when you're playing with toys and they are made to go up.
- Say "down" when you're putting down your child.
- Say "down" to describe your child as she is getting down or climbing down.
- Say "down" any time you are putting down an object.
- Say "down" when you roll down a shade or pull down a window.
- Say "up" and "down" together when something or someone is moving up and down.
- You can say things such as:
  - "Do you want me to pick you up?"
  - "The airplane goes up, up, up!"
  - "Let's pull the shade up."
  - "Down."
  - "You climbed down."
  - "Get down!"
  - "I'm pulling the shade down."
  - "The bird goes up and down, up and down."

Open and *close*

- Say these words every time you open or close something.
- You can say things such as:
  - "Open."
  - "Close."
  - "Open the door."
  - "Close the box."
  - "Open the raisins."

Eat and *drink*

- Say these words to let your child know it is time to eat or drink something.
- Say these words to describe what someone is doing.
- Say these words to find out if your child is hungry or thirsty.
- Say these words to encourage your child to eat or drink something.
- You can say things such as:
  - "Eat."
  - "Drink."
  - "Do you want to eat?"

- □ "Eat some."
- □ "Take a drink."
- □ "Mommy wants to eat."
- □ "Here's your drink."

Stop and go

- Say "stop" to discipline your child when it's appropriate.
- Say "stop" to indicate an activity is finished.
- Say "go" to indicate to your child that she is to do something.
- Say "go" to determine a starting time for a motion or an activity.
- Say "go" to indicate that you're going somewhere.
- Say "stop" and "go" together to describe the motion of something.
- You can say things such as:
  - □ "Stop!"
  - □ "Please stop!"
  - □ "Stop it!"
  - □ "Let's stop."
  - □ "You may stop."
  - □ "Go ahead."
  - □ "Let's go!"
  - □ "Do you want to go?"
  - □ "Go on."
  - □ "Make it go."
  - □ "The car can stop and go, stop and go, stop and go."

Light, off and on

- Say these words any time you use a light switch.
- As you enter or leave a room with your child, point to the light and label it.
- Allow your child to turn the light on and off with a wall switch.
- Say "on" and "off" with other things that can be turned on and off, such as a sound-making toy, the washer/dryer, water faucet, etc.
- You can say things such as:
  - □ "It's off."
  - □ "It's on."
  - □ "Light."
  - □ "That is a light."
  - □ "Turn the light on/off."
  - □ "The light is on/off."
  - □ "Turn the water on/off."

Eyes, nose, mouth **and** *ears*

- Label and point to them on your child.
- Label and point to them on your own body.
- Label and point to them on a doll, a stuffed animal or a toy.
- Label and point to them in a picture or a book.
- You can say things such as:
  - "Eyes."
  - "Nose."
  - "Mouth."
  - "Ears."
  - "(child's name)'s eyes."
  - "Where is Mommy's nose?"
  - "Blue eyes."
  - "There's your nose."
  - "That's my mouth."
  - "Two ears."

Sleep **and** *night-night*

- Say these words when it's time to put your child to bed.
- Say these words to describe someone who is asleep.
- Say these words to encourage your child to go to sleep.
- You can say things such as:
  - "Go to sleep."
  - "Time for sleep."
  - "Daddy went to sleep."
  - "Night-night."

More

- Say "more" when you are giving your child more of something.
- Say "more" when your child wants more of something.
- You can say things such as:
  - "More?"
  - "More."
  - "More juice."
  - "No more."
  - "You want more applesauce?"

Mine

- Say "mine" for your child when she indicates something is hers.
- Say "mine" to indicate something is yours.

- You can say things such as:
  - ☐ "Mine."
  - ☐ "That's mine."
  - ☐ "It's mine."
  - ☐ "No, that's mine."

Ball

- Say "ball" every time you see or play with a ball.
- You can say things such as:
  - ☐ "Ball."
  - ☐ "Here's a ball."
  - ☐ "Get the ball."
  - ☐ "Where's the ball?"
  - ☐ "Throw the ball."
  - ☐ "That's my ball."
  - ☐ "The ball is big."

Baby

- Say "baby" in the love talk you use with your baby.
- Say "baby" when you look in the mirror with your baby.
- Say "baby" to label any baby you see.
- Say "baby" when you see a picture of a baby.
- You can say things such as:
  - ☐ "Baby."
  - ☐ "You're my baby."
  - ☐ "I love my baby."
  - ☐ "There's a baby."
  - ☐ "Aw, look at the baby."
  - ☐ "The baby is crying."

Outside

- Say "outside" to let your child know you will take her outside.
- Say "outside" for your child if she indicates she wants to go outside.
- Say "outside" when you look out the window.
- You can say things such as:
  - ☐ "Outside."
  - ☐ "You want to go outside."
  - ☐ "Look outside."
  - ☐ "Mommy's outside."
  - ☐ "Do you want to go outside?"
  - ☐ "Let's go outside and play."

Shoe and *sock*

- Say these words when dressing or undressing your child.
- Say these words to label the clothes people are wearing.
- You can say things such as:
    - "Shoe."
    - "Sock."
    - "(child's name)'s shoe."
    - "Where is your shoe?"
    - "A blue sock."
    - "Get your shoe."
    - "Daddy's sock."
    - "Let's get shoes and socks."

Hot and *cold*

- Say "hot" to teach your child that hot things are dangerous.
- Say "hot" to describe drinks or water or cold foods or other items.
- You can say things such as:
    - "Hot."
    - "Be careful, the stove is hot!"
    - "Blow, the soup is hot."
    - "No, no, the fire is hot!"
    - "Ouch, the water is hot!"
    - "Cold juice, yummy!"
    - "That water feels cold. Brr!"

Push, pull and *move*

- Say these words when someone or something is being pushed, pulled or moved.
- Say these words to ask your child to push, pull or move something.
- Say these words to ask your child not to push or pull.
- Say "push" when pushing your child on a swing.
- Say "push" with toy vehicles.
- Say "pull" with toys on a string that can be pulled.
- You can say things such as:
    - "Push! Push! Push!"
    - "Move, please."
    - "Push and pull."
    - "Push your truck."
    - "Pull the string."
    - "Don't push."
    - "Move over."
    - "Move the pillow."

No

- Say "no" to respond to her requests when it is appropriate, even if her requests are nonverbal.
- Say "no" to discipline her when it is appropriate.
- You can say things such as:
  - "No, no!"
  - "(child's name), no, no!"
  - "No, not now."
  - "No, I don't want the (object)."
  - "No more."
  - "No hitting."

Action words *(ex: walk, run, jump, cry, fall down)*

- Many young children are on the go and give you lots of opportunities to use simple action words as you talk together. Your child can learn verbs such as these, as well as others that come up, through the simple interaction that accompanies routines and play activities. Use your child's activity to suggest action words for your word list. Then, just listen and talk to go along with the situation.
- You can say things such as:
  - "Please walk."
  - "No running."
  - "Jump . . . jump . . . jump."
  - "Aw, don't cry."
  - "Oh no, you fell down!"

Exclamations *(Uh-oh! Oh no! Ow! Wow! Yuck! Hooray! Peek-a-boo! All gone! Mmm!*)*

- Use exclamations with your child every time you get the chance.
- Say the words with emphasis.
- You can use exclamations by themselves or with a related word or phrase.
- Say "Uh-oh!" or "Oh no!" every time a problem or mess occurs near or with your child.
- Say "Ow!" when your child or you are hurt.
- Say "Wow!" to express excitement about something your child does, says or sees.
- Say "Yuck!" or "Yucky!" when reacting to messes or dirt.
- Say "Hooray!" to praise your child.
- Play Peek-a-Boo! whenever you can. Hide behind a blanket or chair — or just cover your face with your hands.
- Say "All gone!" to describe something that is finished or emptied.
- Say "Mmm!" about tasty foods or drinks your child enjoys.

*typically associated with situations that interest young children

Dog, cat and other animal names

■ Animal labels and animal sounds are of great interest to young children. Choose several animals that your child actually sees live and several represented by toys or by pictures in books. Try to choose many animals that make a recognizable sound you can make. Sometimes it's more appropriate to use the animal's label. Sometimes you can use the label and the animal's sound together. For some animals that don't make a sound, you might want to use an associated action.

■ Some animal labels and sounds you might use are:

- ■ dog   "woof, woof, woof"
- ■ cat/kitty   "meeeow"
- ■ bird   "tweet tweet"
- ■ cow   "moooo"
- ■ horse   "neigh"
- ■ duck   "quack quack"
- ■ sheep   "baaaaaa baaaaa"
- ■ pig   "oink oink oink"
- ■ chicken   "cluck cluck" or "cock-a-doodle-doo"
- ■ rabbit   "hop hop hop"
- ■ frog   "ribbit" or "croak"
- ■ bee   "bzzzz"

Don't be concerned if your child learns the sound before learning the animal's name. These sounds are interesting and fun. Many children with typical hearing learn them before learning the animal names, too.

Other words

You might think of other words you want to add to your word list. Use words your child is likely to hear dozens or even hundreds of times each week. Go for it!

A Listen Box

A **listen box** is a small container filled with 15 or more age-appropriate toys and items to stimulate a child's listening and language abilities. Playing with a listen box provides a very structured activity to practice fun, yet repetitive language with your child. Each item has a certain word or sound used to label it. As is true with the word list, some parents will find a listen box and the corresponding activity helpful and others will find it to be too much.

A listen box activity requires you to set aside a time each day to provide focused language stimulation and planned communication with your child. At first, you may spend only three minutes on an activity. As your child's attention improves, you can build up to five minutes and eventually to 10 or 15. If possible, do the same activity several times daily. Several short periods are even better than one long one. Remember, it's normal for a young child to have a short attention span!

You can make a listen box yourself. An ideal container is an opaque, rectangular, plastic storage container about 12x15x6″ with a lid. This type of container opens and closes easily and prevents the child from seeing the items inside. It has a flat surface you can use as your play area.

The container should:
- hold 15 to 20 hand-size toys and objects
- have a lid or latch to open and close it
- be opaque, so the items inside are not visible
- be plastic or wooden so when you shake it the items make a loud noise
- be portable and storable

The objects should:
- fit in *your* hand
- be large enough to prevent a choking hazard
- be safe without small breakable parts
- be visually interesting or produce an interesting sound

Here are some suggested items for your child's listen box:

baby	cup	plane
ball	dog	rabbit
bell	duck	rattle
bird	fire truck	scarf
boat	frog	sheep
bus	hat	shoe
car	horse	sock
cat	mirror	spoon
chick	phone	toys that make sounds
cow	pig	

Simply collect the items in the container and select a place out of your child's reach to store it when not in use. These materials should be used only for this purpose and not during undirected or unsupervised play. This is necessary to maintain your child's interest in the materials and the activity.

Steps for Using a Listen Box

- Assemble the listen box.
- Choose a quiet place and try to play in the same place each time. Sitting and playing in a high chair is ideal to keep your child from crawling or walking away; however, you may prefer the couch, with your child seated and you on the floor in front of her.
- Play with the listen box for 5 to 15 minutes. Keep it fun.

- Say "Listen!" and shake the container before opening it. Comment on the sound you hear.
- Talk about opening and closing the box each time.
- Be in control of the box, but follow your child's lead with the items.
- Use one or two items at a time and put each item back before taking out others. Usually, you will take out one item at a time to talk about it. However, sometimes it's good to use two items together. This allows you to demonstrate putting a hat on a baby or pretending to stir with a spoon in a cup.
- Use a clear voice with expression and changing intonation.
- Label objects and actions and talk simply about the items. Vary what you do with and say about the items. Try to vary your placement of the word for the item or action, using it sometimes at the beginning, sometimes in the middle and sometimes at the end of your phrases and sentences. Make any relevant sounds associated with the item or action.
- Talk about parts of each item such as eyes, nose, mouth, ears, wheels, buttons and so on. Try to say the same things about each item each time, in addition to adding new, simple comments. Try labeling the ball and throwing it at first; but then roll it, bounce it or describe it.
- Reinforce your child's attention, nonverbal or vocal imitations, vocalizations, verbalizations and interactions with you. You can praise her by smiling, responding, imitating her or patting her on the back.
- Be creative and have fun! It's fine to use the scarf to play Peek-A-Boo! Or throw it into the air or move it back and forth to cover a sleeping baby or animal.
- Stop the activity before your child loses interest. This will encourage her to want to play again another time.

Variations on the Listen Box

If your child needs a bit of variety, try some of these ideas:
- Hide the items and find them. Talk about each item as you put it in the listen box.
- Use only the plastic items and play with them in an inch of water in the listen box. Talk about each as you put it in the water, play and remove it to get the next one.
- Use half the total items for two weeks. Exchange them for the other half for the next two weeks.
- Play in a different room. Try the living room couch, your bed, the high chair or a blanket on the floor.
- Have two of some toys so you and your child both can hold one. Your child can imitate your vocalizations and actions using that toy.
- Extend your child's learning by using the same vocabulary from the listen box during other activities or routines, such as while reading together, playing outside or eating.

Chapter 16

Play

Play is one of the most important activities your child does during the day. Children learn through play. They learn about themselves and their bodies, as well as their thoughts, feelings and abilities through play. They learn about the world through play. They learn about other people through play. Play allows children to develop every single category of age-appropriate skills:

- cognitive
- listening
- language
- speech
- problem-solving
- literacy
- pre-academic
- gross motor
- fine motor
- social
- creativity

In essence, play allows children to learn new skills and information, to interact and socialize and to communicate or express feelings, ideas, wants and needs. Children *need* play to develop these skills. Many people believe play is what children do to give parents or caregivers a break. Likely, there are times this is true for you. Yet one of the best ways you can help your child develop all of her skills is playing with her. There are lots of ways to play. Through playing, you can correctly model play skills and language while spending quality time with your child. She will love this and so will you!

Categories /Stages of Play

In 1932, a researcher named Mildred Parten developed a theory and classification of the stages of children's play. Since then, hundreds of other researchers have studied its complexities. To fully understand your child's development of play skills, it's important to know the categories, or stages, of play. You may want to review the following list and see what kind of play your child is using now. Then continue to watch her skills develop over time (Frost et al., 2008; Brain & Mukherji, 2005; Rosetti, 2001).

Associative play occurs when children become more interested in each other than the toys they're using. Children have individual goals for their play, which may be similar, but there is no formal organization or set rules. They play with the same set of toys or trade toys. This is the first stage that involves social interaction between the children while they play. It begins in toddlerhood and extends through preschool.

Cooperative play occurs around age 5 when children develop play based on an organized set of rules with a goal in mind and at least one leader. This begins in the late preschool period.

Creative play is play in which children use materials for artistic expression. This includes drawing with crayons, markers, pencils or other drawing materials, painting with paint or water color, building with clay or doodling with shaving cream, pudding or other goopy substances. Creative play can be independent or interactive and social.

Constructive play involves making things with objects, such as a town built from blocks.

Dramatic play is play in which children act out experiences they've had or situations they've observed in their lives. As with symbolic play, children use symbols to represent people and things. Further, dramatic play requires rules and set goals. To act out a baby/mother schema, a child represents the mother and uses a doll to represent the baby. Rules include keeping to actions a mother would usually perform with her baby — giving the baby a bottle, getting the baby dressed, changing the baby's diaper, rocking the baby in a rocking chair and putting the baby to bed. It would be against the rules to stuff the baby in the pot on the play stove and stir it around with a spoon.

Exploratory/functional/sensorimotor play involves exploring objects and learning about their properties, the ways they can change and the ways they can be used. Exploratory play helps a child understand new experiences and the environment through the senses — tasting, smelling, hearing, touching and seeing. It can involve repeating simple body movements or actions the child enjoys. This stage of play begins in infancy and continues throughout childhood or life.

Manipulative play is play in which a child controls materials and her environment through her actions. Manipulative play helps a child understand how things work and how her actions alter her environment. A baby drops something just to see someone pick it up or pushes a button on a toy to see the lights flash. A child a little bit older manipulates puzzle pieces into a puzzle tray, and an even older child assembles intricate block configurations.

Onlooker play occurs when a child takes an interest in other children's play but does not join in. The child may ask questions or just talk to other children, but the main activity simply is to watch. This type of play usually starts during toddler years, but it can take place at any age.

Parallel play occurs when a child plays alongside other children or mimics other children's play but doesn't actively engage with them. For example, the child may use the same kind of toy as another child and mimic the other child's actions, but they are not engaged with one another. Parallel play usually is associated with toddlers, although it happens in any age group. Children play side by side with similar toys, but there is no group involvement.

Physical play includes kicking, rolling, crawling, running, jumping, climbing, biking, moving around and rough and tumble play. For babies, physical play is often independent, although it becomes much more interactive and social as children grow older. Physical play can be free from rules, such as running in a park or playing with playground equipment, or it can be organized and rule-based, such as playing Duck-Duck-Goose, Ring Around the Rosie, Tag or Double-Dutch jump rope.

Pretend play is described in detail below.

Solitary play occurs when a child is completely engrossed in playing and does not seem to notice other children. This begins in infancy and is common in toddlers because of their limited social, cognitive and physical skills. However, it's important for all age groups to have some time to play by themselves.

Symbolic play uses symbols to mimic people and objects imaginatively. Symbolic play doesn't follow rules or have specific goals. This could include using a block as a telephone, pushing a hairbrush around like a car or holding a teddy bear like an adult would hold a baby.

Unoccupied play occurs when a child is relatively stationary and appears to be performing random movements with no apparent purpose.

Sound the Trumpets for . . .
. . . Pretend Play!

By the time typically developing children are about 5 years old, they're able to integrate the skills required for many kinds of play — such as associative play, cooperative play, symbolic play and dramatic play — to then participate in the be-all-end-all of play . . . pretend play. Pretend play is the most complicated kind of play because a child must have developed play skills in other categories and stages before accomplishing pretend play. **Pretend play** is the ability to represent familiar experiences with many steps in the correct sequence and to re-enact events with new outcomes. It includes role-playing and requires a significant amount of world knowledge, or knowledge about how things are. Pretend play requires children to have certain cognitive and language skills. Each action in the play is in response to the other players, yet the play follows specific rules about the role of each character. Pretend play also includes goals toward which children work as they engage in play together.

In a doctor/patient play scenario, one child plays doctor while the other plays patient. The doctor follows the rules of play by acting out specific doctor behaviors — she feels the patient's forehead, looks at the patient's throat, gives the patient a shot, tells the patient to take some medicine and sends the patient home. The patient follows the rules of play by acting out specific patient behaviors: She enters the office acting ill, tells the doctor her symptoms, lies on the doctor's table, says, "Ouch" when she gets a shot and thanks the doctor as she leaves. The goal of this play may be that the patient is treated and feels better after her visit to the doctor.

Children who are truly able to use pretend play can alter the events in the scenario while continuing to follow the rules and work toward the goal. If the children mentioned above were to switch roles, the patient might tell the doctor her ankle hurts. The doctor would then examine her ankle, tell her it's broken and put a cast on it. The patient would thank the doctor and limp out of the office. These children are able to consider events associated with a doctor/patient scenario, to act out the events in the correct order and, in future play using this same schema, to alter the events to create new outcomes. Both children work toward the goal of making the patient's ankle better.

Beyond real-life experiences, children who engage in pretend play also can re-enact events they didn't actually experience but learned about from someone else or through books or other media. For example, children often act out the events of a story like *Goldilocks and the Three Bears*. They might pretend to be astronauts who take a space shuttle to the moon, walk around on various planets and interact with aliens. They might pretend to be cavemen who live among dinosaurs. These are obviously not experiences they've actually had, but through books, television, movies and other experiences on these topics and the associated events, they can use their language skills, play skills and imaginations to create scenarios that follow rules and work toward common goals.

Relationship Between Language and Play

By definition, **language** is a formal set of symbols and rules. It is very abstract. Language requires a person to mentally store and retrieve the words for objects, actions and descriptors in addition to the rules for combining those words. Language itself is a symbol, and it requires a person to be able to mentally represent reality (Westby, 2000).

Examples:
- To initiate something using language, one has to think about it first.
- To request something using language, one has to think about it first.
- To tell what happened using language, one has to mentally picture the occurrence and the result.

Similarly, symbolic play requires a person to represent one thing with something else, such as when using a banana to represent a phone, using a miniature toy horse to represent a real horse, or even zooming a little block through the air like an airplane. Play also requires a person to be able to mentally represent reality (Westby, 2000).

Both language and play require a person to mentally represent reality (Westby, 2000).

The relationship between language and play is close and symbiotic. Symbolic play is a prerequisite to learning language. A child must be able to represent reality with symbols before she can learn to use language. Once a child can represent reality with symbols, she is ready to learn language as a set of symbols. Then, as the child develops language skills, she also prepares to use pretend play. When a child engages in pretend play, she is using symbols — toys, miniature objects, her imagination — to represent reality. Pretend play can develop only so far without specific language skills.

Play skills and language skills work like rungs on a ladder. The ladder represents success. Every other rung of the ladder represents language skills, and the other half of the rungs represent play skills. For a person to move one hand to a "language skills rung" on the ladder, she must have a solid grip with the other hand on the "play skills rung" right below. Then she has to have a solid grip on that "play skills rung" before she can move up to the next rung, "language skills." Children build up to high-level play and language skills by working their way up from low-level play and language skills. Language and play skills are acquired in an alternating fashion. Children who don't have age-appropriate play skills usually don't have age-appropriate language skills. Children who don't have age-appropriate language skills usually don't have age-appropriate play skills.

Relationship Between Play and Language Skills for Children With Hearing Loss

You may be wondering why you, as a parent or caregiver, should be concerned about your child's play skills. The relationship between play and language skills is particularly crucial for children with hearing loss learning to listen and talk. If a child's play skills are delayed, you can expect her language skills to also be delayed. If a child's language skills are delayed, it's possible her play skills might be delayed. Many people assume children's play skills just happen because children are naturally curious and motivated by toys. In the same way children with hearing loss don't learn spoken language as readily as children with typical hearing, children with hearing loss often don't understand or pick up on the intricacies of real-life events as thoroughly as children with typical hearing do. Pretend play requires a child to have a good, solid understanding of experiences and the language that goes with those experiences. For this reason, it's imperative for parents of young children with hearing loss and the professionals working with them to monitor both language progress and play skill development. One area cannot develop fully without the other.

Relationship Between Play, Language and Literacy Skills

Language and literacy skills are very closely related, and language and play skills are very closely related (as you read above). Therefore, it makes sense that play skills are closely related to literacy skills as well. The use of language, the social interaction of play and the ability to read require a child to have the following prerequisite skills:

- **Mental model**

  A mental model is a person's thought process about an event or series of events. Pretend play requires a child to represent people, objects and experiences with symbols. A mental model is needed to picture in one's mind the people, objects and experiences before they can be recreated with symbols. Similarly, understanding a story read from a book requires a child to build in her mind a representation of the situation described in the text (Cain & Oakhill, 2007).

- **Episodic memory**

  Episodic memory is memory of experiences and the series of events that make up that experience. It is the ability to picture an experience in one's mind and tap into that memory when talking about it. It requires a person to relate the present moment to something that already has happened as well as something that could happen in the future (Tulving, 1993). Episodic memory is required for telling stories, recognizing relationships, understanding cause and effect, making predictions and making inferences.

  Episodic memory can be developed through play, which gives children a rehearsal of the experience (Westby, 2008). Promoting episodic memory skills can be done using the following procedures:
  - Have an experience.
  - Talk about the experience.
  - Discuss feelings about the experience to tap into emotional states that support memory.
  - Act out the experience. This helps develop memories of events.

- **Theory of mind**

  Theory of mind is the ability to understand that others have beliefs, desires and intentions that are different from one's own. This ability can be developed through pretend play when a child takes on a character and acts the way that character would act (Gopnik & Astington, 1988; deVilliers, 2005; Westby, 2008).

- **Metacommunicative strategies**

  Metacommunicative strategies are cues indicating how language should be interpreted. They include intonation, facial expressions and gestures. For example, saying "That's a nice shirt" with an excited intonation is different from saying "That's a nice shirt" with a sarcastic intonation.

- **Decontextualized language**

  Decontextualized language is language that conveys meaning by using only grammar and vocabulary. Using decontextualized language effectively requires the ability to provide enough appropriate language for another person to understand without background knowledge or contextual clues such as intonation, facial expressions or gestures. Children must understand decontextualized language to comprehend written text. Text requires the reader to understand the details through language alone. In addition, children must be able to use decontextualized language to provide high-level and abstract details in their spoken language (Curenton & Justice, 2004; Westby, 2008).

- **Metalinguistic language**

  Metalinguistic language is language used to tell about language. For example, "He said . . ." or "She told me to. . . ."

- **Metacognitive language**

  Metacognitive language is language for telling what one is thinking. For example, "I know . . ." "I wonder . . ." or "I'm thinking that . . ."

Language and Play for Children with Hearing Loss

For some children with hearing loss, symbolic play skills are well developed by age 3. These children then specifically need to learn the language and vocabulary required to engage in that play with others. Other children with hearing loss have delayed play skills. For these children, the first order of business is to practice early play that doesn't require language. They need early play skills before they can learn the language and vocabulary to be successful in more complex play. To understand which play skills develop early and which are more complex, it may be helpful to read the milestones of play starting on page 245.

Language Requirements for Typical Preschool Play Skills

Appropriately plays with toys designed for preschool-aged children Examples: - drives little vehicles around a toy garage, airport or train set - feeds a doll with a bottle; holds, burps, rocks and dresses a doll - builds structures with blocks - completes puzzles	Language is not required.
Understands preschool concepts through experiences Play skills require children have many "experiences" in in their lives. Experiences include everything a child sees and does everywhere she goes. Experiences include baking, cooking, doing laundry, raking leaves, riding in a car, washing a car, bathing, shopping, eating at a restaurant, building things, gardening, going to the zoo and so on. Experiences allow children to learn about and understand their world. Examples: - understands the steps to washing a car - knows the parts of a car and general location of parts - knows the steps in washing a baby - knows the steps in taking a baby on a walk	Language is *not* required, but is helpful. Typically developing preschoolers have language at this stage.
Pretends real-life experiences Pretending real-life experiences requires that a child actually has the experiences, some understanding of the basic concepts associated with them and the ability to talk about the play scene. Examples: - pretends to drive a car - pretends to bake a cake or make dinner - pretends to be a passenger or ticket collector at a train station - pretends to hail a taxi to the airport and get on an airplane - pretends to be a school teacher or student - pretends to be a waitress or restaurant patron	Language is required.

Milestones of Play and Corresponding Language Skills

You may be interested to know some of the play skills and associated language skills children typically develop in the first years of life. This chart may be useful to share with your child's early interventionist or preschool teacher.

8–12 Months (Pre-Symbolic Level I)

Play skills

- is aware objects exist when not seen and associates an object with a location (ex: finds a toy hidden under a cloth)
- attains a toy by pulling a cloth on which the toy is resting
- attains a toy by a pulling string
- touches an adult to continue activity
- explores moveable parts of a toy
- does not mouth all toys
- uses different kinds of play (ex: patting, banging, turning, throwing)
- plays in different ways with multiple and different objects

Language skills

- demonstrates joint attention on a toy and person
- uses language tied to context and only associated with certain actions or situations (ex: "Bye-bye.")
- shows and gives objects
- requests using gestures and/or words
- commands using gestures and/or words
- shares emotions

12–17 Months (Pre-Symbolic Level II)

Play skills

- is aware that objects exist when not seen or when not in the regular location
- finds objects hidden in first one place and then in a second or third location
- understands things can go into other things
- recognizes that an object can be in a container and works to find a way to get the object out
- hands a toy to an adult if unable to operate
- hands a toy to an adult to get attention
- uses index finger to point to a desired object
- recognizes operating parts of toys (attends to knobs, buttons and levers)
- discovers operation of toys through trial and error

- constructs relationships between toys (ex: puts one toy in another such as figure in car)
- uses familiar objects appropriately (puts a comb through hair)
- plays with blocks by stacking and knocking down
- plays by filling and dumping/pouring

Language skills

- use of single words depends on context (ex: is able to use the word *car* when riding in a car, but not when she sees a car)
- makes requests using gestures and/or words
- gives commands using gestures and/or words
- interacts using gestures and/or words
- uses gestures and/or words to communicate feelings
- protests using gestures and/or words
- labels using gestures and/or words
- responds using gestures and/or words
- greets using gestures and/or words

17–19 Months (Symbolic Level I)

Play skills

- uses tools (ex: uses a stick to reach a toy)
- finds a toy that is invisibly hidden
- pretends using life-like props
- uses common objects and toys appropriately
- requires props to engage in pretend play
- pretends familiar, everyday activities (ex: eating, sleeping) in which she has been an active participant
- demonstrates single, short pretend actions
- is the only character in her pretend play (ex: pretends to go to sleep, eat from a spoon or drink from an empty cup)

Language skills

- uses language to direct others by requesting
- uses language to direct others by commanding
- uses language to engage others
- uses language to protest
- uses language to protect self-interests
- uses language to label objects and activities
- uses language to comment on personal feelings
- uses single words and phrases representing a variety of grammatical categories

19–22 Months (Symbolic Level II)

Play skills

- represents activities done by familiar people (ex: cooking, cleaning, shaving)
- uses two related toys together in pretend play (ex: puts a spoon in a pan)
- demonstrates short, isolated combinations of pretend play with actions or toys (ex: rocks a doll then puts it to bed, pours from a pitcher into a cup, feeds a doll from a plate with a spoon)
- performs pretend actions on passive recipients (brushes a doll's hair, puts a blanket on a toy bear)
- performs pretend actions on more than one object or person (ex: feeds herself, then feeds her doll)
- pretends roles of familiar caregivers

Language skills

- refers to objects and people not present
- requests information
- begins to use two-word combinations (ex: "Mommy eat" "throw ball" "Daddy cup")

2 Years (Symbolic Level III)

Play skills

- represents daily experiences with realistic and life-sized objects (ex: plays house and acts as mommy, daddy or baby)
- pretends elaborate single daily experiences with details
- shows awareness that certain people do certain things and that people are different by pretending differently depending on the role (ex: rocks a baby doll when playing mommy and sprays the hose while playing firefighter, but doesn't spray the hose when playing mommy)

Language skills

- comments on her own actions (ex: "Get apple.")
- comments on others' actions (ex: "Baby sleep.")
- uses phrases and short sentences
- attempts to use present progressive verbs
- attempts to use plurals
- attempts to use possessives

2½ Years (Symbolic Level IV)

Play skills

- represents less-frequent events that were personally experienced (ex: shopping, going to the doctor)
- continues to represent short and isolated events with realistic props and many shifts in roles
- talks to dolls
- reverses complementary roles (doctor-patient, shopper-cashier)

Language skills

- responds appropriately to questions beginning with *What, Who, Whose, Where* and *What . . . do*
- asks questions beginning with *What, Who, Whose, Where* and *What do*
- responds inappropriately to *Why* questions when about unfamiliar routines
- asks *Why* questions, but often inappropriately, and does not attend to the answer

3 Years (Symbolic Level V)

Play skills

- re-enacts experienced events and modifies original outcomes
- engages in evolving episodes that are unplanned (ex: mixes cake batter, bakes it and washes the dishes; doctor checks the patient, calls the ambulance and takes the patient to the hospital)
- transforms self into a role
- engages in associative play — children do similar activities and may share roles, but have no organized goals or rules

Language skills

- uses language to report
- uses language to predict
- uses language to attempt to narrate or tell a story
- uses past tense (ex: "I ate the cake." "I walked.")
- uses future aspect (ex: "I'm gonna do it.")

3 to 3½ Years (Symbolic Level VI)

Play skills

- carries out pretend activities with replica toys (ex: doll house and people, barn and animals)
- uses one object to represent another (ex: stick is a comb, chair is a car)

- uses blocks to build enclosures for imaginative play (blocks represent a fence for animals or a house for dolls)
- pretends observed events in which she was not an active participant (ex: policeman, fireman, characters from TV shows)
- assigns roles to other children
- negotiates play with others
- uses multiple reversible roles (ex: child is ticket seller, pilot and flight attendant, but co-player is always the passenger)
- talks for a doll or puppet
- takes reciprocal roles with dolls (ex: child talks for the doll and acts as parent of the doll)

Language skills

- gives dialogue, including projected desires, thoughts and feelings, to dolls or puppets
- uses indirect requests (ex: "Mommy lets me have cookies for breakfast.")
- changes speech depending on the listener
- uses reasoning by integrating reports, predictions, projections and information
- uses cues that indicate how language should be interpreted, including intonation, facial expressions and gestures
- reasons by integrating information gained from reports, predictions and projections
- uses descriptive words associated with shape, size, color, texture and spatial relationships
- uses language to tell about language (ex: "He said . . . ")
- uses language for telling what one is thinking (ex: "I know . . . ")

3½ to 4 Years (Symbolic Level VII)

Play skills

- uses language to invent props and set the scene
- builds three-dimensional structures with blocks
- improvises and varies pretend play themes
- plans varied scripts with outcomes that differ from what was observed (ex: "I'm the mom and I'm going to cook this dinner called pizza, marshmallow and coffee soup.")
- hypothesizes (ex: "What would happen if . . . ")
- organizes scripts by telling what will happen (ex: "Since I'm the fireman, I get to spray the hose.")
- uses dolls and puppets to act out scripts
- takes on multiple roles or assigns multiple roles to a doll (ex: mother/wife, fireman/husband/father)

Language skills

- uses language to take the role of characters in play
- uses language to direct other children during play
- uses language to create the story line in play
- uses modals* (ex: *can, could, may, might, would*)
- uses conjunctions*(ex: *and, but, so, because, if*)
- gives some appropriate responses to *Why* and *How* questions that require reasoning

5 Years (Symbolic Level VIII)

Play skills

- uses language to set the scene, actions and roles, perhaps without realistic props
- uses highly imaginative activities that integrate parts of events the child has never participated in or observed (ex: astronaut builds a space shuttle, flies to a strange planet, explores the planet, eats unusual food and talks with creatures)
- plans several sequences of pretend events
- organizes children and objects that are needed
- coordinates several scripts occurring simultaneously (ex: "While I'm the girl spinning straw, you have to climb up the castle wall and get my necklace.")
- engages fully in collaborative play with coordinated roles, rules and common goals

Language skills

- uses relational terms* (ex: *then, when, first, next, last, while, before, after*)*

How to Play with Your Child

At some point in your day, even if just for a short time, you likely need your child to play while you accomplish some other necessary duty like unloading the dishwasher, taking a shower or making dinner. Yet playing *with* your child provides a great opportunity to integrate all the tips, tricks and skills you've been reading about in this book — for example, keeping devices on, vocabulary exposure and practice, following your child's lead, singing songs, etc. In addition, your child needs you to play with her so you can model appropriate play for her. This is a little scary for some parents mostly because they are unsure about what to do. If that describes you, then fear no more! The following descriptions of games can be your guide for successfully playing with your child.

*Note: Full competence with these modals, conjunctions and relational terms does not develop until 10–12 years old (Westby & White, 2014).

Games to Play with Your Baby or Young Child

There are lots and lots of ways you can play with your child . . . *lots*! Some are listed here, but don't be afraid to come up with your own special games, particularly if you find something really fun and motivating for your child. You and your child will love it!

The games and activities described below are designed to let your young child know that communication is fun and rewarding. They are appropriate from the beginning, as you get started teaching your child to talk, and later, as alternatives to the other routine and play activities of your day.

One thing to consider is your use of an expressive voice with varied intonation. Most babies and some children are captivated by this kind of voice. If it works for you and your child, keep it up. For other children, that kind of expression and intonation doesn't matter much. In fact, they respond just as well when you talk to them like you would anyone else — in an interesting yet matter-of-fact way. Try both, see what feels comfortable to you and learn what interests your child.

Peek-a-boo!

All you need is any piece of clothing, paper, a towel or just your hands for hiding behind. You can play this game almost anywhere. You know how to play. Get behind something, pause and then pop up with a surprised look on your face, saying "Peek-a-boo!" This is sure to elicit attention and giggles. Once you've done this many times, see if your child will hide behind the blanket or other object. Wait to see if she vocalizes when she pops out at you. If so, you can praise her, clap and shout, "Yay!" If she doesn't vocalize, then you can say it for her, give her a big smile and then praise her anyway.

Pat-a-cake

Use the words and actions of any version of this well-known nursery rhyme with your child. After you've done it a number of times, encourage her to copy the actions and to vocalize as you play it again. (See Chapter 17 if you need the words and actions.)

Monkey see, monkey do

This is a simple game based on the concept of "I'll do it, then you do it." First, do something with your arms, hands, face or legs. Next, say what you did (maybe "Clap, clap."). Lastly, get your child to copy you. If she doesn't copy you on her own, help her copy you (for example, by clapping her hands for her). If your child has been playing this with you for a while, turn the tables and copy something she does, then continue the back-and-forth communication. You can say the appropriate words or just imitate her vocalizations.

Telephone

Get a toy telephone and face your child as you talk into it. Hand the phone to your child, pause and give her an expectant look. Many children have seen adults engage in this activity before and will readily vocalize when handed a phone. For your turn, you can say any of the following or anything else you want:

- "Hello? Hi!"
- "Who is this? Oh, yes. Okay. Thanks. Bye."
- "Oh, hi, Grandma. I'm fine. How are you? Are you coming over later?"
- "Great! See you then. Bye!"

Praise your conversationalist when she chatters in any way!

Bounce the baby

This game can be any version you know or make up. Just put your child on your lap or on your extended legs and bounce her a bit. Remember to take it easy; safety is always a priority.

- You can recite a nursery rhyme:
  "Horsey, horsey through the town. Horsey bounces up and down."
- You can repeat the same word: "Bounce . . . bounce . . . bounce."
- You can talk and move in the same rhythm: "Up and down, up and down."

Dance to the music

Use a radio, mp3 player or cd player and play some energetic music. Pick up your child and dance. Set her down and dance to the music. Try many types of music with differing rhythms. Sing along sometimes.

You talk and I'll talk

Hold your child comfortably and just talk to her. Use "love talk" that is sweet, slow and drawn out, kind and loving. Then pause and smile at your baby expectantly so she learns that it's her turn. Pat, rub and hug your baby if she responds, hopefully with talk. Then take another turn again and let your baby take another turn.

"Hi" and "Bye"

Use rooms, doors and mirrors to play "Hi" and "Bye." Each time someone goes in or out of a room say "Hi" or "Bye." Get behind a door that opens and closes and play "Hi" and "Bye." Pick up your child, go to a mirror, say "Hi" and then walk away. Go back to it and say "Hi" again.

Eyes, nose, mouth and ears

Touch and label these on your baby, on yourself, on dolls and on toys. Let other family members touch and label their eyes, nose, mouth and ears. Encourage your baby to copy. You can expand this into the more traditional "Head, Shoulders, Knees and Toes" song and game if you and your child enjoy it. Slow down the pace a bit and move with the rhythm of your song.

Push or roll

Get a toy car or something else to push. Say "Push!" and push it toward your child. Keep playing and praise your child the day she vocalizes or tries to say "Push" when it's her turn. In similar fashion, play "Roll" with a ball. Keep in mind that your child's beginning vocalizations will not sound exactly like the words "push" or "roll." That's okay!

Point, pause and label

You can play this game anytime or anywhere. Point out something of interest, pause, get your child's attention and label the item. Use your child's interest as a guide. You might want to begin this with only a couple of items (such as dogs and airplanes), but point, pause and label every time you see one. Soon your child will point and pause and either wait for you to label the object or vocalize herself.

Introduce books

Your child may not yet be ready to sit down with you while you read her an entire story. However, she is ready to be introduced to books even as an infant. Books are very important for her learning, and you can use them in many ways. In the beginning, find a book with a page showing an object you have around the house. Show and label the picture and then show and label the real object. You also can find an action pictured in the book and copy it by doing the action yourself, showing both to your child and labeling both. Talk simply about familiar objects and actions pictured in books. Sit with your child and just look at some of the pictures together. Label any objects or actions that interest her or that you think she will like. You also can make noises associated with objects (such as "Moo" for a cow) and actions (such as "Knock, knock" for a door).

Don't worry about going in order or seeing every page of the book. You can label or talk about a picture when your child attends to you. Let your child help turn the pages. Also give your child several sturdy books to look at for a quiet-time activity such as at rest time. If there aren't other toys in reach, she'll take a look at the books. Some young children build the habit of looking at books in bed. This is a great step toward becoming a lifelong lover of books!

These games and activities may give you ideas for others, such as reciting nursery rhymes or finger plays or playing simple games with something to do and something to say. Be creative! Improvise! Have fun! It's all useful in helping your child learn to listen and talk!

Floor Time

One sure-fire way to get a young child involved in play is to get down on the floor with her and play with toys. Pretend to be someone or something. Do a puzzle together. Move animals in and out of a toy barn. Hold a doll and pretend to give her a bottle. There are tons of things to do and tons of possibilities for toys. You also can use kitchen items such as pots and spatulas to play drums or pretend to cook something.

No matter what kind of play activities you do with your child, this is a wonderful time to build a happy and trusting relationship with her. Playtime also allows for great listening, language and speech modeling. Use lots of appropriate, natural language that describes your actions and the play you are doing. This may become one of your child's favorite times during the day . . . and yours, too!

References

Brain, C. & Mukherji, P. (2005). Play and Friendships. *Understanding Child Psychology* (pp. 131–143). Nelson Thornes: Cheltenham, United Kingdom.

Cain, K. & Oakhill, J. (2007). Reading comprehension difficulties: Correlates, causes, and consequences. In K. Cain & J. Oakhill (Eds.), *Children's Comprehension Problems in Oral and Written Language* (pp. 41–75). New York: Guilford.

Curenton, S.M. & Justice, L. (2004). African American and Caucasian preschoolers' use of decontextualized language: Use of literate language features in oral narratives. *Language, Speech and Hearing Services in the Schools, 35,* 240–235.

deVilliers, P. (2005). The role of language in theory-of-mind development: What deaf children tell us. In J.W. Astington and J.A. Baird (Eds.), *Why Language Matters for Theory of Mind.* New York: Oxford.

Frost, J.L., Wortham, S.C. & Reifel, S. (2008). *Play and Child Development* (3rd ed.) (pp. 142–146). Upper Saddle River, NJ: Pearson.

Gopnik, A. & Astington, J. (1988). Children's understanding of representational change and its relation to the understanding of false belief and the appearance-reality distinction. *Child Development, 59,* 26–37.

McGuigan, F. & Salmon, K. (2004). The time to talk: The influence of adult-child talk on children's event memory. *Child Development, 75(3),* 669–686.

Rossetti, L. (2001). *Communication Intervention: Birth to Three.* (pp. 131–133). Oshkosh, WI: Singular.

Tulving, E. (1993). What is episodic memory? *Current Directions in Psychological Science, 2,* 67–70.

Westby, C. (2000). A scale for assessing development of children's play. In K. Gitlin-Weiner, A. Sandgrund and C. Schaefer (Eds.), *Play Diagnosis and Assessment.* New York: Wiley.

Westby, C. & Wilson, D. (2008). *Promoting Emergent Literacy Skills in Deaf Preschool Children Through Play.* Unpublished manuscript, Brigham Young University, Provo, UT.

Westby, C. & White, E. (2014). *CID Preschool Symbolic Play Rating Form.* St. Louis: CID – Central Institute for the Deaf.

Chapter 17

The Benefits of Music

As is true for many people, music may be an important part of your life. Many parents of children with hearing loss worry their children will miss out on the robust and various effects of music. Because of today's advancements in hearing device technology, children with hearing loss, even profound hearing loss, are able to access sound in such a way that they, too, can and do benefit from music. Those benefits are the same for children with hearing loss as they are for children with typical hearing: enjoyment, relaxation, stimulation, motivation and so on.

Not only can your child with hearing loss benefit from exposure to music in the way all of us do, she may experience additional benefits. Research suggests that music positively affects development of listening, language, vocabulary, literacy and motor skills. With this in mind, music can be a source of great enjoyment for your child, with the added bonus of promoting listening and spoken language. Jackpot!

Mainstream Music

You may be wondering what kind of music is most beneficial. Tons of evidence suggests that certain kinds of music promote brain development, increase productivity and alter mood. Yet it's important to choose music for your child that you can easily incorporate into your daily life. Play music you usually listen to. For example, if you like bluegrass music, play that for your child. There's no need to buy a bunch of classical music when it's not what you already own or even like. If you like classical music, then play that for your child. Although many parents want to expose their children to all types of music, you never have to feel like you're short-changing your child or her auditory progress if you stick to music you prefer. Conversely, if you want to expose your child to a variety of genres, go for it! Check out the music selection online or at your local library — or borrow cds or mp3s from friends.

Are you wondering about the effect of music on listening situations? It may seem that music would significantly increase background noise. It's true that when you expose your child to the language of your day — during meals, playtime, getting dressed or undressed, cleaning up, etc. — you want her to be able to focus on the talk that comes from you. Background music could interrupt that talk. So when your child is a new listener, and therefore needs a clear signal from you without any background noise, avoid playing music at those frequent language stimulation times. Choose a few points in your day that are good for listening to music. Riding in the car might be a good time. You also might choose to play music while your child plays on the kitchen floor as you make dinner, or when you need to make the bed, fold laundry or write a grocery list. Naturally, there are times in the day when you have to tend to your household, so try to use these as times your child can spend enjoying music.

Once your child is a more astute listener, you might want to try having a conversation with her while music is playing. After all, children with typical hearing can have conversations with music in the background, and your child will eventually learn to do that, too. So you might choose to practice this occasionally. If your child seems inattentive or frustrated by the music playing while you're talking, take a break from the music and try again another time.

Movement and Dance

Music can be a fun and interesting way to promote motor skill development and vestibular development related to balance and body awareness. Through music, you can help your child listen for the beat and clap or tap along to it. You can move your body to the beat, modeling for your child how to do that. Clap your hands, wiggle your hips or bob your head. Do the Twist, a country line dance, the Robot or some Beyonce moves. You don't have to be a good dancer to help your child move to the music. You can show her how fun it is to dance, listen to music and express yourself. She'll see how much fun you're having and want to join in.

Rhythm, Music and Language Development

In addition to mainstream music you can borrow or purchase in cd or mp3 form, there are lots of other ways to bring rhythm and music into your child's life. Specifically for young children, you can use finger plays, nursery rhymes and children's songs. As an added benefit, these forms of rhythm and music also can support communication, fine and gross motor skills and, most importantly, language skills.

Music for Children with Hearing Loss

Some professionals, called music therapists, have specialized training in music intervention for children with special needs. One such therapist, Chris Barton, has extensive experience working with children with hearing loss. Check out her website to learn more. www.christinebarton.net

Finger Plays

Finger plays are simple vocal games with accompanying motions of the fingers, hands or body. They're like songs, but less melodic. Finger plays are essentially a cross between poems and songs — often using rhyme like poems, but more chant-like than "singable." Finger plays are useful to:

- expose children to music-like rhythm and cadence
- promote listening skills
- promote imitation of gross and fine motor skills
- encourage vocalizations
- promote imitation of language
- promote imitation or approximation of speech
- be fun and playful

When you first introduce finger plays to your baby, expect her to watch you with curiosity. She will likely be interested in both the rhythm of your voice and the accompanying finger, hand or body movements. If you see she isn't so interested, try another finger play or stop for now and try again later. Some children take longer to become interested in finger plays, while others are interested from the beginning.

If your child shows a lot of interest in finger plays, help her do the movements with you. Move her little hands and body for her. Eventually, you'll work up to her imitating your movements on her own. This gross and fine motor imitation is a precursor to vocal imitation. It's important to note the point at which your child can imitate motor movements because it's a first step to her eventual ability to imitate your talk. Remember, we all learn to talk by imitating what others around us say. Your child will learn how to talk this same way.

With lots of exposure to finger plays over time, you'll see which ones your child enjoys most and which ones she's most interested in doing herself. Work toward vocalizations. With continued practice, she'll begin to approximate the words of the finger plays while doing the movements.

Some finger plays require no materials at all, except for you and your child. You can use props with some finger plays to help the child bridge the gap between the words and your motions. Props can help clarify the meaning, and they are fun to hold and manipulate.

Introducing a Finger Play to Your Child

It will take some time and effort to help your child get to the point where she can do a finger play along with you. You first need to introduce the finger play and model how it's done. Then encourage her to do it. Here are some steps in that process:

1. Sit (or stand) on the floor facing one another so she can see and hear you well.
2. Make it interesting! Practice your entertaining skills by being spirited, enthused and happy about the finger play. This will help motivate your child to imitate you.

3. Repeat the finger play a few times as long as she is still showing interest. If she loses interest, move on to another finger play — or just try again the next day.

4. Repeat the finger play, but this time, model the motions with your hands or body, then pause to help your child make the motions herself. Encourage her to imitate your movements. Remember, imitation of gross and fine motor movements often precedes imitation of vocalizations.

5. Remember to be patient. You may have to model the finger play many, many times before she imitates you at all. That's okay!

6. Praise your child when she imitates your movements and when she tries to imitate your vocalizations. She's working really hard, so remember to tell her how great she is!

7. There are many finger plays that you might choose to do with your child (see the list on the next few pages). At first, just pick a couple. As she learns to imitate you, add another one or two. New finger plays will help keep her interest over time and will help you from getting burned out on the same ones.

Finger Plays to Teach Your Child

Five Little Bears

Five little bears were dancing on the floor. (Wiggle and dance in your spot.)
One fell down and that left four. (Pretend to fall down.)
Four little bears climbed up a tree. (Move hands in climbing motion.)
One found a beehive — that left three. (Wiggle your pointer finger like a flying bee.)
Three little bears were wondering what to do.
    (Bend your arms at the elbow and hold palms up.)
One chased a bunny rabbit — that left two.
    (Make bunny ears with two fingers and hop them along.)
Two little bears were looking for some fun.
    (Put your flat hand over your eyes as if searching.)
One took a swim and that left one. (Move your arms in a swimming motion.)
    One little bear, sitting all alone. (Sit in place.)
He looked all around then ran home.
    (Look around. Then move your arms in a running motion.).

Five Fat Peas

Five fat peas in a pea pod pressed. (Hold hand open, then in a fist.)
One grew, two grew and so did the rest. (Put fingers up one by one.)
They grew and grew and did not stop. (Raise hand in air slowly.)
Until one day the pod went POP! (Clap hands together.)

Five Little Firefighters

(Start in a standing position.)

Five little firefighters (Show five fingers.)
Sleeping in a row. (Put two hands to cheek, tilt head and close eyes.)
Ring goes the bell
Down the pole they go. (Pretend to slide down pole.)
They jump on the engine (Jump up.)
And put out the fire. (Pretend to squirt with a hose.)
Now they're back at the station.
My, they are tired. (Stretch and yawn.)

Five Little Monkeys (Bed)

Five little monkeys jumping on the bed. (Show five fingers and bounce on other hand.)
One fell off and bumped his head. (Bump fist into head.)
Momma called the doctor and the doctor said (Make phone with thumb and pinky. Put to ear.)
No more monkeys jumping on the bed. (Shake finger.)

Four little monkeys jumping on the bed. (Show four fingers and bounce on other hand.)
One fell off and bumped his head. (Bump fist into head.)
Momma called the doctor and the doctor said (Make phone with thumb and pinky. Put to ear.)
No more monkeys jumping on the bed. (Shake finger.)

Three little monkeys jumping on the bed. (Show three fingers and bounce on other hand.)
One fell off and bumped his head. (Bump fist into head.)
Momma called the doctor and the doctor said (Make phone with thumb and pinky. Put to ear.)
No more monkeys jumping on the bed. (Shake finger.)

Two little monkeys jumping on the bed. (Show two fingers and bounce on other hand.)
One fell off and bumped his head. (Bump fist into head.)
Momma called the doctor and the doctor said (Make phone with thumb and pinky. Put to ear.)
No more monkeys jumping on the bed. (Shake finger.)

One little monkey jumping on the bed. (Show one finger and bounce on other hand.)
He fell off and bumped his head. (Bump fist into head.)
Momma called the doctor and the doctor said (Make phone with thumb and pinky. Put to ear.)
No more monkeys jumping on the bed. (Shake finger.)

No more monkeys! (Shrug shoulders.)

Five Little Monkeys (Tree)

Five little monkeys swinging from a tree. (Swing hand showing five fingers.)
Teasing Mr. Alligator — can't catch me, can't catch me. (Put thumbs in ears. Wiggle fingers.)
Aloooooong comes Mr. Alligator, hungry as can be…
   (Slowly push your open hand along ground.)
And SNAP! that monkey right out of that tree!
   (Clap two hands together like an alligator mouth.)

Four little monkeys swinging from a tree. (Swing hand showing four fingers.)
Teasing Mr. Alligator — can't catch me, can't catch me. (Put thumbs in ears. Wiggle fingers.)
Aloooooong comes Mr. Alligator, hungry as can be…
   (Slowly push your open hand along ground.)
And SNAP! that monkey right out of that tree!
   (Clap two hands together like an alligator mouth.)

Three little monkeys swinging from a tree. (Swing hand showing three fingers.)
Teasing Mr. Alligator — can't catch me, can't catch me. (Put thumbs in ears. Wiggle fingers.)
Aloooooong comes Mr. Alligator, hungry as can be…
   (Slowly push your open hand along ground.)
And SNAP! that monkey right out of that tree!
   (Clap two hands together like an alligator mouth.)

Two little monkeys swinging from a tree. (Swing hand showing two fingers.)
Teasing Mr. Alligator — can't catch me, can't catch me. (Put thumbs in ears. Wiggle fingers.)
Aloooooong comes Mr. Alligator, hungry as can be…
   (Slowly push your open hand along the ground.)
And SNAP! that monkey right out of that tree!
   (Clap two hands together like an alligator mouth.)

One little monkey swinging from a tree. (Swing hand showing one finger.)
Teasing Mr. Alligator — can't catch me, can't catch me. (Put thumbs in ears. Wiggle fingers.)
Aloooooong comes Mr. Alligator, hungry as can be…
   (Slowly push your open hand along ground.)
And SNAP! that monkey right out of that tree!
   (Clap two hands together like an alligator mouth.)

No more monkeys! (Shrug shoulders.)

Five Little Turkeys

Five little turkeys by the barn door. (Hold up five fingers.)
One waddled off, then there were four. (Move arms to waddle. Then hold up four fingers.)
Four little turkeys out under the tree. (Hold up four fingers.)
One waddled off, then there were three. (Move arms to waddle. Then hold up three fingers.)
Three little turkeys with nothing to do. (Hold up three fingers.)
One waddled off, then there were two. (Move arms to waddle. Then hold up two fingers.)
Two little turkeys in the noonday sun. (Hold up two fingers.)
One waddled off, then there was one. (Move arms to waddle. Then hold up one finger.)
One little turkey — better run away! (Move arms in running motion.)
Soon will come Thanksgiving Day!

Little Mouse

Slowly, slowly, very slowly goes the little mouse.
 (Circle your pointer finger around in your child's palm.)
Slowly, slowly, very slowly to his little house. (Close your child's palm around your finger.)
Quickly, quickly, very quickly goes the little mouse. (Tickle her palm with your fingers.)
Quickly, quickly, very quickly right up to your house.
 (Run your tickling fingers up your child's arm and tickle her chin.)

One, Two, Buckle My Shoe

One, two, buckle my shoe. (Pretend to buckle your shoe.)
Three, four, shut the door. (Pretend to shut a door.)
Five, six, pick up sticks. (Pretend to pick up sticks.)
Seven, eight, lay them straight. (Pretend to lay sticks out in front of you.)
Nine, ten, a big, fat hen! (Puff your cheeks, put your hands under your arms and flap.)

Pat-a-Cake

(Sit facing your child.)
Pat-a-cake,
 (Clap your hands, then put them out for your child to hit with her hands.
 Repeat for each line.)
Pat-a-cake,
Baker's man!
Bake me a cake
As fast as you can
Roll it and pat it (Pretend to roll and pat the dough.)
And mark it with a B. (Draw a B in the air or on your child's hand with your pointer finger.)
Put it in the oven (Clap your hands then put them out for your child to hit with her hands.)
For Baby and me.

Rain

Pitter-pat, pitter-pat (Drum your fingers on the floor.)
The rain goes on for hours.
And though it keeps me in the house,
    (Hold hands palms up and close into fists in front of you.)
It's very good for flowers. (Open fists and lift hands to imitate flowers growing up.)

This Little Piggy

This little piggy went to market. (Wiggle your child's pinky toe.)
This little piggy stayed home. (Wiggle your child's next smallest toe.)
This little piggy had roast beef. (Wiggle your child's middle toe.)
This little piggy had none. (Wiggle your child's second-to-largest toe.)
And this little piggy went, "Wee, wee, wee!" (Wiggle your child's big toe.)
All the way home. (And tickle your fingers up her leg, belly and under her chin.)

Thumbs

(Start with thumbs out and move them in the way mentioned in the song.)
My thumbs go up, up, up.
My thumbs go down, down, down.
My thumbs go out, out, out.
My thumbs go in, in, in.
My thumbs go round and round and round.
My thumbs go fast!!!!!!!!
My thumbs go slow.
Stop! (Hold up two hands with palms facing your child. Praise and look expectantly at her.)
Go!

Nursery Rhymes

Nursery rhymes are fun and interesting for all children, including your child with hearing loss. They are chant-like and less melodic than finger plays, but they don't involve finger, hand or body movements the way finger plays do. Nursery rhymes often are very old and not exactly relevant to modern-day life. That can make the content difficult to understand. Yet most young children are able to recite at least some of them from memory. Your child also will learn to recite nursery rhymes without necessarily understanding what they mean, and that's just fine.

It may be helpful to find a picture of each nursery rhyme you'd like to teach your child. There are lots of books full of common nursery rhymes. In addition, you can do a quick Internet search and find a picture of almost any nursery rhyme ever created. You can use the picture as a prompt for your child to associate with the words of the rhyme. Each time you say a certain nursery rhyme, show her the picture. She'll learn that when she sees a certain picture, she can expect certain words to go with it. Eventually, she'll be able to imitate or approximate some of those words, and later she'll be able to recite the nursery rhyme with you in her sweet little voice.

Nursery Rhymes to Teach Your Child

Goodnight

Goodnight, sleep tight.
Don't let the bed bugs bite.

Hey, Diddle, Diddle

Hey, diddle, diddle!
The cat and the fiddle,
The cow jumped over the moon.
The little dog laughed
To see such sport,
And the dish ran away with the spoon.

Hickory, Dickory, Dock

Hickory, dickory, dock,
The mouse ran up the clock.
The clock struck one,
The mouse ran down.
Hickory, dickory, dock.

Humpty Dumpty

Humpty Dumpty sat on a wall,
Humpty Dumpty had a great fall.
All the king's horses and all the king's men
Couldn't put Humpty together again.

It's Raining

It's raining, it's pouring,
The old man is snoring.
He went to bed
And bumped his head
And couldn't get up in the morning.

Jack and Jill

Jack and Jill went up the hill
To fetch a pail of water.
Jack fell down and broke his crown
And Jill came tumbling after.
Then up Jack got and off did trot,
As fast as he could caper.
To old Dame Dob, who patched his nob
With vinegar and brown paper.

Jack Be Nimble

Jack be nimble, Jack be quick,
Jack jumped over the candlestick.

Jack Sprat

Jack Sprat could eat no fat.
His wife could eat no lean.
And so between the two of them
They licked the platter clean.

Little Boy Blue

Little boy blue, come blow your horn.
The sheep's in the meadow. The cow's in the corn.
But where is the little boy tending the sheep?
He's under the haystack fast asleep.
Will you wake him? No, not I.
For if I do, he's sure to cry.

Little Bo Beep

Little Bo Peep has lost her sheep
And doesn't know where to find them.
Leave them alone and they'll come home,
Wagging their tails behind them.

Little Miss Muffet

Little Miss Muffet
Sat on a tuffet
Eating her curds and whey.
Along came a spider
Who sat down beside her
And frightened Miss Muffet away.

Mary, Mary Quite Contrary

Mary, Mary, quite contrary,
How does your garden grow?
With silver bells and cockleshells,
And pretty maids all in a row.

Old King Cole

Old King Cole was a jolly old soul
And a jolly old soul was he.
He called for his pipe
And he called for his bowl
And he called for his fiddlers three.

Peas Porridge Hot

Peas porridge hot.
Peas porridge cold.
Peas porridge in the pot,
Nine days old.
Some like it hot.
Some like it cold.
Some like it in the pot,
Nine days old.

Peter, Peter Pumpkin Eater

Peter, Peter pumpkin eater
Had a wife and couldn't keep her.
He put her in a pumpkin shell
And there he kept her very well.

See a Penny

See a penny, pick it up.
All day long you'll have good luck.

Star Light

Star light, star bright,
First star I see tonight.
I wish I may, I wish I might
Have the wish I wish tonight.

There Was an Old Lady

There was an old lady who lived in a shoe.
She had so many children, she didn't know what to do.
She gave them some broth without any bread.
She scolded them meanly and sent them to bed.

Three Little Kittens

Three little kittens lost their mittens
And they began to cry,
"Oh mother dear, we sadly fear,
Our mittens we have lost."
"What? Lost your mittens?
You naughty kittens.
Then you shall have no pie.
Then you shall have no pie."

Songs

Singing songs is another great way to expose your child to music, rhythm and the language of songs. Songs are motivating and fun, and they help children develop listening, language and speech skills. Many children's songs are listed below for you to consider singing to and with your child. Some of these songs have hand or body motions to accompany them; others don't. You can always make up your own movements for any song. In addition, you might consider finding a related little toy, such as a rubber ducky for *Five Little Ducks* or a picture of the song's content. You can use the toy or picture as a prompt for your child to associate with the song. Each time you sing a certain song, show her the toy or picture. She'll learn to expect that song when you show her the corresponding prop. Eventually, she'll be able to imitate or approximate some of those words and later she'll be able to sing along with you. How exciting!

Songs to Sing With Your Child

Alphabet Song

(Tune: "Twinkle, Twinkle Little Star")
A-B-C-D-E-F-G,
H-I-J-K-L-M-N-O-P,
Q-R-S, T-U-V,
W-X, Y and Z.
Now I know my ABCs.
Next time won't you sing with me?

Ants Go Marching

(Sit with criss-crossed legs. Alternately pat your hands on each thigh.)
The ants go marching one by one, hurrah, hurrah.
The ants go marching one by one, hurrah, hurrah.
The ants go marching one by one. The little one stops to suck his thumb.
    (Momentarily pretend to suck your thumb. Then return to patting thighs.)
And they all go marching down, to the ground, to get out of the rain.
Boom, boom, boom. Boom! Boom, boom, boom.

The ants go marching two by two, hurrah, hurrah.
The ants go marching two by two, hurrah, hurrah.
The ants go marching two by two.
The little one stops to tie his shoe.
    (Momentarily pretend to tie your shoe. Then return to patting thighs.)
And they all go marching down, to the ground, to get out of the rain.
Boom, boom, boom. Boom! Boom, boom, boom.

The ants go marching three by three, hurrah, hurrah.
The ants go marching three by three, hurrah, hurrah.
The ants go marching three by three.
The little one stops to climb a tree.
    (Momentarily pretend to climb. Then return to patting thighs.)
And they all go marching down, to the ground, to get out of the rain.
Boom, boom, boom. Boom! Boom, boom, boom.

The ants go marching four by four, hurrah, hurrah.
The ants go marching four by four, hurrah, hurrah.
The ants go marching four by four.
The little one stops to shut the door.
    (Momentarily pretend to shut the door. Then return to patting thighs.)
And they all go marching down, to the ground, to get out of the rain.
Boom, boom, boom. Boom! Boom, boom, boom.

The ants go marching five by five, hurrah, hurrah.
The ants go marching five by five, hurrah, hurrah.
The ants go marching five by five. The little one stops to take a dive.
    (Momentarily pretend to dive. Then return to patting thighs.)
And they all go marching down, to the ground, to get out of the rain.
Boom, boom, boom. Boom! Boom, boom, boom.

Apple Song

(Tune: "B-I-N-G-O") (Clap each time you say "crunch.")
I know a fruit that's good to eat and apple is its name, oh.
A-p-p-l-e, a-p-p-l-e, a-p-p-l-e, and apple is its name, oh.

I know a fruit that's good to eat and apple is its name, oh.
Crunch-p-p-l-e, crunch-p-p-l-e, crunch-p-p-l-e, and apple is its name, oh.

I know a fruit that's good to eat and apple is its name, oh.
Crunch-crunch-p-l-e, crunch-crunch-p-l-e, crunch-crunch-p-l-e, and apple is its name, oh.

I know a fruit that's good to eat and apple is its name, oh.
Crunch-crunch-crunch-l-e, crunch-crunch-crunch-l-e, crunch-crunch-crunch-l-e,
    and apple is its name, oh.

I know a fruit that's good to eat and apple is its name, oh.
Crunch-crunch-crunch-crunch-e, crunch-crunch-crunch-crunch-e, crunch-crunch-
    crunch-crunch-e, and apple is its name, oh.

I know a fruit that's good to eat and apple is its name, oh.
Crunch-crunch-crunch-crunch-crunch, crunch-crunch-crunch-crunch-crunch, crunch-
    crunch-crunch-crunch-crunch, and apple is its name, oh.

Bear Went Over the Mountain

(Tune: "For He's a Jolly Good Fellow")
The bear went over the mountain,
The bear went over the mountain,
The bear went over the mountain,
To see what he could see.
To see what he could see, to see what he could see.

The other side of the mountain,
The other side of the mountain,
The other side of the mountain,
Was all that he could see.
Was all that he could see, was all that he could see.
The other side of the mountain,
Was all that he could see!

Baa, Baa, Black Sheep

(Tune: "Twinkle, Twinkle, Little Star")
Baa, baa, black sheep, have you any wool?
Yes sir, yes sir, three bags full.
One for the master, and one for the dame.
One for the little boy who lives down the lane.
Baa, baa, black sheep, have you any wool?
Yes sir, yes sir, three bags full.

Baby Bumblebee

I'm bringing home a baby bumblebee. (Cup hands together as if holding a bee.)
Won't my mommy be so proud of me?
I'm bringing home a baby bumblebee —
Ouch! It stung me! (Shake hands as if just stung.)

I'm squishing up the baby bumblebee. (Squish the bee between palms of hands.)
Won't my mommy be so proud of me?
I'm squishing up the baby bumblebee —
Ooh! It's yucky! (Open up hands to look at mess.)

I'm wiping off the baby bumblebee. (Wipe hands off on shirt.)
Won't my mommy be so proud of me?
I'm wiping off the baby bumblebee —
Look! All clean! (Hold hands up to show they are clean.)

BINGO

There was a farmer, had a dog, and Bingo was his name, oh.
B-I-N-G-O, B-I-N-G-O, B-I-N-G-O, and Bingo was his name, oh.

There was a farmer, had a dog, and Bingo was his name, oh.
[Clap]-I-N-G-O, [Clap]-I-N-G-O, [Clap]-I-N-G-O, and Bingo was his name, oh.

There was a farmer, had a dog, and Bingo was his name, oh.
[Clap]-[Clap]-N-G-O, [Clap]-[Clap]-N-G-O, [Clap]-[Clap]-N-G-O,
    and Bingo was his name, oh.

There was a farmer, had a dog, and Bingo was his name, oh.
[Clap]-[Clap]-[Clap]-G-O, [Clap]-[Clap]-[Clap]-G-O, [Clap]-[Clap]- Clap]-G-O,
    and Bingo was his name, oh.

There was a farmer, had a dog, and Bingo was his name, oh.
[Clap]-[Clap]-[Clap]-[Clap]-O, [Clap]-Clap]-[Clap]-[Clap]-O,
[Clap]-[Clap]-[Clap]-[Clap]-O, and Bingo was his name, oh.

There was a farmer, had a dog and Bingo was his name, oh.
[Clap]-[Clap]-[Clap]-[Clap]-[Clap], [Clap]-[Clap]-[Clap]-[Clap]-[Clap], [Clap]-[Clap]-
    [Clap]-[Clap]-[Clap], and Bingo was his name, oh.

Clap Your Hands

Clap, clap, clap your hands,
Clap your hands together.
Clap, clap, clap your hands,
Clap your hands together.
Tra-la-la, la-la-la-la,
Tra-la-la-la-la.
Tra-la-la, la-la-la-la,
Tra-la-la-la-la.
Hey!

The Farmer in the Dell

The farmer in the dell.
The farmer in the dell.
Heigh-ho, the derry-o,
The farmer in the dell.

The farmer takes the wife.
The farmer takes the wife.
Heigh-ho, the derry-o,
The farmer takes the wife.

The wife takes the child.
The wife takes the child.
Heigh-ho, the derry-o,
The wife takes the child.

The child takes the nurse.
The child takes the nurse.
Heigh-ho, the derry-o,
The child takes the nurse.

The nurse takes the cow.
The nurse takes the cow.
Heigh-ho, the derry-o,
The nurse takes the cow.

The cow takes the pig.
The cow takes the pig.
Heigh-ho, the derry-o,
The cow takes the pig.

The pig takes the dog.
The pig takes the dog.
Heigh-ho, the derry-o,
The pig takes the dog.

The dog takes the cat.
The dog takes the cat.
Heigh-ho, the derry-o,
The dog takes the cat.

The cat takes the mouse.
The cat takes the mouse.
Heigh-ho, the derry-o,
The cat takes the mouse.

The mouse takes the cheese.
The mouse takes the cheese.
Heigh-ho, the derry-o,
The mouse takes the cheese.

The cheese stands alone.
The cheese stands alone.
Heigh-ho, the derry-o,
The cheese stands alone.

Fireflies at Night

(Tune: "Open, Shut Them")
Winking, blinking,
Winking, blinking,
See the little light.
Now it's here and now it's there
And now it's out of sight.

Five Green and Speckled Frogs

Five green and speckled frogs (Using one hand, hold up five fingers in the air.)
Sat on a speckled log (Bounce your five fingers on the other hand.)
Eating the most delicious bugs. (Pretend to eat.)
Yum! Yum!! (Rub your tummy.)
One jumped into the pool (Point your finger up and then down like jumping.)
Where it was nice and cool. (Rub your hands on the opposite arms to indicate you're cold.)
Now there are four green speckled frogs. (Hold up four fingers.)

Four green and speckled frogs (Using one hand, hold up four fingers in the air.)
Sat on a speckled log (Bounce your four fingers on the other hand.)
Eating the most delicious bugs. (Pretend to eat.)
Yum! Yum!! (Rub your tummy.)
One jumped into the pool (Point your finger up and then down like jumping.)
Where it was nice and cool. (Rub your hands on the opposite arms to indicate you're cold.)
Now there are three green speckled frogs. (Hold up three fingers.)

Three green and speckled frogs (Using one hand, hold up three fingers in the air.)
Sat on a speckled log (Bounce your three fingers on the other hand.)
Eating the most delicious bugs. (Pretend to eat.)
Yum! Yum!! (Rub your tummy.)
One jumped into the pool (Point your finger up and then down like jumping.)
Where it was nice and cool. (Rub your hands on the opposite arms to indicate you're cold.)
Now there are two green speckled frogs. (Hold up two fingers.)

Two green and speckled frogs (Using one hand, hold up two fingers in the air.)
Sat on a speckled log (Bounce your two fingers on the other hand.)
Eating the most delicious bugs. (Pretend to eat.)
Yum! Yum!! (Rub your tummy.)
One jumped into the pool (Point your finger up and then down like jumping.)
Where it was nice and cool. (Rub your hands on the opposite arms to indicate you're cold.)
Now there is one green speckled frog. (Hold up one finger.)

One green and speckled frog (Using one hand, hold up one finger in the air.)
Sat on a speckled log (Bounce your one finger on the other hand.)
Eating the most delicious bugs. (Pretend to eat.)
Yum! Yum!! (Rub your tummy.)
He jumped into the pool (Point your finger up and then down like jumping.)
Where it was nice and cool. (Rub your hands on the opposite arms to indicate you're cold.)
Now there are no green speckled frogs. (Hold up your fist.)
Glub. Glub. (Make a sad face.)

Five Little Ducks

Five little ducks went out to play (Hold up five fingers.)
Over the hills and far away.
   (Move your five fingers "over a hill" and then behind your back.)
Mama Duck said "Quack, quack, quack, quack!"
   (Make your other hand quack like a duck's bill.)
Four little ducks came waddling back.
   (Show the hand behind your back again, but with four fingers.)

Four little ducks went out to play (Hold up four fingers.)
Over the hills and far away.
   (Move your four fingers "over a hill" and then behind your back.)
Mama Duck said "Quack, quack, quack, quack!"
   (Make your other hand quack like a duck's bill.)
Three little ducks came waddling back.
   (Show the hand behind your back again but with three fingers.)

Three little ducks went out to play (Hold up three fingers.)
Over the hills and far away.
   (Move your three fingers "over a hill" and then behind your back.)
Mama Duck said "Quack, quack, quack, quack!"
   (Make your other hand quack like a duck's bill.)
Two little ducks came waddling back.
   (Show the hand behind your back again, but with two fingers.)

Two little ducks went out to play (Hold up two fingers.)
Over the hills and far away.
   (Move your two fingers "over a hill" and then behind your back.)
Mama Duck said "Quack, quack, quack, quack!"
   (Make your other hand quack like a duck's bill.)
One little duck came waddling back.
   (Show the hand behind your back again, but with one finger.)

One little duck went out to play (Hold up one finger.)
Over the hills and far away. (Move your finger "over a hill" and then behind your back.)
Mama Duck said "Quack, quack, quack, quack!"
    (Make your other hand quack like a duck's bill.)
No little ducks came waddling back.
    (Show the hand behind your back again but with a closed fist.)

Mama duck said "QUACK, QUACK, QUACK, QUACK!"
    (Shout with your hand quacking like a duck's bill.)
Five little ducks came waddling back.
    (Show the hand behind your back with all five fingers.)

Head, Shoulders, Knees and Toes
(Point to the body parts as you sing them.)
Head, shoulders, knees and toes.
Knees and toes.
Head, shoulders, knees and toes.
Knees and toes.
Eyes and ears and mouth and nose.
Head, shoulders, knees and toes, knees and toes.

How Much Is that Doggie in the Window

How much is that doggie in the window? Woof, woof!
The one with the waggly tail.
How much is that doggie in the window? Woof, woof!
I do hope that doggie's for sale.

Hush Little Baby

Hush little baby, don't say a word.
Papa's gonna buy you a mocking bird.
If that mocking bird don't sing,
Papa's gonna buy you a diamond ring.
If that diamond ring turns brass,
Papa's gonna buy you a looking glass.
If that looking glass gets broke,
Papa's gonna buy you a billy goat.
If that billy goat won't pull,
Papa's gonna buy you a cart and bull.
If that cart and bull turn over,
Papa's gonna buy you a dog named Rover.

If that dog named Rover won't bark,
Papa's gonna buy you a horse and cart.
If that horse and cart fall down,
You'll still be the sweetest little baby in town.

If You're Happy and You Know It

If you're happy and you know it, clap your hands. (Clap twice.)
If you're happy and you know it, clap your hands. (Clap twice.)

If you're happy and you know it, then your face will surely show it.
If you're happy and you know it, clap your hands. (Clap twice.)

If you're happy and you know it, stomp your feet. (Stomp twice.)
If you're happy and you know it, stomp your feet. (Stomp twice.)

If you're happy and you know it, then your face will surely show it.
If you're happy and you know it, stomp your feet. (Stomp twice.)

I'm a Little Teapot

(Start in a standing position.)
I'm a little teapot short and stout.
    (Squat down and round your arms out to the side for stout.)
Here is my handle, here is my spout.
    (Put one hand on your hip for a handle and the other arm pointed out like a spout.)
When I get all steamed up, hear me shout, "Tip me over and pour me out."
    (Lean over on the spout side and pretend to pour tea.)

Itsy Bitsy Spider

The itsy bitsy spider went up the waterspout.
    (Touch your pointer fingers to opposite thumbs and "crawl" upward.)
Down came the rain and washed the spider out. (Wiggle fingers on both hands down like rain.)
Out came the sun and dried up all the rain. (Connect hands over head like the sun.)
And the itsy bitsy spider went up the spout again.
    (Touch your pointer fingers to opposite thumbs and "crawl" upward.)

I've Been Working on the Railroad

I've been workin' on the railroad
All the live-long day.
I've been workin' on the railroad
Just to pass the time away.
Can't you hear the whistle blowing?

Rise up so early in the morn.
Can't you hear the captain shouting,
"Dinah, blow your horn?"

Dinah, won't you blow,
Dinah, won't you blow,
Dinah, won't you blow your horn?
Dinah, won't you blow,
Dinah, won't you blow,
Dinah, won't you blow your horn?

Someone's in the kitchen with Dinah.
Someone's in the kitchen I know.
Someone's in the kitchen with Dinah,
Strummin' on the old banjo.

Singin' fee, fie, fiddly-i-o,
Fee, fie, fiddly-i-o-o-o-o,
Fee, fie, fiddly-i-o,
Strummin' on the old banjo.

Line Up Song

(Tune: "Mama's Little Baby Loves Shortnin' Bread")
Everybody line up, line up, line up.
Everybody line up at the door.
Not on the ceiling, not on the floor. (Point up, then point down.)
Everybody line up at the door.

Little Dog

Oh where, oh where has my little dog gone?
Oh where, oh where could he be?
With his ears cut short and his tail cut long,
Oh where, oh where could he be?

London Bridge

London Bridge is falling down, falling down, falling down.
London Bridge is falling down, my fair lady.

Take the key and lock her up, lock her up, lock her up.
Take the key and lock her up, my fair lady.

Mary Had a Little Lamb

Mary had a little lamb, little lamb, little lamb.
Mary had a little lamb whose fleece was white as snow.
Everywhere that Mary went, Mary went, Mary went.
Everywhere that Mary went, the lamb was sure to go.
It followed her to school one day, school one day, school one day.
It followed her to school one day, which was against the rules.
It made the children laugh and play, laugh and play, laugh and play.
It made the children laugh and play to see a lamb at school.

My Bonnie Lies Over the Ocean

My Bonnie lies over the ocean.
My Bonnie lies over the sea.
My Bonnie lies over the ocean.
Oh, bring back my Bonnie to me.

Bring back, bring back,
Oh, bring back my Bonnie to me, to me.
Bring back, bring back,
Oh, bring back my Bonnie to me.

Old MacDonald Had a Farm

Old MacDonald had a farm.
E-I-E-I-O!
And on the farm he had a pig.
E-I-E-I-O!
With an oink, oink here
And an oink, oink there.
Here an oink, there an oink,
Everywhere an oink, oink.
Old MacDonald had a farm.
E-I-E-I-O!
   (Repeat and substitute other animals and the sounds they make.)

Open, Shut Them

Open, shut them. (Open hands in front of you, then shut them into fists.)
Open, shut them. (Open hands in front of you, then shut them into fists.)
Give a little clap! (Clap.)
Open, shut them. (Open hands in front of you, then shut them into fists.)
Open, shut them. (Open hands in front of you, then shut them into fists.)
Lay them in your lap. (Lay your hands in your lap.)

Creep them, crawl them. (Walk fingers of both hands up your body towards your mouth.)
Creep them, crawl them. (Continue walking fingers up over your throat.)
Right up to your chin. (Continue walking fingers up and stop at your chin.)
Open up your little mouth. (Say this line, then open your mouth dramatically.)
But do not let them in! (Say this line quickly, shut your mouth and press lips together.)

Open, shut them. (Open hands in front of you, then shut them into fists.)
Open, shut them. (Open hands in front of you, then shut them into fists.)
Give a little peek. (Cover your eyes with your hands, then peek out between them.)
Open, shut them. (Open hands in front of you, then shut them into fists.)
Open, shut them. (Open hands in front of you, then shut them into fists.)
Time to go to sleep. (Press palms together and put them to your cheek. Pretend to sleep.)
Wake up! (Open your eyes wide.)

Right Hand, Left Hand

Up to the ceiling, (Raise your hands up.)
Down to the floor, (Lower your hands down.)
Left to the window, (Point left with your left hand.)
Right to the door. (Point right with your right hand.)
This is my right hand. (Show you right hand.)
Raise it up high. (Raise your right hand.)
This is my left hand. (Raise your left hand while your right hand is still up.)
Reach for the sky. (Reach and stretch up high.)
Right hand, left hand, (Put your right hand out in front and then your left.)
Twirl them around. (Twirl hands one over another.)
Left hand, right hand, (Put your left hand out in front and then your right.)
Pound, pound, pound. (Hit fists together like when you give "knuckles.")

Ring Around the Rosie

(Stand in a circle, join hands and move around in a circle.)
Ring around the Rosie.
Pockets full of posies.
Ashes, ashes, we all fall down. (Fall down on the floor.)
The cows are in the meadow.
Eating buttercups.
Hush-a, hush-a, they all stand up. (Jump up.)

Rock-a-Bye Baby

Rock-a-bye baby in the tree top. (Interlace your arms and rock them as if you have a baby.)
When the wind blows the cradle will rock.
When the bough breaks the cradle will fall, (Quickly pull your arms apart.)
And down will come baby cradle and all. (Pretend a baby is falling.)

Row, Row, Row Your Boat

(Pretend to hold a paddle and row on each side of you.)
Row, row, row your boat
Gently down the stream.
Merrily, merrily, merrily, merrily,
Life is but a dream.

She'll Be Coming Around the Mountain

She'll be coming around the mountain when she comes.
She'll be coming around the mountain when she comes.
She'll be coming around the mountain, she'll be coming around the mountain,
She'll be coming around the mountain when she comes.

She'll be driving six white horses when she comes. Yee-haw!
She'll be driving six white horses when she comes. Yee-haw!
She'll be driving six white horses, she'll be driving six white horses,
She'll be driving six white horses when she comes. Yee-haw!

Oh we'll all come out to meet her when she comes. Howdy!
Oh we'll all come out to meet her when she comes. Howdy!
Oh we'll all come out to meet her, oh we'll all come out to meet her,
Oh we'll all come out to meet her when she comes. Howdy!

Take Me Out to the Ballgame

Take me out to the ballgame.
Take me out to the crowd.
Buy me some peanuts and crackerjacks.
I don't care if I ever get back.
For it's root, root, root for the Cardinals.
If they don't win it's a shame!
For it's 1,–2,–3 strikes you're out
At the old ballgame!

Teddy Bear

(Begin standing and do each motion as it's mentioned in the song.)
Teddy bear, teddy bear, turn around.
Teddy bear, teddy bear, touch the ground.
Teddy bear, teddy bear, touch your nose.
Teddy bear, teddy bear, touch your toes.

There Was an Old Lady Who Swallowed a Fly

There was an old lady who swallowed a fly.
I don't know why she swallowed a fly.
Perhaps she'll die.

There was an old lady who swallowed a spider
That wiggled and wiggled and tickled inside her.
She swallowed the spider to catch the fly.
I don't know why she swallowed the fly.
Perhaps she'll die.

There was an old lady who swallowed a bird.
How absurd to swallow a bird.
She swallowed the bird to catch the spider
That wiggled and wiggled and tickled inside her.
She swallowed the spider to catch the fly.
I don't know why she swallowed the fly.
Perhaps she'll die.

There was an old lady who swallowed a cat.
Imagine that, she swallowed a cat.
She swallowed the cat to catch the bird.
She swallowed the bird to catch the spider
That wiggled and wiggled and tickled inside her.
She swallowed the spider to catch the fly.
I don't know why she swallowed the fly.
Perhaps she'll die.

There was an old lady who swallowed a dog.
My, what a hog, to swallow a dog.
She swallowed the dog to catch the cat.
She swallowed the cat to catch the bird.
She swallowed the bird to catch the spider
That wiggled and wiggled and tickled inside her.

She swallowed the spider to catch the fly.
I don't know why she swallowed the fly.
Perhaps she'll die.

There was an old lady who swallowed a cow.
I don't know how she swallowed a cow.
She swallowed the cow to catch the dog.
She swallowed the dog to catch the cat.
She swallowed the cat to catch the bird.
She swallowed the bird to catch the spider
That wiggled and wiggled and tickled inside her.
She swallowed the spider to catch the fly.
I don't know why she swallowed the fly.
Perhaps she'll die.

I know an old lady who swallowed a horse . . .
She's dead of course. She swallowed a horse!

This Old Man

This old man, he played one.
He played knick-knack on my thumb
With a knick-knack paddywhack
Give the dog a bone.
This old man came rolling home.

This old man, he played two.
He played knick-knack on my shoe
With a knick-knack paddywhack
Give the dog a bone.
This old man came rolling home.

This old man, he played three.
He played knick-knack on my knee
With a knick-knack paddywhack
Give the dog a bone.
This old man came rolling home.

This old man, he played four.
He played knick-knack on my door
With a knick-knack paddywhack
Give the dog a bone.
This old man came rolling home.

This old man, he played five.
He played knick-knack on my hive
With a knick-knack paddywhack
Give the dog a bone.
This old man came rolling home.

This old man, he played six.
He played knick-knack on my sticks
With a knick-knack paddywhack
Give the dog a bone.
This old man came rolling home.

This old man, he played seven.
He played knick-knack up in heaven
With a knick-knack paddywhack
Give the dog a bone.
This old man came rolling home.

This old man, he played eight.
He played knick-knack on my gate
With a knick-knack paddywhack
Give the dog a bone.
This old man came rolling home.

This old man, he played nine.
He played knick-knack on my spine
With a knick-knack paddywhack
Give the dog a bone.
This old man came rolling home.

This old man, he played ten.
He played knick-knack once again
With a knick-knack paddywhack
Give the dog a bone.
This old man came rolling home.

Three Blind Mice

Three blind mice, three blind mice.
See how they run, see how they run.
They all ran after the farmer's wife
Who cut off their tails with a carving knife.
Have you ever seen such a sight in your life
As three blind mice?

Thumbkin

Where is thumbkin? (Hold thumbs up behind your back.)
Where is thumbkin?
Here I am, (Move one thumb out in front of you.)
Here I am. (Move the other thumb out in front of you.)
How are you today, sir? (Make the first thumb "talk" to the other.)
Very fine, I thank you. (Make the second thumb "talk" to the other.)
Run away. (Move one thumb behind your back.)
Run away. (Move the other thumb behind your back.)

Twinkle, Twinkle Little Star

Twinkle, twinkle little star. (Hold your hands out in front and open and close them.)
How I wonder what you are. (Put your palms face up to your sides as if asking a question.)
Up above the world so high (Point both pointer fingers up over your head.)
Like a diamond in the sky. (Make a diamond with your pointers and thumbs.)
Twinkle, Twinkle little star. (Hold your hands out in front and open and close them.)
How I wonder what you are. (Put your palms face up to your sides as if asking a question.)

Twinkle, Twinkle Traffic Light

(Tune: "Twinkle, Twinkle Little Star") (Sit with criss-crossed legs.)
Twinkle, twinkle traffic light.
    (Put your right elbow on your right knee with arm up and palm facing your child.)
Standing on a corner bright.
    (Open and close your fingers in and out of a fist like a flashing light.)
Red means stop. (Flip your palm as if to say "stop.")
Green means go. (Roll your fists around each other very quickly.)
Yellow means go very slow. (Roll your fists around each other slowly.)
Twinkle, twinkle traffic light. (Put your palms face up to your sides as if asking a question.)
Standing on a corner bright.
    (Open and close your fingers in and out of a fist like a flashing light.)

Wash Your Hands

Wash, wash, wash, your hands.
Play our handy game.
Rub and scrub, scrub and rub.
Germs go down the drain.
Hey!

Wheels on the Bus

The wheels on the bus go 'round and 'round,
'Round and 'round, 'round and 'round.
The wheels on the bus go 'round and 'round
All through the town.

Additional verses:
The driver on the bus says "Move on back."
The people on the bus go bumpity-bump.
The baby on the bus says "Wah, wah, wah!"
The mommy on the bus says "Shhh, shhh, shhh!"
The wipers on the bus go swish-swish-swish."
The horn on the bus goes beep-beep-beep.

Yankee Doodle

Yankee Doodle went to town
Riding on a pony.
Stuck a feather in his hat
And called it macaroni.

You Are My Sunshine

You are my sunshine,
My only sunshine.
You make me happy
When skies are gray.
You'll never know, dear,
How much I love you.
Please don't take my sunshine away.

Reference

Kindermusik (2008). *The Impact of Music on Language and Literacy: A Research Summary in Support of Kindermusik's ABC Music & Me*. Greensboro, NC: Kindermusik International.

Chapter 18

Early Literacy Development

One of the most important indicators for success in life is literacy. A myriad of research is available connecting literacy to success. In other words, the more proficient a person is at reading, the more likely she is to be successful in her adult life. Obviously, this is important! As parents, we are called to instill a love of books and reading in our children at a very young age so they will grow to be literate and successful adults. It's never too early to start reading books with your child. In fact, some parents read to their babies before they're even born! Whether you did this or not, you now can read aloud to your child and expose her to books as much as possible.

Relationship Between Books and Language

Books provide a very important avenue of learning for your child. Language and reading are very closely related. Because books provide language that describes our lives and world in written form, you can use them as a tool for teaching your child language. Like all children, your child will be able to learn a lot about the world from reading. However, reading is especially important for a child with hearing loss. Much of what is missed by not hearing everything around her can be learned from books. It's very important to teach skills that lead to literacy. Developing a love of books in early childhood is the first step. Also, well before your child learns to read, books provide opportunities to stimulate language and introduce new language. You cannot show your child an actual example of every object or situation you want her to know about in early childhood, but you almost always can find something pictured or addressed in a book.

Creating a Literacy-Rich Environment

One of the first and most important things you can do to help your child develop a love of books and reading is to create a literacy-rich environment in your home. Any environment that is considered "literacy-rich" is one that promotes active reading, writing, listening and speaking. You can do this in a physical way by having print, books and writing all around. The environment can also be enhanced by your attitude toward books and reading as you consistently exude the importance of them in your life. Here are a few concrete tips for building a literacy-rich environment in your home:

1. Have books all around and read them. Get books from the library and buy some too, if possible. Sturdy board books are best for babies. Add regular picture books when your child is ready. Select books with good illustrations that interest your child.
2. Dedicate some time each day to looking at and reading books with your child. Make it part of your routine. This will convey the attitude that reading and books are important — in fact, important enough to do every day.
3. Let your child see you and others reading. If you model the behavior, she will know it's an important part of your lives. Show her how to treat books with care.
4. Point out environmental print such as words on a cereal box, familiar signs, a recipe or directions to a game.

Reading Aloud

The U.S. Commission on Reading stated: "The single most important activity for building the knowledge required for eventual success in reading is reading aloud to children" (Anderson et al., 1985). One of the most important things you can integrate into your daily routine is time to read aloud to your child. The many benefits include:

Expanding experiential knowledge
Books allow children to learn about and experience activities they might not have experienced before, either because it's not possible (ex: taking a rocket ship to the moon) or because they simply haven't experienced it (ex: climbing a mountain or jumping into a pond from a rope swing). This experiential knowledge is key to both learning how to talk and learning to understand what we read.

Developing episodic memory
Episodic memory is memory of personal experiences and the series of events that make up that experience. This is the ability to picture a personal experience in one's mind and tap into that memory when talking about it or hearing a story about it.

Developing vocabulary
Books are filled with great vocabulary. Vocabulary development is so crucial to being able to talk. The more vocabulary your child can learn, the better. Reading aloud exposes your child to lots of new and interesting words.

Providing pleasant associations to books
Many of the books you read to your child will contain wonderful stories with take-home messages. Children learn about life, the world, feelings and social interactions from the people and characters in stories. In addition, the special time you spend reading with your child will be something she always will remember about her childhood. Your attention at that time and your tenderness as she sits on your lap or snuggles up next to you is comforting and special, and she'll always treasure this experience.

▪ Providing exposure to the language of books

Books contain the written form of our language. Even though that's true, the way we talk is often different from what's written in text. For example, if you were explaining about your day, you might say:

> Well, I went to the grocery store and there was this lady giving out free samples of some stuff that looked really good so I asked her if I could try one and she said "yeah." So I picked the one that said it was chicken salad, but then it was so spicy I didn't like it so I threw most of it away . . . and I think she was a little surprised, but I asked her if I could have one of the other things she was giving out and she said okay, but seemed a little bit hesitant cuz she probably was like, "Well if you're just gonna throw it away then I don't really wanna give you another one."

If you were reading a book aloud, you might read:

> Once upon a time, there was a little girl named Goldilocks. Goldilocks loved to frolic and play in the forest. One day while she was playing in the forest, she noticed she had walked farther than she usually did. After a while, she came upon a darling little cottage deep in the woods. Goldilocks looked in the windows and didn't see anyone. She knocked on the door, but no one answered. So Goldilocks walked right in. She was feeling very hungry after her long walk. At the table in the kitchen, there were three bowls of porridge — a big bowl, a medium bowl and a small bowl. She tasted the porridge from the big bowl. "This porridge is too hot!" she exclaimed. So she tasted the porridge from the medium bowl. "This porridge is too cold," she said. Then she tasted the porridge from the small bowl. She said happily, "This porridge is just right!" and she ate it all up. After she'd eaten some breakfast, Goldilocks realized her feet were tired from her long walk in the woods. She walked into the living room, where she saw three chairs — a big chair, a medium chair and a small chair. She sat in the first chair. "Oh dear, this chair is too hard!" said Goldilocks.

Although this story may sound very familiar to you, if you look closely you'll notice it contains language we rarely use to talk. We rarely use the phrase *once upon a time* or the word *exclaimed* unless we're reading, although it's important to recognize these are part of many stories. We also would rarely use such complete and proper sentence structures. Although this *is* the way stories are written, it's not the way we talk. It would sound unnatural if we talked like that. Yet we learn to understand text written that way. The more you expose your child to stories, the better she will become at understanding the meaning within those stories and the meaning of the language of books. Children exposed to books early learn to love the stories within those books. They often ask to read the same stories over and over. That's a great sign! The more you read aloud to your child, the more likely your child will develop a love of books and reading.

■ **Creating mental models**

A mental model is a person's thought process about an event or series of events. A mental model is needed to think about people, objects and experiences. It's the idea of picturing something in your head. The ability to create mental models is necessary for language development. Moreover, understanding a story read from a book requires a child to build in her mind a representation of the situation described in the text (Cain & Oakhill, 2007).

■ **Developing theory of mind**

Theory of mind is the ability to understand that others have beliefs, desires and intentions different from one's own. Until theory of mind develops, a child believes the way she feels about something is the way everyone else feels about it, too. Once theory of mind is developed (at around age 4 or 5 in typically developing children), a child is able to understand that others might feel and think differently from how she does; she can also understand how others can feel differently from one another (Gopnik & Astington, 1988).

Reading story books allows children to develop theory of mind by providing a source for characters who think, feel and act in certain ways. In the story *Cinderella*, we all feel for poor Cinderella, who gets locked in the attic on the night of the ball. Even though that didn't happen to us, we realize she must be so sad and angry. The ability to take on those feelings for her is the concept of theory of mind.

Theory of mind is a vast and complicated subject. A lot of information is available, particularly in relation to children with special needs. Children with hearing loss often show significant delay in their development of theory of mind. Likely, this is due to language delay, particularly social language delay. Although books aren't the only tool for developing theory of mind, they are great ones — especially story books.

■ **Developing an understanding of decontextualized language**

Decontextualized language is language that conveys meaning by using only grammar and vocabulary. Children must understand decontextualized language to comprehend written text without visual support such as pictures. Text requires the reader to understand the details through language alone. Children begin to comprehend stories read aloud by using their experiences, mental models and the story's pictures to support their understanding. Eventually, they learn to comprehend stories using their personal experiences and mental models without pictures in the stories. This is the ability to understand decontextualized language (Curenton & Justice, 2004; Westby, 2008).

■ **Developing an understanding of metalinguistic language**

Metalinguistic language is language used to tell about language. For example, "He said . . ." or "She told me to . . ." Comprehension of metalinguistic language is necessary to understand many stories.

■ **Developing an understanding of metacognitive language**

Metacognitive language is language used for telling what one is thinking. For example, "I know . . ." or "She wondered . . ." or "He's thinking that . . ." Comprehension of metacognitive language is necessary to understand many stories.

■ **Introducing basic concepts of print and books**

Besides being exposed to the language of books, it's also important for children to be physically exposed to books. Many parents and family members love to tell stories that aren't from books, although they often use the language of books. That's great. Keep doing that and encourage your family members to do that with your child, too. In addition, your child benefits from physically holding and managing books. This exposure helps her develop three important skills over time:

Print awareness

Print awareness is the recognition of print all around, including the print in books. We want children to recognize and be aware of print because it helps them understand that print is meaningful. This exposure also helps children learn that print describes people, things, actions and situations, all of which often are illustrated in pictures.

Conventions of print

Conventions of print are consistent rules about how to create print and accurately represent language through print. There are many conventions of print, but by the time your child is finished with preschool, she should have been repeatedly exposed to these specific conventions:

☐ Letters represent sounds in our language (the Alphabet Principle).
☐ Letters have certain shapes.
☐ Letters can be capital and lower case.
☐ Letters have names.
☐ We can write what we say, we can read what we write, and we can say what we read. In other words, what we say can be turned into print and our print can be spoken.
☐ We read print from left to right and from top to bottom.
☐ Illustrations are meaningful.
☐ Spaces separate words.
☐ There is specific vocabulary related to reading (ex: *page, cover, title, author, letter, word, sentence*).

(Gunning, 2013; Irwin et al., 2012; *Missouri Early Learning Standards for Literacy,* 2009)

Book handling/book orientation

Children learn book handling and orientation skills through exposure to books and by imitating how the adults around them handle books. You can do this while you read aloud to your child. By the time she is finished with preschool and ready for kindergarten, she should be able to do the following:

☐ Handle books carefully.

☐ Hold books right-side-up.

☐ Look at pictures in books.

☐ Tell stories from pictures in books.

☐ Look at books from front to back.

☐ Turn pages one at a time.

☐ Tell the titles of books.

☐ Look at print in books.

☐ Attempt to read print in books.

☐ Follow print from left to right.

☐ Ask questions about stories.

☐ Ask to reread interesting books.

☐ Put books away properly when finished.

(Irwin et al., 2012; *Missouri Early Learning Standards for Literacy,* 2009)

As you can see, your child benefits in so many ways simply by your reading aloud to her. Try to make it part of your daily routine. Even if you're uncomfortable reading aloud, eventually it will become second nature. She has so much to gain from this time spent with you — and so do you!

How to Read Aloud to Your Child

For some parents, reading aloud is a snap. For others, it feels awkward and strange. If you're comfortable reading aloud to your child, keep it up! If it feels uncomfortable, it may be that your child just isn't used to looking at books, and it will take some time and effort to get there. Consider these suggestions for developing the readiness skills to enable your child to sit with you and listen as you read and talk about books:

1. Help your child develop a love of books and reading from birth. It may seem silly to read to an infant who can barely focus on a page — or who falls asleep in the middle of the book. But reading aloud to your child from an early age helps her develop an interest in books that will prove invaluable in her life.

2. For a child who is a little wigglier, start with very short periods of reading and stop before your child loses interest. Over time, she will become more interested, and you can increase the amount of time you spend with books each day.

3. Try to sit so your child can see the book and hear you. At first, you might want her to see you, too, so she can watch your facial expressions as you use the language of the book. This might involve a face-to-face setup with the book facing your child, yet up-side down to you. You can also try having your child sit on your lap so she can look at the book and see where you're pointing in the book while she listens to you read or tell about the story.

4. Use the pictures in the book as a guide for things to talk about. In the beginning don't plan to read the entire book as it is written. It's okay not to read at all in the beginning. Just talk about what's happening in the pictures, label objects and actions and use lots of enthusiasm to describe what you see. Skip over some pages if you need to in order to keep your child interested.

5. Help your child get involved by pointing to items and turning the pages if she wants. Many children's books are interactive, including lift-the-flap and touch-and-feel books.

6. If your child isn't interested in books, try to figure out a way to make books more inter-esting. You might need to simplify the talk and add drama. You might help your child match pictures in the book to toys or real objects around the house. You could assemble some stuffed animals or dolls and read to the group along with your child. You might need to provide books when your child is tired and ready for a quiet activity.

7. Add some drama! Use facial expressions and body language. Actually act out something pictured.

8. Over time, you will be more able to actually read the text. If the sequence of the book is relevant, go through the book in front to back order. If your child isn't ready to look at each page yet, just skip over some to keep her interested. Eventually, and after reading her favorite books hundreds of times, she'll want you to read every word on every page, and she'll catch you when you skip pages. Won't that be so great?

Increasing Your Expectations While Reading Aloud

There are several different ways to enjoy books with your child. In the beginning, you will have different expectations than you might after reading aloud for months or years. At first, you probably will spend less time reading and more time labeling pictures without even tell-ing the story in order to keep her interested. Later, you will work up to reading every word of the stories, and she will learn to be interested and excited about them. Here are some steps for increasing your expectations while reading aloud:

- **Talk about the pictures.**
  In the beginning, you can just think of the pictures in the book as a good source for something to talk about. Pace the activity so you can get through a story book in one sitting. Picture books can be used for short or long periods and may be of interest to children not ready for the story aspect. Name objects and actions of interest and pause

to let your child vocalize. If she is able, encourage her to name things or talk about the pictures. Don't worry if you don't get to every picture or page in the book. Just go back to the book another time and talk about other pages. Your young child will see that books have covers, that books stimulate conversation, that there is an expected order of looking at pages and so on.

■ **Simplify the story.**
When your child is ready, use the pictures to create a simple rendition of the story and events depicted. Include words you commonly use with your child and use other familiar words when possible. Tell the story in small chunks. Create pauses for your child to look at pictures that particularly interest her. Be sure to pause to let your child vocalize or comment on something in the book, too. Sounds made by animals, vehicles and people are likely interesting to your child, so incorporate them as you look at books with pictures.

■ **Read some of the text.**
If your child can attend to books for 10 or more minutes and if she has some developing comprehension of language, you can read some parts of story books just as they're written. On some pages, you might read the exact text and then pause to let your child respond. On other pages, you might just talk about the pictures and then pause so she can respond. Pace the activity to your child's attention and then pause to allow her time to think and talk about the language, pictures and story line.

■ **Read the whole text.**
Eventually, you will get to the point where your child will sit and listen while you read a short story exactly as it's written. Be comfortable with inserting explanations to help your child understand, and be comfortable labeling objects of interest or pictures of objects/actions that are new for your child. If your child becomes disinterested, you may need to finish later, choose another book or simplify the story line to make comprehension a bit easier. In any case, you want this activity to be enjoyable, so keep it fun.

■ **Ask questions.**
Once you are truly reading whole stories to your child, you can increase your expectations by asking her some questions. Typically developing preschoolers are able to answer three kinds of questions by the time they're ready for kindergarten. You can start with the simplest kinds of questions and move on from there as your child is able.

☐ *Literal questions*
Ask your child about the details of the story that literally come right from the text. For example, if you were reading *The Three Little Pigs*, the text might say "The first little pig bought some hay for his house." Then you could ask:
- "Who bought hay for his house?"
- "What did the first little pig buy?"

Literal questions also are good for asking about the sequence of events in a story. In the same story, you could read about how each pig bought a certain material for building the houses. Then you could ask:

- "The first little pig bought hay for his house. What did the second little pig buy? And what did the third little pig buy?"
- "Where did the Big Bad Wolf go first? And then where did he go? And then where?"
- "What happened to the first little pig?"

☐ **Inferential questions**

Inferential questions involve having some background knowledge about details of the story that aren't specifically mentioned in the text. These questions are helpful for teaching your child to draw conclusions, make predictions and make personal connections. You might ask:

- "How did the pigs feel when the wolf came to the house?"
- "Why are the pigs making a fire in the fireplace?"
- "What do you think will happen if the pig didn't run fast enough?"

☐ **Evaluative questions**

These questions include an opinion or judgment. They are the highest-level type of questioning, and the most difficult to answer. You might ask:

- "Did you like the story? Why? Why not?"
- "The pigs are making soup in the fireplace. What kind of soup do you like?"

Give Your Child a Lifetime of Reading

Knowing the importance of literacy, you certainly can do a lot now to foster literacy development, even for a baby or very young child. You can start instilling in her a love of books, stories and reading. Ideally, read books with your child every day. Many families enjoy books before bedtime as a last activity of the day.

Some children love to read all day long. No matter when you read with your child, ensure she is wearing her hearing devices during this time. You want her to get as much out of reading as possible! Most of all, being close to Mom or Dad during story time builds language, loving relationships and a lifelong love of reading!

References

Anderson, R.C., Hiebert, E.H., Scott, J.A. & Wilkinson, I.A.G. (1985). *Becoming a Nation of Readers: The Report of the Commission on Reading.* Champaign-Urbana, IL: Center for the Study of Reading.

Cain, K. & Oakhill, J. (2007). Reading comprehension difficulties: Correlates, causes and consequences. In K. Cain and J. Oakhill (Eds.), *Children's Comprehension Problems in Oral and Written Language* (pp. 41–75). New York: Guilford.

Curenton, S.M. & Justice, L. (2004). African American and Caucasian preschoolers' use of decontextualized language: Use of literate language features in oral narratives. *Language, Speech and Hearing Services in the Schools, 35,* 240–235.

Gopnik, A. & Astington, J. (1988). Children's understanding of representational change and its relation to the understanding of false belief and the appearance-reality distinction. *Child Development, 59,* 26–37.

Gunning, T. (2013). *Creating Literacy Instruction for All Students* (8th ed., p. 139). Boston: Pearson.

Irwin, J., Moore, D., Tornatore, L. & Fowler, A. (2012). Expanding on early literacy: Promoting emerging language and literacy during story time. *Children and Libraries. Summer/Fall 2012,* 20–23, 28.

Missouri Early Learning Standards for Early Literacy. (2009, January). Retrieved from http://dese.mo.gov/eel/el/PreK_Standards/documents/Literacyteacher.pdf.

Westby, C. & Wilson, D. (2008). Promoting emergent literacy skills in deaf preschool children through play. Unpublished manuscript, Brigham Young University, Provo, UT.

Chapter 19

Early Intervention Services

In the United States, a child between birth and 3 years old with an established condition, disability or special need that affects development or that may affect her education (or a child at risk of developing a condition, disability or special need) is eligible to receive early intervention services (Wright & Wright, 2015). Participation in early intervention programs is optional. **Early intervention services** include supporting the child and educating the caregivers in order to appropriately meet the child's needs and to lessen the effects of the condition, disability or special need. Certain evaluations and assessments are required to qualify for early intervention services. Early intervention services are referred to simply as early intervention (or EI) and are most effective when started as soon as the condition, disability or special need is identified, often just after a child's birth. Service provision is expected to occur within natural environments for the child. **Natural environments** are the everyday settings in which children of the same age and who are developing typically pass their time. For many, the most natural environment is the home in which a child lives with her family, although natural environments also may include a childcare center, park or other community setting (Danaher & Goode, 2013; Wright & Wright, 2015).

Although early intervention services are managed by individual state governments, much of the financial support comes from a federal grant called the *Program for Infants and Toddlers with Disabilities,* or Part C of the **Individuals with Disabilities Education Act (IDEA).** IDEA is the law governing services provided to children with disabilities. **Part C of IDEA** is specific to infants and toddlers. Its main purpose is to recognize "an urgent and substantial need to enhance the development of infants and toddlers with disabilities; reduce educational costs by minimizing the need for special education through early intervention; minimize the likelihood of institutionalization, maximize independent living, and enhance the capacity of families to meet their child's needs" (Wright & Wright, 2015). The areas of development considered in Part C include physical development, cognitive development, communication, social and emotional development and adaptive behavior.

Most parents get involved with early intervention because they're concerned about their child or their child's healthcare provider makes a recommendation for services. One of the eligibility requirements for early intervention services is a diagnosed physical or mental condition with a high probability of resulting in a developmental delay. Hearing impairment can result in a communication delay, so children with a diagnosed hearing loss often qualify for services. When an infant or toddler is diagnosed with hearing loss, the diagnosing professional should refer the parents or caregivers to early intervention if appropriate.

Child Find

Child Find is a continuous process of public awareness activities, screening and evaluation designed to locate, identify and refer as early as possible all young children with disabilities and their families in need of Early Intervention Program (Part C) or Preschool Special Education (Part B) services of IDEA.

Getting started with the process can be as simple as doing an Internet search for early intervention services in your state. Each state has its own early intervention matrix and a corresponding website where you can find contact information for professionals who work with children with certain conditions, disabilities or special needs. Your pediatrician or pediatric audiologist also can provide contact information.

Families also can begin receiving early intervention services by getting in touch with a private school or clinic offering services specifically for children with hearing loss. Many of these programs emphasize listening and spoken language. These programs are part of a consortium of schools called OPTION schools. You also can find early intervention providers by contacting one of the OPTION schools in your area. OPTION schools are not located in every community, but you may find independent providers who offer early intervention services for children with hearing loss. Some independent providers have special training to work with children whose families choose listening and spoken language. These providers can guide you through the process of navigating early intervention in your community.

Once enrolled in the early intervention system for your state, you are assigned an **early intervention service coordinator**. Your service coordinator can explain early intervention policies to you and arrange for your child's evaluation, if needed. If your child is eligible for services, a team is formed to help determine what services are necessary using the information gained from evaluations and assessments. The service coordinator can serve as your main point of contact by which to organize the team meetings and services.

ECTA Center

ECTA stands for Early Childhood Technical Assistance. The ECTA Center primarily serves to provide technical assistance on how to interpret IDEA and implement services on a practical level. Service coordinators and administrators call upon the ECTA Center when developing programs or modifying services. As a parent, you may have no need to interact directly with the ECTA Center, although you likely will benefit from programs they advise. You may find their website offers helpful lists of publications, events and guidance documents related to IDEA (ectacenter.org).

Evaluations and Assessments

Evaluations and assessments are an important part of your child's journey. They are tests used to determine your child's abilities in specific areas of development. These tests are ways to gather information to help your child by appropriately meeting her needs. **Evaluations** provide information about whether your child qualifies for early intervention services. If your child qualifies for services, **assessments** are used to determine the specific services necessary to meet her needs.

Eligibility

Eligibility for early intervention services can be determined in two ways:

1. A diagnosis derived from evaluation, which results in automatic eligibility

2. Documentation of a developmental delay *or* documentation of behaviors or conditions that indicate the child is at risk for a developmental delay

The criteria for these determinations differ among individual states.

Evaluations

It's likely your child has had at least one hearing evaluation to identify her hearing loss. This initial evaluation often occurs due to a referral for further testing after the initial hearing screening in the hospital. The result of the initial evaluation, a diagnosis, provides the starting point for determining early intervention eligibility within your state.

In addition to a hearing evaluation, your child may have multidisciplinary evaluations to determine other necessary early intervention services. These evaluations provide information about abilities in five areas of development: adaptive behavior, cognition, communication, physical development and social-emotional development. Evaluations are required because their results are the starting point by which services are provided.

Evaluations are derived from a medical model, which means they're intended to be objective and reliable. A formal diagnosis is required to receive early intervention services and can provide some basic indication of what intervention and support services may be needed. Yet the diagnosis itself doesn't provide information about developmental delays caused by the diagnosed condition and therefore certainly doesn't provide enough information to determine specific individualized services for the child and family. Early intervention services are intended to address the delays caused by the diagnosis, not the diagnosis itself. This is why assessments are necessary.

Assessments

If your child's evaluation determines she is eligible for early intervention services, more testing is needed. These further tests are referred to as assessments and are used for the following purposes:

- to obtain samples of behavior from your child and your child's interactions with you and other family members
- to document a delay in one or more developmental areas
- to determine areas of strength and areas in need of continued support
    When it's time to write the IFSP (Individualized Family Service Plan), assessments can guide your conversations with your early intervention provider. They can also help you identify the goals you want for your child and family. (See more on IFSPs later in this chapter.)
- to indicate appropriate services and illustrate why your child should qualify for specific services
- to guide the use of specific intervention strategies with your child and family
- to track progress over time

Assessments can be used after services have begun to demonstrate the appropriateness of the goals and intervention strategies.

The two main types of assessments are standardized (formal) and functional (informal). No matter what assessment is used, one is never enough. Each assessment is based on a one-time observation of your child, so it's not unusual for a single assessment to present a limited picture of her abilities. A variety of assessments provides much more information.

Your child with hearing loss may have assessments in all developmental domains to assess the following skills:

- motor
- cognitive
- social
- emotional
- receptive language
- expressive language
- pragmatic language
- play
- adaptive/self-help

"Assessment is any activity, either formal . . . or informal . . . designed to elicit accurate and reliable samples of infant-toddler behavior upon which inferences relative to developmental skill status may be made"(Rossetti, 1990, p. 92).

Standardized Assessments

Standardized assessments are tests given in a consistent manner and scored based on comparison. The standardized assessments your child is given are scored in comparison to other children her same age. For example, if your child is given a standardized language assessment when she is 3 years old, her standard score indicates your child's language skills compared to other 3-year-olds with typical hearing. To better understand standardized assessments, it's important to understand the following terms:

The **average range** for a standardized test is the range of scores considered to represent the middle 68 percent of people on which the scores are based (or normed). About 16 percent of people tested naturally fall above the average range. About 16 percent of people tested naturally fall below the average range. This is important to know because when your child is given a standardized assessment, you want to see if she is functioning in or above the average range. If she isn't, certain interventions or services should be provided to help her catch up to the average range. For many standardized assessments, the average range is 85–115.

Normed assessment scores are based on the performance of a certain group, representative of the population. A normative group includes many children who represent a particular age group as well as some other factors, including gender, ethnic background, geographic area of residence, socioeconomic status, etc. For example, if a language test is normed on children with typical hearing, your child's language score is compared to the scores of children with typical hearing her age. If a language test is normed on children with hearing loss, your child's score is compared to other children with hearing loss her age. Test such as these are referred to as **norm-referenced** tests.

A **standard score** is derived from the raw score. (A raw score is the actual number of points a person gets on a test.) Standard score is used to describe the score in comparison to the norm. For example, if the average range for an assessment is 85–115 and your child's standard score is 102, your child is said to have scored within the average range. This score is especially important in that it provides a meaningful comparison from year to year.

Closing the Gap

It's important to use standardized assessments to determine the level at which your child functions in certain areas compared to other children her age. With any delay, the goal is to provide interventions that help her move from being delayed to being average. The process of moving from a below average score to a score within the average range is referred to as **closing the gap**.

Standardized Assessments Typically Used in Early Intervention

Many standardized assessments are used with young children with hearing loss. Every school or program has its favorites. Some standardized assessments are:

■ *Developmental Assessment of Young Children, Second Edition (DAYC-2)*

The *DAYC-2* identifies developmental delays and deficits in children from birth through age 5. *DAYC-2* scores are useful when designing an early intervention program. The test is composed of five subtests, each focusing on a domain mandated for assessment by IDEA: adaptive behavior, cognition, communication, physical development and social-emotional development. The test format allows data collection through observation, direct assessment and parent/caregiver interviews.

■ *Preschool Language Scales, Fifth Edition (PLS-5)*

PLS-5 is a normed language assessment for children ages birth to 7 years, 11 months. Areas assessed include attention, play, gesture, vocal development, social communication, semantics, language structure, interactive language skills and emergent literacy skills. The assessment yields both standard scores and age-equivalent scores. Testing includes a caregiver questionnaire, observation of child/caregiver interactions and an examiner's assessment of the child.

■ *Receptive-Expressive Emergent Language Test, Third Edition (REEL-3)*

REEL-3 is a normed language assessment for children ages birth to 3 years. It provides standard and age-equivalent scores for receptive language, expressive language and vocabulary. It is administered to an individual child or as a parent interview.

■ *Vineland Adaptive Behavior Scales, Second Edition (Vineland-II)*

The *Vineland-II* looks at a child's personal and social skills needed for everyday living. It is a norm-referenced tool for gathering baseline data on a child. This assessment yields standard scores and age-equivalent scores for four behavioral domains: communication, daily living skills, socialization and motor skills. Although the *Vineland-II* can be administered to anyone between birth and 90 years old, for infants and young children it's administered as a parent/caregiver interview.

Functional (Informal) Assessments

The purpose of functional assessments is to acquire more information about your child and family so appropriate services can be determined and continued. A functional assessment is **criterion-referenced,** meaning that it compares your child to herself by indicating her abilities in a specific area and her progress in that area over time. The information acquired is specific to the delay caused by the diagnosed condition. It therefore provides indicators for what services will benefit your child and family by decreasing the effects of the delay. Many functional assessments can be used with young children with hearing loss. Every school or program has its favorites. Functional assessments include:

■ *CID Early Childhood Vocabulary Rating Form*

The *CID Early Childhood Vocabulary Rating Form* is a criterion-referenced assessment designed for use with children birth to age 5 with hearing loss. It outlines vocabulary at five levels — functional vocabulary, first 100 words, more basic vocabulary, theme-based vocabulary and preschool-specific vocabulary.

■ *CID Teacher Assessment of Grammatical Structures (TAGS)*

CID TAGS is a series of three rating forms used to evaluate a child's understanding and use of the grammatical structures of English. The forms provide a representation of grammatical structures for children with hearing loss who develop grammatical structures in smaller increments and at slower rates compared to children who are typically developing. The grammatical structures are organized into three levels: TAGS-1, TAGS-2 and TAGS-3.

■ *CID Preschool Symbolic Play Rating Form*

The relationship between language and play is a close and symbiotic one. A child with delays in either area will potentially show delay in the other. Symbolic play is a prerequisite for learning language. Before being able to use language, a child must be able to represent reality with symbols. Play skills must develop to a certain level before the corresponding language skills are possible. The *CID Preschool Symbolic Play Rating Form* is used to track play skills and their related language skills in children 8 months to 5 years old.

■ *CID Speech Perception Instructional Curriculum and Evaluation (SPICE)*

CID SPICE is used to help young children with cochlear implants and/or hearing aids develop auditory skills. It's designed to make learning easy and fun for both the teacher/clinician and the child.

■ **CID Speech Skills Rating Form**

The *CID Speech Skills Rating Form* is a criterion-referenced assessment designed for use by teachers of the deaf, speech-language pathologists and other professionals working with children with hearing loss. The rating form is divided into five detailed sections — voice, suprasegmental aspects of speech, vowels, consonants and blends and clusters.

■ **CID Toddler Developmental Rating Form**

While most CID forms track skills in areas of expected delay for children with hearing loss, these forms are used to track typical development of self-help, social and emotional, cognitive, fine motor and gross motor skills in children 1 and 2 years old. Teachers and parent educators use these in conjunction with other CID forms to monitor whole-child development.

■ **Cottage Acquisition Scales for Listening, Language, and Speech (CASLLS)**

CASLLS is a series of scales, or checklists, used to track a child's skills in listening, speech, language and cognition. It is used with children from birth to approximately 8 years old. *CASLLS* includes five separate criterion-referenced scales based on typical language development: preverbal, pre-sentence, simple sentence, complex sentence and sounds and speech.

■ **Hawaii Early Learning Profile 0–3 (HELP 03)**

The *HELP 03* is a global assessment tool for children birth to 3 years old. With a comprehensive list of 685 developmentally-sequenced skills, it's intended to look at the whole child. The *HELP* is used to identify needs, to track growth and development and to determine target objectives for the child and family. It offers play-based activities and intervention strategies for each skill and includes useful handouts and supplemental resources for parents.

■ **Rossetti Infant-Toddler Language Scale**

The *Rossetti Infant-Toddler Language Scale* is designed to provide the clinician with a comprehensive, easy-to-administer and relevant tool to assess the preverbal and verbal aspects of communication and interaction in the young child.

■ **Sensory Kids Impaired Home Intervention Language Development Scale (SKI-HI 2004)**

The *SKI-HI* is a parent observation scale listing the receptive and expressive language skills of children from birth to 5. It is specifically designed for children with hearing loss.

Team of Experts

If evaluation results indicate your child is eligible for services, your early intervention service coordinator facilitates a team of experts to determine needed services using the information gained from assessments and experience with your child.

From the start, it may be helpful to know about all of the experts with whom you might be in contact as you learn more about hearing loss and work to meet your child's needs. These people are there to help you. Each team member contributes to your child's health, growth and development in various ways. Below are descriptions of possible team members and their roles on your team, along with information about how to choose professionals who are a good fit for your family.

▪ **Parents, caregivers and family**

It's important to remember that, no matter what, *you* are the most important expert on your child. You know her better than anyone else. At times, you may feel like you don't know what to do, and so other people will be there to coach you; however, you will always have that special connection with your child no other team member has. All of your expertise is important while working with other team members. You know your child's moods, her willingness to participate and the signals she sends right before she shuts down. Your ability to read these cues and share them with the other team members is extremely valuable.

▪ **Pediatric audiologist**

Your pediatric audiologist supports you through your child's diagnosis and audiologic services. In addition, she may be part of the IFSP team that creates a plan of action for your child. She can give specific information on your child's present levels or audiologic performance and auditory development needs.

▪ **Ear, nose and throat doctor and pediatrician**

Although your child's physicians may not be present at your IFSP meetings to determine outcomes for your child, their input is very valuable. Be sure to ask your ENT doctor or pediatrician any questions you have so you can feel confident about your child's medical history and health.

▪ **Early intervention service coordinator**

An **early intervention service coordinator** is a professional charged with knowing your state's early intervention system inside and out. She keeps your team on track, manages paperwork and meetings and ensures you receive the services your child and family need. Essentially, a service coordinator is your case manager for early intervention while each service provider actually meets with you to provide the services your child needs.

■ **Early intervention service provider**

Once your child is deemed eligible for early intervention services and is ready to begin sessions, the family is assigned to one or more early intervention service providers. An **early intervention service provider,** or early interventionist, is a trained professional who works with you, your child and family to provide appropriate services in a specialty area. One area of specialty is hearing loss. Your service provider who specializes in hearing loss is a teacher of the deaf and is responsible for:

☐ meeting with you initially to get to know you and your child. This includes an interview, also called a **routines-based interview**, in which the provider asks you about your child and her daily routines. The first meeting is intended to be an engaging experience — for you to begin developing a positive relationship with your provider and for your provider to learn about your child and family.

☐ meeting regularly with you at your home or the place where your child spends most of the day

☐ helping you understand the nature of your child's diagnosis of hearing loss

☐ giving you and other caregivers unbiased information about the choices and options for your child

☐ coaching you and other caregivers on how to accomplish the goals you have for your child — for example, how to help your child learn how to listen and talk

☐ coordinating services with other service providers

This can include helping you arrange audiology services. It also could include working with other service providers your child might have as a result of other diagnoses. For example, if your child has a diagnosed gross motor delay, you may be assigned a service provider who specializes in physical therapy. If your child has a diagnosed eating or swallowing disorder, you may be assigned a feeding specialist. The service providers work together to provide comprehensive services to support the needs of you and your family.

Other Early Intervention Service Providers

Depending on your child's abilities and your family's goals, you may have a variety of other professionals on your team.

■ A **speech-language pathologist (SLP)** has many responsibilities related, but not limited to, communication development. Some work specifically with children. Some are more experienced working with children with hearing loss than others. Some speech-language pathologists also specialize in feeding or swallowing support.

■ An **occupational therapist (OT)** who works with children specializes in sensory needs, feeding or oral motor issues, fine motor delay and functional living skills.

■ A **physical therapist (PT)** who works with children specializes in gross motor developmental delays such as problems with sitting up, crawling, walking, running, etc.

■ An **orientation and mobility (O&M) specialist** helps children with vision impairments navigate their environment and learn to move safely and independently.

■ A **nutritionist** or **dietician** helps children with food aversion or weight gain concerns.

■ A **developmental therapist/special instructor** is responsible for monitoring children with global delays and for providing services to help them make progress.

■ A **social worker** may assist the team by connecting the family with community resources, counseling or social supports.

Individualized Family Service Plan

Under Part C of IDEA, any child eligible for early intervention services has an **Individualized Family Service Plan (IFSP)**. Along with a team of professionals, the child's parents, caregivers and family members create this document. The IFSP contains a plan of action for the child and family. At the meeting for writing the IFSP, the team must ensure the content of the IFSP reflects parents' concerns, is developed in conjunction with parents, builds on and utilizes family strengths and resources and addresses the family's needs as well as the child's needs.

The IFSP development meeting includes the following people that make up the **IEP (Individualized Education Plan) team**:

■ the child's parents or caregiver(s)

■ other family members as requested by parent(s)

■ family advocate at parental request

■ service coordinator (meeting facilitator)

■ one or more members of the evaluation and assessment team

■ providers expected to deliver services

The IFSP contains the following information:

■ present levels of development in all developmental domains

■ child's strengths and needs

■ family's strengths, needs, resources, priorities and concerns

■ desired outcomes expected in the next 6–12 months for the child and family

  □ methods for accomplishing outcomes

  □ anticipated timing of outcomes

  □ criteria for measuring progress of outcomes

■ list of services necessary to meet the needs of the child and family

■ anticipated dates for initiation and duration of each service

■ statement justifying the use of settings other than "natural environments"

■ listing of persons responsible for implementing individual services as well as parties (persons or agencies) responsible for payment

■ steps for transition of needed services when the child turns 3

■ name of the service coordinator

Determining Outcomes

You and your family must consider the big picture goal, or desired outcome, for your child with hearing loss. One approach for deciding on a desired outcome is to think about what you want for your child when she is grown up. From that, work backward and consider the method of communication your child will need to achieve that outcome. Your team of experts can support your decision by providing information and by helping you determine specific family goals as you work toward your long-term desired outcome for your child. Examples of long-term desired outcomes are as follows:

- As an adult, my child will listen, talk and fully integrate in the hearing world.
- As an adult, my child will listen and talk, yet feel connected to Deaf culture by also communicating with sign language.
- As an adult, my child will be an active participant in Deaf culture by living among people who are deaf and communicating in sign language without the use of spoken language.

Early Intervention Services

The actual services your child receives depend on the results of her evaluations and assessments in addition to your family's goals and priorities. No matter what the specific services are, two general types of service provisions help families achieve their desired outcomes:

- **Family support and training**
  Early intervention is family-centered, meaning your family's concerns and priorities drive all the services you receive. Sometimes your provider talks with you about what's on your mind concerning your child. Other times your provider literally "provides" the information you need to know about your child's condition, disability or special need. Quality early intervention providers offer support in various ways. This includes providing information, emotional support, resources and referrals to other experts. Quality early intervention providers work well with the entire IFSP team and the various professionals working with your child.

  In addition, your provider coaches you and other caregivers on strategies that can be incorporated into daily routines. The provider will model an activity or the use of a specific strategy. Next, she'll give you a chance to try it with her as she guides you. Then, you can feel confident trying it on your own with your child when the provider isn't there. Remember, the provider is a coach, and part of coaching is to allow you to try while guiding you along the way. This is an important step on the way to feeling empowered to interact effectively with your child toward meeting your desired outcomes.

■ **Direct services**

Your child may receive specialized therapy and/or instruction to help her develop skills to counteract the effects of her condition, disability or special need. Your early intervention provider provides these services directly to your child while you observe. In these cases, you are not typically an active participant.

Quality Early Intervention Providers and Programs

Some parents of infants or toddlers with hearing loss have few choices about who provides early intervention services. Other parents have a choice. In some geographical areas, only one early intervention provider may work with families of infants and toddlers with hearing loss. In other areas, early intervention programs may employ a number of early intervention providers with the relevant skills. If you have a choice, you may find it difficult to know how to choose unless you know what differences to expect among providers and programs. Quality early intervention programs have certain characteristics you might choose to seek out. After all, the goal of early intervention is to support you and teach you ways to foster your child's development. Your goal in finding an appropriate program or provider should be to find one you believe can offer you the support you and your child need.

Quality early intervention providers are prepared to counsel you effectively on specific topics related to your child's hearing loss and communication needs. In other words, your provider who specializes in working with parents of infants and toddlers with hearing loss will help you gain an understanding of the following:

■ audiology and assistive technology
■ listening and auditory skill development
■ receptive language
■ expressive language
■ typical child development
■ speech and articulation
■ family rights/laws pertaining to early childhood special education
■ counseling/social support/community resources

As a parent searching for the right early intervention program and the right providers, remember to trust your gut and choose a program that feels right for your family. Some questions to help you decide on a program are:

■ **What developmentally-appropriate practices does the program use?**

The specific practices of early intervention programs vary greatly. The best, highest-quality programs use specific developmentally-appropriate practices researched and put into practice based on evidence showing they work. **Developmentally-appropriate practices** are those that fit a child's age and level of development. For example, you wouldn't expect a 2-year-old to learn by sitting at a desk and listening to a teacher lecture. Some developmentally appropriate practices for early intervention include:

- □ informing parents of typical milestones and expectations for children at certain ages
- □ demonstrating for parents and caregivers activities suitable for the child and her age they can try at home or daycare
- □ spending time observing the parent interact with the child during daily routines and activities, then giving the parent feedback and additional strategies to try
- □ collaborative problem solving between parents and providers as they discuss parents' concerns
- □ asking parents to reflect about daily activities that go particularly well and those that don't

■ **Are services provided in the natural environment?**
Part C of IDEA specifically requires early intervention providers to carry out family visits in the most natural environment for the child. For most children, the natural environment is the home or daycare setting. Although it's best for family visits to occur in the natural environment, this may be difficult if you live far from your early intervention center. Some early intervention providers are willing to drive up to an hour away to provide a family visit in the home or daycare setting. If you don't live far from your provider, be sure the majority of your family visits occur in your home or daycare setting. As a last resort, you may need to have family visits at the early intervention center because it's just not practical or economical for providers to drive. Services provided outside the natural environment may require special documentation.

An early intervention program is truly only as good as its providers. Depending on where you live, you may or may not have a choice of the provider assigned to you. If you do have a choice, use the following questions as a guide for acquiring information so you can make an informed decision. You may not be able to find a provider who has all the attributes you're looking for. If that's the case, choose the person likely to be the best match for your child according to your own family dynamics and priorities. If you

Virtual Intervention

With the state-of-the-art technology available today, it's possible for families who live a great distance from a qualified early intervention service provider or center to use tele-intervention. Tele-intervention is the provision of services using technology such as videoconferencing. Using small cameras and computers, the family and early interventionist can see one another and converse. In fact, the early interventionist can offer the same information she would if she were physically in the same room with the family.

don't have the option of selecting a provider, you still might want to ask these questions about the person working with your child and family. In any case, you have the right to ask about the professional qualifications of a potential early intervention service provider. Questions you might ask include:

☐ What is the provider's formal training?

☐ Does the provider have a degree in deaf education? If so, is her area of expertise spoken language instruction, manual communication or some other area?

☐ Does the provider have a degree in speech-language pathology?

☐ Does the provider have a degree in special education?

☐ Is the provider knowledgeable about child development?

☐ Is the provider knowledgeable about all modes of communication for children with hearing loss?

☐ Is the provider knowledgeable about the specific mode of communication you have selected for your child?

☐ Is the provider knowledgeable about evaluations and assessments and able to explain them in parent-friendly terms?

☐ Is the provider knowledgeable about the early intervention system?

☐ Is the provider willing to help you and your family navigate the early intervention system?

☐ Is the provider willing to listen as well as talk?

☐ Is the provider willing to share good resources and connections?

☐ Is the provider a good counselor and interviewer?

☐ Is the provider comfortable with concerns and priorities not directly related to hearing loss?

☐ Is the provider a lifelong learner who seeks to constantly learn more?

"I've learned that people will forget what you said, people will forget what you did, but people will never forget how you made them feel."
— Maya Angelou

Family Visits

Family visits are events in which an early intervention provider meets with the child and parents or caregivers. Sometimes more than one early intervention provider is at the family visit. Other times, there is only one early intervention provider. For the most part, family visits should occur in the home unless there is a specific reason for having a visit at the early intervention center, daycare or alternate location.

Home Visits

The majority of your family visits should be in your home with your child and family. This is important because the family visits are intended to help you know how to support your child when the early intervention provider isn't there. You may meet with your provider for an hour each week, but for the rest of that week, you need to use what you learned during that hour to meet your child's needs. Although the early intervention provider often wants to talk to you about listening and spoken language development, feel free to talk about anything you'd like related to the well-being and development of your child. Early intervention providers are there to help and coach you for the good of your child. Sometimes the issues you want to talk about aren't specific to deafness or learning to talk. That's okay! If it's related to your child's welfare, it's okay to bring it up.

Center-Based Visits

You might have a center-based visit if your child needs a specific evaluation that can't be performed in your home or daycare setting. For example, audiologic testing must occur at the audiology center because so much equipment is involved in testing.

You also may agree to meet occasionally at an early intervention center due to travel distance. In that case, your early intervention provider and other professionals on the team can meet you there. In some cases, your early intervention provider can meet you for a family visit that is really an appointment — perhaps at the ENT doctor's office or at an audiology center located in a hospital or elsewhere.

What Happens at a Family Visit?

The agenda for family visits can vary significantly. Some families need to talk about specific issues before they can begin to talk about hearing aid use and language development. Other families are ready to learn everything they can about how to create a home environment conducive to learning to listen and talk. Here are some typical discussion topics:

- your child's hearing device use during the week
- issues you're having in the process of reaching full-time use (all waking hours)
- your child's auditory development

- your child's communicative intent
- ways in which your child communicates with the family
- your child's ability to understand and use spoken language
- your child's development as compared to children who are typically developing
- your child's speech and articulation development
- your upcoming appointments and what to expect at those appointments
- your family dynamics and the relationships your child has with others
- your feelings about how things are going for you and your child

Providing Direct Services

- Your early intervention service provider may work individually with your child to teach specific listening, language, speech, cognitive, play and behavior skills. The provider plans a series of fun and motivating activities, including games and various play-based activities. These activities are designed to help develop your child's skills in various areas as well as to give your provider an idea of your child's abilities and progress. In the case of direct service provision, you're likely to take the role of an observer. It can be really interesting to see a skilled professional work with your child, but the activities in these sessions are not necessarily what you need to try when the provider isn't there.

Modeling or Demonstrating Activities and Strategies

- In addition to providing direct services, your early intervention provider spends time at the family visits coaching you on what to do to encourage your child's development. *This* is what you can try later, when the provider is no longer at your house. Really great providers are able to demonstrate activities for you using only the materials and toys you already have in your home. This makes sense since those household materials and toys are what you'll have to work with after the provider leaves. The provider uses your child's toys to demonstrate how you can talk to and play with your child. She will ask you to join in the play so you can practice and she can coach you as you learn certain strategies. This should feel supportive, friendly and worthwhile. It's no fun to feel like you aren't doing it right or like you don't know anything. Quality early intervention providers guide you as you learn these new strategies for helping your child learn to listen and talk.

Toys Don't Equal Play

Beware of activities that aren't play-based! If your child is looking at picture cards or simply labeling toys without playing with them, this is not play. Remember, young children learn best and most efficiently through active play!

Family Support

■ Many parents and families benefit from the support quality early intervention providers are trained to offer. You might benefit if you're experiencing grief because of your child's identified hearing loss. This also includes support for families living in crisis, whose basic needs such as food, shelter and clothing are not met. Support can come in many forms and for many reasons. Some family sessions include time for providing you with this kind of support if needed. Remember, a quality early intervention provider would never want you to feel uncomfortable. If you don't want to talk about certain topics, that's okay. Bring up what you're comfortable talking about, any questions you have, things you need help with or things you wonder about.

Group Instruction for Toddlers

Besides family sessions and audiologic services, some children benefit from engaging in group instruction in a class specifically designed for toddlers with hearing loss learning to listen and talk. Research indicates successful outcomes for children enrolled in early intervention with an intensive toddler class designed specifically for children with hearing loss (Moog & Geers, 2010). If you have a toddler class in your area, you can discuss the possibility of enrolling your child. Many toddlers benefit greatly from the social aspect and positive effects of peer interaction associated with group instruction. Research shows that children, even infants, benefit from interactions with one another. When given appropriate interactive situations, infants and toddlers can learn to communicate with each other, imitate each other, share their experiences with each other, develop social understanding, enjoy social play and function in joint play activities (Shin, 2012). Your early intervention provider or service coordinator can help you determine if there is a toddler class in your area that may be appropriate for your child and, if so, help you inquire about whether your child is a candidate for that class.

Transition from Part C to Part B

As you read earlier in this chapter, early intervention services through Part C of IDEA are provided only for children up to age 3. In many cases, when a child turns 3, she still may require special services due to her special need. The federal law called IDEA also has a Part B that is specific to services provided to school-aged children. This includes children ages 3 to 21. When your child turns 3, she will "transition" from services provided through Part C to services provided by Part B. This requires special meetings, discussion and paperwork.

When your child is about 2½ years old, your early intervention service coordinator will convene a transition meeting with all the members of your child's IFSP team. A representative from the school district in which you live will be present to discuss the desired outcomes you had for your child while receiving early intervention services and whether you

Some young children with hearing loss transition from Part C into a general education classroom with no special education services. This happens only if the team, including you and the group of professionals, decides the child doesn't require special education services to make adequate progress each school year.

and your family achieved those outcomes with support from your early intervention providers. In addition, you will discuss the procedures necessary to prepare your child and family for a change in the way services are provided. For example, when your child turns 3, you will no longer have family visits with an early intervention provider; instead, your child may be enrolled in a more direct service model, perhaps in a classroom if she is eligible. The team discusses what kinds of support you and your family need as you transition from one type of service model (family visits) to another (preschool or early childhood program).

At the transition meeting, you will have an opportunity to grant permission for your school district to gain access to your child's records. This includes evaluations, assessments, IFSPs and other documents. Your district representative may request additional testing or observations. The district uses this information to determine eligibility for early childhood education services, to ensure continuity of services and to learn more about your child as they make plans to appropriately provide her with the services she needs to progress. This is the beginning of the IEP process. Every child between the ages of 3 and 22 who receives special education services has an IEP, an **Individualized Education Plan.** This legal document outlines educational and developmental goals for your child to achieve within one year. The IEP is developed with an IEP team consisting of professionals from your school district, professionals relevant to your child's development, you and other family members. See chapter 20 for more information on IEPs and the process for developing and reviewing IEPs.

Finally, you will discuss potential placements for your child. **Placement** is a term used in special education to describe the setting in which a child will receive educational services dependent upon the child's needs. The possibilities for placement are nearly endless, and this makes sense since educational decisions for children with special needs always should be individualized. Placements include a special education classroom, a general education classroom, a general education classroom with support services from various professionals and a self-contained school that provides special education services for children with specific needs, such as a school for children with hearing loss. After discussing potential placements, you can make a plan for visiting those schools or classrooms. You can ask members of the IFSP team to join you as you tour potential placements. They can remind you to ask about specific details, such as classroom acoustics and the audiologic services available at this school. They can guide you as you learn about the individual programs and consider placement for your child. This is a big decision. The team members are there to support you.

Advocacy Skills and Resources for Parents

One of the best ways to help your child is to advocate for her. This is not always easy, but it is effective. "Advocacy is the process of striving to improve the quality of life for someone else" (Byington & Whitby, 2011). Advocating for your child is the best way to give her a voice so she can get the services she needs to succeed. We live in a great country that offers these services to children who need them. As her parent, you know your child best, and you can help the others charged with her education to know her, too. This will ensure she is appropriately represented.

One important part of being a good advocate for your child is to understand her rights as a child with special needs and your rights as her parent. The following is a list of resources you might find useful:

- **Advocacy support**
  Hands and Voices

- **Parent advocacy training**
  Listening and Spoken Language Knowledge Center
  Alexander Graham Bell Association for the Deaf and Hard of Hearing

References

Byington, T. & Whitby, P. (2011). Empowering families during the early intervention process. *Young Exceptional Children, 14,* 44–56.

Danaher, J. & Goode, S. (2013, May 10). *Early Intervention Program for Infants and Toddlers with Disabilities: Part C of IDEA.* Retrieved from http://ectacenter.org/partc/partc.asp.

Moog, J.S. & Geers, A.E. (2010). Early educational placement and later language outcomes for children with cochlear implants. *Otology & Neurotology, 31*(8), 1315–1319. doi:10.1097/MAO.0b013e3181eb3226.

Rossetti, L. (1990). *Infant-Toddler Assessment: An Interdisciplinary Approach* (p. 92). Boston: Little, Brown & Company.

Shin, M. (2012). The role of joint attention in social communication and play among infants. *Journal of Early Childhood Research, 10*(3), 309–317.

Wright, P.W.D. & Wright, P.D. (2015, February 17). *Early Intervention: Part C of IDEA.* Retrieved from http://www.wrightslaw.com/info/ei.index.htm.

Chapter 20

Educational Programs for Preschoolers with Hearing Loss

Whether or not your child with hearing loss receives early intervention services, eventually, you may find yourself looking for an appropriate early childhood special educational (ECSE) preschool program. Preschool programs serve children ages 3 to 5. Programs for preschoolers with hearing loss vary greatly in practices, philosophy, funding, number of students and number of teachers.

Assessments for Eligibility

For a child with hearing loss, assessments are an important part of the journey. They are necessary to determine whether your child is eligible for early childhood special education services in the preschool years. Assessments, both standardized and informal, provide information about your child's educational needs so eligibility can be determined and educational needs can continue to be met.

Standardized Assessments

Standardized assessments are tests given in a consistent manner and scored based on comparison. The standardized assessments your child is given are scored in comparison to other children her same age. For example, if your child is given a standardized language assessment when she is 3 years old, her standard score indicates her language skills compared to other 3-year-olds with typical hearing. To better understand standardized assessments, it's important to have an understanding of the following terms.

The **average range** for a standardized test is the range of scores considered to represent the middle 68 percent of people on which the scores are based (or normed). About 16 percent of people tested naturally fall above the average range. About 16 percent of people tested naturally fall below the average range. This is important to know because when your child is given a standardized test, you want to see if she is functioning in or above the average range. If she isn't, certain interventions or services should be provided to help her catch up. For many standardized assessments, the average range is 85–115.

Normed scores are based on the performance of a certain group, one representative of the population. A norm group includes many children who represent a particular age group as well as some other factors — gender, ethnic background, geographic area of residence, socioeconomic status, etc. For example, if a language test is normed on children with typical hearing, your child's language score is compared to the scores of children with typical hearing her age. If a language test is normed on children with hearing loss, your child's score is compared to the scores of other children with hearing loss her age. Tests such as these are referred to as **norm-reference** tests.

The **standard score** is derived from the raw score. (The raw score is the actual number of points a person gets on a test.) The standard score is used to describe the score in comparison to the norm. For example, if the average range for an assessment is 85–115 and your child's standard score is 102, your child is said to have scored within the average range. This score is especially important in that it provides a meaningful comparison from year to year.

Closing the gap

It's important to use standardized assessments to determine the level at which your child is functioning in certain areas compared to other children her age. With any delay, the goal is to provide interventions that help her move from delayed to average. The process of moving from a below average score to a score within the average range is referred to as **closing the gap**.

Standardized Assessments Typically Used with Preschoolers

Many standardized assessments can be used with young children with hearing loss. Every school or program has its favorites. Some standardized assessments are:

- **Language**
  Peabody Picture Vocabulary Test — 4th Edition (PPVT-4)
  Expressive Vocabulary Test — 2nd Edition (EVT-2)
  Preschool Language Scale-V (PLS-5)
  Clinical Evaluation of Language Fundamentals-Preschool 2 (CELF-P2)
  Preschool Language Assessment Instrument-2 (PLAI-2)

- **Speech**
  Goldman-Fristoe Test of Articulation 2 (GFTA-2)

- **Early literacy**
  Test of Preschool Early Literacy (TOPEL)
  HearBuilder Story Retell Test

Functional (Informal) Assessments

The purpose of functional assessments is to acquire more information about your child so appropriate services can be determined and continued. A functional assessment is **criterion-referenced,** meaning it compares your child to herself by indicating her abilities in a specific developmental area and her progress in that area over time. The information acquired is specific to the delay caused by the diagnosed condition. These assessments provide information about how your child is functioning, her educational needs and her progress. Many functional assessments are designed for use with young children with hearing loss. Every school or program has its favorites. Some functional assessments include:

- *CID Early Childhood Vocabulary Rating Form*

  The *CID Early Childhood Vocabulary Rating Form* is a criterion-referenced assessment designed for use with children birth to age 5 with hearing loss. It outlines vocabulary at five levels: functional vocabulary, first 100 words, more basic vocabulary, theme-based vocabulary and preschool-specific vocabulary.

- *CID Teacher Assessment of Grammatical Structures (TAGS)*

  CID TAGS is a series of three rating forms used to evaluate a child's understanding and use of the grammatical structures of English. The rating forms provide a representation of grammatical structures for children with hearing loss who develop grammatical structures in smaller increments and at slower rates compared to children who are typically developing. The grammatical structures listed are organized into three levels: TAGS-1, TAGS-2 and TAGS-3.

- *CID Preschool Pragmatic Language Rating Form*

  The *CID Preschool Pragmatic Language Rating Form* is a criterion-referenced assessment designed for use with 3- to 5-year-old children with hearing loss. Based on research with children with typical hearing and the experience of seasoned teachers of the deaf, this assessment lists the most common and useful pragmatic language skills for preschoolers.

- *CID Preschool Symbolic Play Rating Form*

  The relationship between language and play is a close and symbiotic one. A child with delays in either area will potentially show delay in the other. Symbolic play is a prerequisite for learning language. Before being able to use language, a child must be able to represent reality with symbols. Play skills must develop to a certain level before the corresponding language skills are possible. The *CID Preschool Symbolic Play Rating Form* is used to track play skills and their related language skills in children 8 months to 5 years old.

- ### *CID Speech Perception Instructional Curriculum and Evaluation (SPICE)*

  CID SPICE is used to help young children with cochlear implants and/or hearing aids develop auditory skills. It is designed to make auditory learning easy and fun for both the teacher/clinician and the child. CID SPICE focuses on foundational auditory skills.

- ### *CID SPICE for Life*

  CID SPICE for Life is an auditory learning curriculum designed to help individuals with hearing loss overcome real life listening challenges. *SPICE for Life* focuses on functional auditory development. It includes practice with auditory memory, listening in noisy settings, listening to music, localizing sounds, listening to voices, listening in conversation, listening on the telephone and more. This kit is designed to be used with children age 5 and older. *SPICE for Life* contains activities for structured lessons, suggestions for practicing skills in a classroom or therapy session and pages to encourage parents to practice skills at home. *SPICE for Life* can be used to help children develop auditory skills even if they have low language skills.

- ### *CID Speech Skills Rating Form*

  The *CID Speech Skills Rating Form* is a criterion-referenced assessment designed for use by teachers of the deaf, speech-language pathologists and other professionals working with children with hearing loss. The rating form is divided into five detailed sections: voice, suprasegmental aspects of speech, vowels, consonants and blends and clusters.

- ### *CID Preschool Developmental Rating Forms (3, 4 and 5)*

  These forms are used to track typical development of literacy, cognitive, social, fine motor and gross motor skills in children 3, 4 and 5 years old. Teachers use these in conjunction with other forms for listening, language and speech to monitor whole-child development.

- ### *Cottage Acquisition Scales for Listening, Language and Speech (CASLLS)*

  CASLLS is a series of scales, or checklists, used to track a child's skills in listening, speech, language and cognition. It's designed to be used with children from birth to approximately 8 years old. *CASLLS* includes five separate criterion-referenced scales based on typical language development. The scales include preverbal, pre-sentence, simple sentence, complex sentence and sounds and speech.

Individualized Education Plan

As stated previously, assessments are used partly to determine eligibility for special education services. Once the team determines your child is eligible for services, a plan is put in place to determine services, set goals and track progress. The plan is called the IEP. An **individualized education plan (IEP)** is a legal document that outlines educational and developmental goals for your child to achieve within one year. Every child from age 3 to 21 who receives special education services has an IEP. The IEP is developed by a team composed of the following people (U.S. Department of Education, 2005):

- at least one general education teacher
- at least one special education teacher or provider
- a representative of the local educational agency (LEA)
- the parents
- the student, if appropriate
- a professional who can interpret the instructional implications of evaluation results
- other people the parents or the school have chosen to invite

A representative from the school district in which you live calls a meeting to write the IEP. The team works together to write the initial IEP based on each team member's knowledge of your child. This includes developing goals. Benchmarks, also known as objectives, are often included, although they are not required under the Individuals With Disabilities Education Act (IDEA). **Benchmarks** are the steps a child takes as she works toward achieving an IEP goal within a year. Having benchmarks enables providers to help a child build toward a larger goal in smaller steps.

After the IEP is written, it's in effect for one year. Your child's teachers and/or therapists help your child achieve each goal, including the associated benchmarks for each goal. Near the end of the one-year period, a representative from the IEP team contacts you to schedule an IEP review meeting. At this meeting, you and the other team members discuss your child's progress toward achieving each goal. Although the initial IEP meeting and the review meeting occur at the beginning and end of the designated year, respectively, any team member, including a parent, has the right to reconvene the team to discuss the details and potentially make changes to the IEP.

Placement

After the IEP document is complete, the team works to find an appropriate **placement** for your child in an early childhood special education program. Placement includes the actual location your child receives educational services, the professionals who provide those services and the other students with whom your child attends preschool. The team may determine multiple possibilities for placement. In this case, with support from the team, you choose the placement that works best for your child and your family.

Components of a High Quality Preschool Program

You are your child's best advocate. As you consider an appropriate program for your child, feel free to ask lots of questions. Consider inquiring about the following components of a preschool program:

National Association for the Education of Young Children (NAEYC)

NAEYC offers a national, voluntary accreditation system that sets professional standards for early childhood education programs and helps families identify high-quality programs. Accredited programs meet 10 NAEYC Early Childhood Program Standards. The standards contain a set of required criteria in each of the following categories: relationships, curriculum, teaching, assessment of child progress, health, teachers, families, community relationships, physical environment and leadership and management (naeyc.org, NAEYC, 1996).

State Early Childhood Accreditation

Be sure the preschools you look into have state early childhood accreditation. To attain state accreditation, preschools must comply with specific standards. Information about U.S. Department of Education preschool standards and individual state preschool standards is readily available online. You might search for preschool standards, early learning standards, early learning initiative or early childhood accreditation.

Program Philosophy

Children with hearing loss need constant support in learning to listen and talk. The environment in which they spend the school day must provide that support. For your preschooler to continue learning to listen and use spoken language, the philosophy of the program you choose should be based on teaching listening and spoken language skills to children with hearing loss. This philosophy requires not only specialized training of teachers and staff, but also a special dedication and attitude toward supporting children as they learn to listen and talk.

In addition, the philosophy of a program should give you insight into the atmosphere of learning. It's important for your child to be surrounded by a community of learners who constantly strive for further learning. This kind of professional learning community makes for a progressive and highly functional environment, and therefore can be an important factor in your child's progress and continued success.

Focus on the Individual Child

Quality programs are able to appropriately serve a variety of children with different strengths, abilities and needs. Look for a program that will treat your child as a true individual and work to meet her needs.

Focus on the Whole Child

Although your child may need special instruction in the areas of listening, language and speech, it's imperative for her to develop in other areas, too. Look for a program that emphasizes all developmentally appropriate skills for preschoolers. These include:

- cognitive skills
- communication skills (listening, language and speech)
- gross motor skills
- fine motor skills
- pre-academic skills
- early literacy skills
- social skills
- emotional skills
- technology skills
- creativity
- play skills

Focus on Play

Have you ever noticed or thought about how children gravitate toward play? They want to play, they like to play and they find ways to play in any and every situation. The fact is that children *need* to play. In preschool, learning is really all about play. A child who is "successful" in preschool is one who is successful at play. Play requires socialization skills, listening skills, language skills, speech skills and the ability to express feelings, ideas, wants and needs. Through play, children work on developing all of these skills. Because of this, quality preschool programs focus on building preschoolers' skills in all areas of development so they can be successful at play.

It's not uncommon for children with hearing loss and delayed language to also have delayed play skills. Children who don't have age-appropriate language skills often don't have age-appropriate play skills. Children who don't have age-appropriate play skills often don't have age-appropriate language skills. For many children with hearing loss, play skills must be directly taught in the same way language skills are taught. Exposure to other children playing and talking is not enough. Teachers must explicitly teach play. Quality preschool programs have a specific and intricate play-based curriculum. When you visit, you will see children playing with other children while teachers model play, guide children in their play and facilitate language during play. For more information on play, see Chapter 16.

Theme-Based Learning

Instruction and learning based on themes allows for exposure to and practice using typical pre-academic concepts, language targets, pragmatic language and vocabulary associated with that theme. Themes provide a foundation for integrated learning. They enable children to learn in many different ways and acquire a deep understanding of concepts while developing various skills.

Audiologic Management

Because your child wears hearing devices, it's imperative for you to have access to quality pediatric audiologic services. This is truly essential. Children who have typical hearing listen all day long. To successfully learn to listen and talk, your child also needs to listen all day long, or at least during all waking hours. You need an audiologist or audiology center that can respond to you quickly and effectively when your child's devices are not working properly or when you need an appointment. Some preschools focused on listening and spoken language instruction have pediatric audiologic services available on-site, which is very convenient. Other programs don't have on-site pediatric audiology. If this is the case, search your area for a pediatric audiologist or audiology center that can meet your needs.

Auditory Development Curriculum

Children with typical hearing don't need to be taught to listen. Listening skills come naturally to children who have had access to the sounds of our world, including spoken language, since before birth. Children with hearing loss inevitably miss out on some opportunities to listen. Quality preschools that teach listening and spoken language have a well-defined and effective auditory development curriculum. Inquire about a prospective preschool's auditory development curriculum and ask about how they ensure quality auditory instruction throughout the day.

Language Curriculum

Since they have missed out on opportunities to listen to spoken language around them, children with hearing loss typically have delayed language skills. A quality preschool program has a well-defined language curriculum for teaching children to understand and use vocabulary, syntax and pragmatic aspects of language. In addition, children with hearing loss and delayed language skills need a variety of language sessions throughout the day that vary in the level of direct instruction provided. In other words, a child might need structured and direct instruction for learning new vocabulary and syntax, as well as practice using that language with support from a teacher or therapist in a less structured and more natural setting. In addition, your child needs time to use the same language in natural situations typical for her age. The goal of language development is to be able to understand and appropriately use language in natural situations with same-aged peers who are typically developing. This means the language goal for your preschooler with hearing loss is to understand and use the same language used by other preschoolers without hearing loss or other delays. Quality preschool programs serving children with hearing loss put a lot of emphasis on their language curricula. When you visit a prospective school, be sure to inquire about the specifics of the language curriculum.

Speech Curriculum

As is true for language development, children with hearing loss typically have delayed speech skills since they have missed opportunities to listen to the speech of others around them. In addition, hearing loss often distorts the sound of speech, so children with hearing loss might not receive a clear speech signal. A quality preschool program has a well-defined speech curriculum for teaching children appropriate articulation (production of the individual sounds of our language), suprasegmental aspects of speech (duration, intensity and pitch) and voice (breath control and voice quality). The speech goal for your preschooler with hearing loss is to produce the same speech produced by other preschoolers without hearing loss (or other delays). Quality preschool programs serving children with hearing loss put a lot of emphasis on their speech curriculum. When you visit a prospective school, be sure to inquire about the specifics.

Focus on Early Literacy

Many people believe success in life relies on proficient reading ability. Reading ability affects academic achievement, prospects for higher education, success in the job market and quality of life. Statistically speaking, the average American student with hearing loss graduates from high school with reading comprehension skills at about the fourth-grade reading level (Luckner & Handley, 2008). This is truly unacceptable. Children with hearing loss should have the same opportunities for success and fulfillment in life as any other children. It's the responsibility of parents and educators alike to ensure children with hearing loss every opportunity to become proficient readers.

Reading proficiency begins in infancy, with exposure to books and print in the environment. During the preschool years, children should have access to an early literacy curriculum that provides instruction and exposure to children's literature. The earlier preschoolers are immersed in literature, the better they will be at learning to read.

Spoken language, reading and writing are all very closely related. When we read, we associate print with what we also can say. When we write, we put the words we otherwise would say into print. It makes sense for children with hearing loss who have delayed language skills to struggle as they learn to read language in print. Moreover, it makes sense that, as we foster preschoolers' language skills, we simultaneously help build their early literacy skills to reinforce that language development. Language development and literacy development go hand-in-hand.

Seek a program focused not only on developing listening and spoken language skills, but also on developing early literacy skills that foster eventual reading proficiency. Some early literacy program components to look for include the following:

- literacy-rich environment
- exposure to the rules of print and books
- theme-based approach to literacy skills development
- building comprehension through read-alouds, pre-teaching vocabulary related to stories, teaching vocabulary within the context of stories, questioning (literal, inferential and evaluative) and using story extension activities
- exposure to attempts at storybook reading
- exposure to experience stories
- practice using tools to form letters
- exposure to phonological awareness concepts
- exposure to phonics concepts
- exposure to patterning and sequencing concepts

Individualized Instruction and Class Size

Because of the intensive instruction children with hearing loss need to develop age-appropriate listening, language and speech skills, your child likely needs to spend some time during the school day receiving direct instruction in a very small group or as the only student. Quality preschool programs design a schedule that allows for differing numbers of students in particular classes. Direct listening, language and speech instruction should occur in individual sessions or in very small groups with like-learners. In addition, your child likely needs to be in larger groups during some part of the day so she has a chance to learn in a setting typical of preschool. Larger groups give her opportunities to observe and interact with children her same age, which promotes the development of social skills.

Inclusion in Typical Settings

It's important for your child to spend some time during the school day integrated into classrooms typical for her age and with same-aged peers. Children with age-appropriate listening, language and speech skills, including children with hearing loss, can successfully integrate into typical preschool settings for the entire school day. Children with delayed listening, language and speech skills need to spend some time in typical classrooms, but also need to be pulled out of typical settings for direct instruction of listening, language and speech. The amount of time a child with delays might spend in typical classrooms varies according to her specific needs.

Focus on Kindergarten Readiness

All quality preschool programs base their curricula on preparing preschoolers for kindergarten. Ask about how prepared a program's preschool graduates were at the time they entered kindergarten. Ensure your child develops all kindergarten readiness skills just as any child would. Although some children with hearing loss are ready to fully mainstream into typical kindergarten, many are not. Nevertheless, ensure your child is in a preschool program that focuses on developing all skills necessary to enter and succeed in kindergarten.

Parental Involvement

Decades of research demonstrate that children whose parents are involved in their education are more likely to succeed in school. Quality preschools emphasize the importance of parent involvement in their children's education. The more you support and engage in your child's education, the more your child is likely to progress in school. Seek a preschool program that emphasizes parent involvement. Ask about specific ways the program communicates with parents and provides opportunities for them to be involved in their child's education, both at and away from school.

Professionals to Look for in a Prospective Preschool Program

Educational Audiologist

An **audiologist** diagnoses, treats and manages individuals with hearing loss. An audiologist determines appropriate treatment of hearing problems by getting a complete hearing and illness history, then administering a variety of hearing assessments. Based upon the diagnosis, the audiologist presents a variety of treatment options. Audiologists dispense, program and fit hearing aids, and they fit and program cochlear implants. They can also help you learn about options for assistive listening devices such as FM/DM systems.

 Educational audiologists are a specialized group. They are trained and have experience working specifically with children. This is very important because the methods for testing, diagnosing and managing children's hearing are much different from the methods used for adults. If the preschool program you're looking at doesn't have an on-site audiologist, ask if there is one at another location associated with the program. If not, search your area for a pediatric audiologist who can meet your needs.

Classroom Teacher of the Deaf

A **classroom teacher of the deaf** is a teacher who specializes in classroom instruction for children with hearing loss. Depending on the program or classroom, the teacher may use only sign language, only spoken language or a combination of sign and spoken language. Classroom teachers include those who teach:

- a class of children, all of whom have hearing loss
- a class of children, most of whom have hearing loss, but some with typical hearing
- a class of children, most of whom have typical hearing, but some with hearing loss
- in a resource room where children with hearing loss are scheduled to work with the teacher of the deaf during certain times and periods of the school day

Itinerant Teacher of the Deaf

An **itinerant teacher of the deaf** generally travels around visiting multiple students with hearing loss in local neighborhood school programs. The itinerant is assigned to work with each child on her caseload for a certain number of minutes or hours each week or month. The itinerant works closely with a child's other teachers in a collaborative effort to meet the child's needs. The itinerant also might be in contact with the family on a regular basis to report on their child's progress. Responsibilities of the itinerant teacher include the following:

- provide direct instruction to the child
- ensure the child has appropriate and adequate services to meet her needs
- monitor the child's language development
- monitor the child's auditory and speech development
- monitor the child's use of auditory equipment

School Speech-Language Pathologist

A **school speech-language pathologist (SLP)** works with children with communication disorders that adversely affect educational performance. School SLPs work in schools with children who have a variety of disabilities that include language, voice, fluency or stuttering, speech/articulation and swallowing (ASHA, 2013).

Roles of the school SLP

- prevent communication disorders, as possible
- identify students at risk for later problems
- assess students' communication skills
- evaluate the results of comprehensive assessments
- develop and implement IEPs
- document outcomes

- collaborate with teachers and other professionals
- advocate for teaching practices
- participate in schoolwide curriculum and literacy teams

SLP services vary depending on students' needs. An SLP may:

- combine communication goals with academic and social goals
- integrate classroom objectives
- help students understand and use basic language concepts
- support reading and writing
- increase students' understanding of texts and lessons
- monitor or periodically screen
- collaborate and consult
- provide classroom-based services
- provide small group or individual sessions
- provide speech therapy

Choosing a Preschool Program: Go with Your Gut

Depending on where you live, you may have only one option for a preschool program. This is the case for many people. Many school districts throughout the U.S. have exceptional programs for children with hearing loss. Ask lots of questions and be sure you get answers. If you feel like something isn't right, bring it up. Talk about it. Starting a dialogue about your concerns is a great way to advocate for your child.

If you happen to have more than one preschool option for your child with hearing loss, then lucky you! This is a *great* position in which to find yourself. Compare the programs and find the one that best meets your child's needs. When faced with multiple programs that are all excellent, some parents find the decision difficult. In this is the case for you, go with your gut. Choose the one that feels like the best fit for you and your child. You will be happy you did.

In any case, take great care finding the right placement and services for your child's preschool years. Gone are the days when preschool was considered no big deal. Now we know preschool is essential because it's at the same time so many important skills are developed. In addition, a preschooler with hearing loss especially needs that exposure to typical preschool life and peers. Maintain a serious and dedicated attitude toward preschool, and your child will reap the benefits!

References

American Speech-Language-Hearing Association (2010). Roles and responsibilities of speech-language pathologists in schools. Retrieved April 9, 2015, from http://www.asha.org/policy/PI2010-00317/.

Luckner, J. & Handley, C. (2008). A summary of the reading comprehension research undertaken with students who are deaf or hard of hearing. *American Annals of the Deaf, 153,* 6–36.

National Association for the Education of Young Children. (1996). Position Statement on Developmentally Appropriate Practice in Early Childhood Programs Serving Children from Birth Through Age 8. Washington, DC: NAEYC.

U.S. Department of Education (2005). Regulations: Part 300 / D / 300.321 IEP Team. Retrieved March 29, 2015, from http://idea.ed.gov/explore/view/p/,root,regs,300,D,300%2E321.

Index